PERCEPTION AND THE
CONDITIONED REFLEX

PERCEPTION
AND THE
CONDITIONED REFLEX

Ye. N. SOKOLOV

Translated by
STEFAN W. WAYDENFELD

Scientific Editors
ROBIN WORTERS
The Manor, Epsom, Surrey

A. D. B. CLARKE
Department of Psychology
The University, Hull, E. Yorks

A Pergamon Press Book

THE MACMILLAN COMPANY
NEW YORK
1963

THE MACMILLAN COMPANY
60 Fifth Avenue
New York 11, N.Y.

This book is distributed by
THE MACMILLAN COMPANY
pursuant to a special arrangement with
PERGAMON PRESS LIMITED
Oxford, England

Published with the assistance of
THE PERGAMON INSTITUTE
AND
THE NATIONAL INSTITUTES OF HEALTH
PUBLIC HEALTH SERVICE,
U.S. DEPARTMENT OF HEALTH, EDUCATION AND WELFARE

Library of Congress Card Number: 62–22210

A translation of the original volume
Vospriyatiye i Uslovnyi Refleks
(Moscow University Press, Moscow, 1958)

*Set in 10 on 12 pt Times New Roman by Santype Ltd, Salisbury, Wilts
and Printed in Great Britain*

Contents

PREFACE TO THE ENGLISH EDITION   ix

AUTHOR'S PREFACE   x

INTRODUCTION   1

PART I—GENERAL ASPECTS OF THE THEORY OF PERCEPTION

CHAPTER 1.   Reflex activity of analysers and the process of perception
A. Reflex control in analysers   5
B. Unconditioned reflexes and the tuning of analysers   10
C. Conditioned reflexes and analyser control   15
D. Intra-analyser and inter-analyser connexions   19

CHAPTER 2.   Measurement of the functional state of analysers
A. Sensitivity and its measurement   22
B. Reactivity and lability   26
C. Poly-effector reaction recording (electropolygraphic technique)   29

PART II—THE PERCEPTION OF NON-SIGNAL STIMULI

CHAPTER 1.   Vascular and cutaneogalvanic components of orienting, thermo-regulatory and defensive reflexes
A. Vascular reactions in various reflex acts   35
B. Vascular reactions in the course of the application of stimuli evoking orienting reflexes   39
C. Vascular reactions to thermal stimulation   42
D. Vascular reactions to painful stimuli   46
E. Sensitivity as measured by orienting and defensive reflexes   49
F. The galvanic skin component of orienting reflexes   53
G. Interrelationships between the orienting, thermoregulatory and defensive reflexes   64

CHAPTER 2.   Orienting and adaptation reflexes in the visual analyser
A. Adaptation and orientation reflexes in the visual analyser   71
B. The electrical manifestations of the orienting reflex in the cortex   78
C. General and local orienting reactions   79
D. The effects of rhythmic photic stimulation   88
E. Central and peripheral components of adaptation reflexes   94
F. Adaptation and orienting reflexes in the control of sensitivity   102
G. Mechanisms of interaction between orienting and adaptation reflexes   109

CHAPTER 3.   Structure of the orienting reflex and the functional state of analysers
A. Tonic and phasic orienting reflexes   116
B. "Over-extinction" of the orientation reflex   119
C. Afferent and efferent links of the orientation reaction   123

103165

D. Electrical reactions in the brain associated with the afferent and efferent elements of orienting reflexes   130

CHAPTER 4.   Elaboration of conditioned adaptation reflexes

A. Adaptation to repeated illumination   132
B. The conditioned adaptation reflex and its relationship to the orienting reflex   137
C. A conditioned orienting reflex in response to a sequence of two non-signal acoustic stimuli   150
D. A conditioned orientation reflex produced by combination of visual and proprioceptive stimuli   154
E. Conditioned adaptation reflexes and the mechanism for excitation of the orienting reaction   158

PART III—PERCEPTION OF SIGNAL STIMULI

CHAPTER 1.   Orienting, thermoregulatory and defensive vascular reflexes produced by signal stimuli

A. Vascular reactions during the elaboration of conditioned motor reflexes   163
B. Vascular reactions during the elaboration of conditioned reflexes with electro-dermal reinforcement   170
C. Measurement of reactivity and sensitivity by means of orienting and defensive reflexes   175
D. The galvanic skin reaction in relation to stimuli acquiring signal significance   187
E. The orientation reflex in the structure of the conditioned reflex   198

CHAPTER 2.   Visual orienting and adaptation reactions during elaboration of conditioned reflexes

A. Enhancement of visual sensitivity and reactivity for non-specific signal stimuli   202
B. Electrographic manifestations of a conditioned motor reflex to photic stimuli   208
C. Visual sensitivity for photic stimuli   223
D. Reactions to signal photic stimuli of threshold intensity   227
E. Extinction of the orienting reaction on consolidation of a motor reflex originating in the visual analyser   236

CHAPTER 3.   Functional state of the analyser during the elaboration of a conditioned reflex

A. Afferent and efferent links of the orientation reaction and analyser reactivity to signal stimuli   239
B. Tonic and phasic orienting reactions associated with the acquisition of signal significance by a stimulus   242
C. Change in reactivity during elaboration of a conditioned motor reflex   244
D. Orienting and specific reflexes in the motor analyser   245
E. Role of the orienting reflex in the closure and functioning of the temporary connexion   247
F. Relationship between conditioned and orienting reflexes   255

PART IV—REFLEX MECHANISMS IN THE ACTION OF STIMULI ON ANALYSERS   261

APPENDIX.   A neuronal model of the stimulus and the orienting reflex

1. Questions in the objective study of sensory integration   282
2. The orienting reflex and its components   283

3. Selective extinction of the orienting reflex   285
4. A neuronal model of stimulus   286
5. The filtering properties of the neuronal model   288
6. The scheme of the orienting reflex   289
7. The neuronal model of the stimulus and the conditioned reflex   291

REFERENCES   295

INDEX   305

Preface to the English Edition

In the West during the last few years, a number of research reports by Sokolov have become available and have aroused great interest. In particular, the London University Lectures given by the eminent Soviet Psychologist, Professor A. R. Luria, in 1957, revealed that Sokolov is an outstanding member of the post-war generation of Soviet Psychologists. This view was subsequently reinforced by a number of lectures given personally by Sokolov outside the U.S.S.R.

The present volume is the first major work of this author to have been translated. It considers the role of conditioned reflexes in the processes of perception, studying in particular the orientation, adaptation and defence reflexes. These and their inter-relationships are shown to play a significant part in the control of sensory processes.

As with other Soviet work in this field, the reader will be impressed by the simplicity yet ingenuity of experimentation, and the interest in processes rather than in "Molar" theories. At the same time, he may note the characteristic relative disinterest both in individual differences and in the quantification of results. Nevertheless, the experimental detail presented will enable the replication and extension of this approach in other laboratories.

We think that this book will be of interest to neurophysiologists, psychologists, psychiatrists, and indeed all who are concerned with the scientific study of human behaviour.

R. W.
A. D. B. C.

Author's Preface

THIS work forms part of a series of investigations on the reflex basis of perception, in the light of Pavlov's teaching. The orientation, adaptation and defence reflexes, and their inter-relationships, play a significant part in the production and control of sensory processes and this has been the chief subject of the present series of investigations.

The experimental part of the study was completed during the period 1952–1957 in the Department of Psychology of the Moscow State University, the Department of Physiology of Higher Nervous Activity of the Moscow State University and in the Institute for Disabled and Mentally Defective Children of the A.P.S. R.S.F.S.R.*

I am greatly indebted to I. G. Bershadskii, O. S. Vinogradova, N. N. Danilova, M. B. Mikhalevskaya and N. P. Paramonova for their help in carrying out the experimental work.

I consider it also my duty to express my deep gratitude to L. G. Voronin, A. N. Leontiev and A. R. Luria for their advice in the course of the work and to thank E. A. Golubev, L. V. Krushinskii, G. D. Smirnov, B. M. Teplov and P. A. Shevarev for their valuable criticism of the manuscript.

* Academy of Pedagogical Sciences of the Russian Soviet Federative Socialist Republic

Introduction

By perception is meant that action of the analyser mechanism which reflects the activity of external agencies. Thus "perception" denotes the process of reception in the wide sense of the word. Sensory processes can and should be analysed as manifestations of the combined conditioned and unconditioned reflex activity of analysers, resulting from the action of certain well-defined stimuli (Pavlov, 1949).

The study of perception as a reflex act of adaptation opens new horizons in the field of sensory processes which so far have not been explored by classical sensory organ psycho-physiology. It will suffice to point out, for example, that the perception of a stimulus depends on what signal significance this stimulus has for the organism. Where man is concerned, there is also the problem of the effect on perception of the verbal stimulations contained in verbal instructions (Gershuni, 1957). This approach to the processes of perception also provides an opportunity for detailed analysis of the structure of the conditioned reflex arc and, in particular, of its afferent limb.

When one is investigating the reflex processes on which the perception of a conditioned stimulus is based, one must also consider perception of the reinforcement, and the specific reactions of the body (the principle of return afferentation, Anokhin, 1949, 1955). Both afferent and efferent limbs of the conditioned reflex will then be seen to consist of a number of individual reflex acts combined together into a single system with adaptional significance for the body as a whole. This approach can be contrasted with "molar" theories, which have been gaining ground recently and which confine themselves to the examination of integrated behaviour (Hull, 1943, 1952).

In this book an attempt is made to interpret the results of such an investigation on man. It consists of three main parts. The first, which is mainly a review of the literature, also discusses the connexions between the reflex processes taking place in the analysers and the processes of perception. Special attention is given to the parts played by orienting, adaptation and defensive reflexes in the control of sensitivity.

Simultaneous polygraphic recording is used because of the complex structure of the somatic reactions to external stimuli employed as indices of the sensitivity and reactivity of analysers. Some general principles governing these reactions are considered in an attempt to standardize such measurements.

1

The second part of the book is concerned with reflex mechanisms in the perception of non-signal (unconditioned) stimuli. The analysis of this form of perception is based on a comparison of the parts played by various reflex actions which produce changes in the sensitivity, reactivity and lability of analyser apparatuses when stimuli of various kinds and intensities are applied repeatedly. Special attention is given in this section to the development of intra-analyser conditioned reflex connexions forming part of the mechanism for cortical control of analyser sensitivity for the perception of stimuli.

The perception of signal (conditioned) stimuli, reinforcing stimuli and the proprioceptive stimulations connected with execution of the response motor reaction are discussed in the third part of the book. The relationship between the perception of any given stimulus and its place in the conditioned reflex arc is discussed in the light of Gershuni's investigations (1949, 1955, 1957). The connexion between the functional state of analysers and the ease with which conditioned reflexes can be established and switched is discussed in detail. Special attention is also given to study of the principles governing the relationship between orientation and conditioned reflexes, and to changes in sensitivity at various stages in the course of the development of temporary connexions.

In the last section we describe some of the general patterns, revealed by our investigations, in the interaction between the various reflexes in the process for perception of indifferent and signal stimuli and we attempt a detailed analysis of the structure of the conditioned reflex arc in man in the light of the results of modern neurophysiological research.

PART ONE

GENERAL ASPECTS OF THE THEORY OF PERCEPTION

CHAPTER 1

Reflex Activity of Analysers and the Process of Perception

A. Reflex Control in Analysers

In psychophysiology the process of stimulus perception is usually considered from the standpoint of transformation of a physical stimulus originating in a receptor and ending in the higher centres of the central nervous system. According to this view, the stimulus sets up a process of excitation at the periphery which, through intermediate stages, reaches the cerebral cortex where complex neural phenomena constituting the basis of perception develop. Analyser activity is considered mainly from the standpoint of the centripetal transmission of excitation. However, such a simplified view of events does not withstand more detailed analysis since the centrifugal wave of excitation, resulting in a substantial change in the effects produced by the stimulus at the periphery, must be taken into consideration. The process of perception of a stimulus appears, therefore, as an uninterrupted reflex act centred on the analyser and consisting of a complicated system of conditioned and unconditioned reflexes.

This concept of perception as a system of reflex acts was developed by Sechenov, who was particularly interested in the "physiology of sensation". Taking as an example the formation of a three-dimensional image, he demonstrated the complex reflex activity of the visual analyser. He considered visual perception to be a complex of "photomotor acts" and "light reflexes" (Sechenov, 1952, p. 217).

Pavlov approached Sechenov's idea from the point of view of conditioned reflex theory and concluded that the basic psychological elements in the physiology of vision (perception of size, form and depth) were merely chains of conditioned reflexes—the simplest elements from the complex activity of the visual analyser (Pavlov, 1949, p. 101).

A visual stimulus sets up a photo-chemical reaction and this gives rise to the whole system of reflexes essential for the formation of retinal image. These reflexes include conjugate movement of the eyes towards the light, convergence, accommodation and contraction of the pupil. The number of active photoreceptors in the retina is also regulated reflexly by the light (Snyakin, 1948). Thus, the chain of reflex activity leads to substantial alterations in the functional state of the receptor system, which in turn determines the effectiveness of the action of the stimulus on the system.

Reflex control of the receptors is exercised by the central organs of the nervous system by means of uninterrupted centrifugal nervous activity or "feedback" in cybernetic terminology. This feedback can be negative, reducing the effect of the stimulus, and thus adaptive in effect, or positive, amplifying the effect and thus sensitizing. The reflex eye movements described above increase the efficacy of the stimulus and exemplify positive centrifugal control. Conversely, the contraction of the pupil in response to increased light intensity is an example of negative centrifugal control. As indicated by Orbeli (1949, p. 413), these two kinds of central influence—constantly interacting, maintain the sensitivity of the peripheral receptor at a certain level.

The reflex controls exercised by the analyser as a result of stimulation are of great importance for an understanding of the principles governing the phenomena of perception (Granit, 1955). This problem became of particular interest because of the failure of many attempts to explain all processes of perception on the basis of peripheral changes in the receptor (Adrian, 1947). Interest in this subject was further stimulated by the rapid development of cybernetics, the science dealing with general principles of automatic regulation, its conclusions being extended to the mechanisms for control of the apparatuses of perception in man and animals (Wiener, 1948; Allport, 1955).

Analysis of the centrifugal effects of the central nervous system on receptors reveals the following main paths for the transmission of these effects.

(1) **Direct Influence of the Centre on Receptor Activity.** Among the many possible effects of the centre on the receptor, direct influences reaching the periphery from the central parts of the analyser stimulated are of greatest interest, and the presence of efferent fibres connecting the centre with the periphery, running in the sensory nerves, have been demonstrated for all sensory organs. Furthermore, the structure of the central end of the analysers is, according to modern research, that of an afferent—efferent organ, which is capable not only of receiving stimuli but also of exercising control over lower formations (Grinshtein, 1956).

The efferent control mechanism of visual receptors merits special attention, as hitherto the eye has been considered as a purely afferent organ. Histological and physiological data, however, point to direct central control of retinal activity. The presence of many efferent fibres which ramify in the retina has been demonstrated histologically in the optic nerve (Cahal, 1909). The cortex evidently plays an important part in this control mechanism, as evidenced by the recently discovered efferent fibres connecting it with the subcortical visual centre (Shkolnik-Yaross, 1955).

It should be pointed out, however, that the function of the efferent fibres in the processes of photoreception has not been satisfactorily explained. They may possibly be concerned primarily with the central control of adaptation (Grinshtein, 1947). A possible mechanism for control of the functional state of the retina is the neural regulation of the regeneration of visual purple, a view which is supported by the diminished concentration of rhodopsin observed in the frog after removal of the brain at the level of the anterior borders of the thalami (Mkrtycheva, 1955).

The influence of the central on the peripheral parts of the visual analyser is mediated by impulses which can be registered in the retina following the stimulation of the lateral geniculate body (Dodt, 1956). Evidence on the influence of the centres on the activity of the retina is to be found in the work of Granit *et al.*, who used microelectrode techniques. Stimulation of thalamic and midbrain nuclei leads to changes in the basal activity of the ganglion cells in the retina and lowers the threshold of retinal sensitivity for an adequate photic stimulus (Granit, 1955).

Certain authors accept perielectrotonic activity as a factor in the control of receptors by higher centres. Thus a focus of parabiotic excitation created in the optic nerve (frog retina preparations) produced rhythmic activity in the retina although no impulse activity could be registered in the nerve (Farber, 1952). However, these perielectrotonic phenomena and their importance in the control of receptor sensitivity require further study by microelectrode techniques.

The existence of cortical control of the functional state of the retina has been confirmed by experiments on intact animals (e.g. rabbit). A stable dominance created in the occipital cortex by means of an uninterrupted flow of constant current, resulted in retinal discharges appearing in response to auditory stimuli which previously produced no electrical activity in the eye (Novikova and Faber, 1956).

Detailed study of proprioceptor control mechanisms showed the presence in motor nerves of thin fibres regulating the conditions of proprioceptor function. When stimulated in isolation from other fibres, these fibres do not cause muscle contraction but influence the state of the muscle spindles, leading to changes in the latter's transducing characteristics (Hunt, 1952; Granit and Henatsch, 1956, and others).

Microelectrode experiments have shown that stimulation of the auditory centres in the medulla has an inhibitory effect on the cochlea's electrical response to auditory stimulation. This inhibitory influence is exerted via descending fibres (Galambos, 1956). These same efferent fibres also play an important role in processes of adaptation (Davis *et al.*, 1952).

B

The presence of descending and ascending chains of neurones in the cortex and the existence of reciprocal connexions between the cortex and subcortical areas compels us to regard the analysers are self-regulating systems of perception, which not only transform and transmit signals from the periphery to the centres but also, through their specific efferent paths, adjust their own functional state for the selection of stimuli arising outside the body. This self-regulating mechanism of the analyser acting as an afferent–efferent organ is based on "a reflex ring" (Bernshtein, 1947) in which the initial afferent stimulation influences the state of the receptor through the system of connexions.

(2) **Propriomuscular Tuning Apparatus of the Receptor.** In addition to the direct influence of the centres on the functional state of receptors, there is also a reflex muscular mechanism for the setting of receptors which can alter their operating conditions materially (Kvasov, 1956). E.g. the sensitivity of the retina varies from point to point and thus the effects of a visual stimulus of constant intensity will vary greatly, depending upon which part of the retina is stimulated, and this in turn depends upon the positioning of the eye within the orbit and the posture of the head and body as a whole. The propriomuscular control of the eye is particularly well developed and is evident in the reactions connected with searching and fixation; there are similar mechanisms in the olfactory organ (sniffing movements) and the organ of hearing (turning of the ears in animals). The propriomuscular apparatus of each receptor is represented in its cortical projection. This is demonstrated by the movements of receptor apparatuses produced by electrical stimulation of the cortical projection of the corresponding analyser during neurosurgical operations on man (Penfield and Rasmussen, 1950) and in experiments on animals (Lagutina, 1955).

(3) **The Autonomic Nervous System in the Control of Receptor Activity.** The direct action of centres on receptors and the activity of the propriomuscular apparatus are supplemented by effects from the higher autonomic centre in the hypothalamus which plays an important part in processes of adaptation. The role of the autonomic nervous system in trophic and adaptation processes depends on the controlling influence of the sympathetic (and also in certain cases, parasympathetic) nervous system on all excitable tissues, including receptors. This again results in tuning of the reflex apparatus of the analysers for performance of its function (Orbeli, 1949). This role of the autonomic nervous system has been particularly well studied in respect of the influence of the sympathetic nervous system on the receptors of the eye (Rappaport and Robinson, 1935; Zagorul'ko, 1937; Arkhangel'skii et al., 1936).

Reactions linked with activity of the autonomic nervous system influence the functional state both of receptors, and of the cortical centres of the analysers. The weakening of all conditioned reflex activity in the dog as a result of superior cervical ganglionectomy (Asratyan, 1939) will serve as an example. It must also be mentioned that the autonomic nervous system is capable of effecting changes in cortical function but is itself under cortical control.

The diffuse effects produced by many kinds of stimuli also include variations in the sensitivity of the cerebral cortex. Recent work indicates that this effect depends on the activity of the reticular formation, which extends from the spinal cord to the diencephalon and comprises systems of connexions in thalamus, hypothalamus, midbrain and medulla oblongata. The structure of the reticular formation is characteristically diffuse and it is surrounded by various nuclei and construction paths. Stimulation of any point in the reticular formation results in an alteration of the functional state of the cortex, as revealed by change in its electrical activity (Moruzzi and Magoun, 1949).

Any type of afferent stimulation traversing the collateral connexions in the brain stem and thalamic area produces excitation in the reticular formation, which in turn maintains the activity of the cortex as a whole (Beritov, 1948; Roitbak, 1955; Gottschick, 1955; Anokhin, 1956). The reticular formation retains its influence on the cortex even when all the specific thalamic nuclei are destroyed. For this reason Jasper (1949) was able to speak of a non-specific, diffuse thalamo-cortical projection apparatus serving for transmission of impulses from the reticular formation to the cortical parts of analysers. The existence of a relation between the activity of the reticular formation and the functional state of the receptors is shown by the increased electrical activity of the retina and the increased instability of certain proprioceptors which results from electrical stimulation of the reticular formation (Granit, 1955).

The humoral element also enters into the system of reflex control of the analysers, in which the vegetative nervous system occupies an important place. This had already been demonstrated by Cannon (1927) who found that a new or unexpected stimulation resulted in a discharge of adrenaline which led to increasing excitability. The part played by the humoral element in the control of reflex activity is also evident after adrenalectomy, when there is lowered cortical activity (Orbeli, 1949).

The experimental application of painful stimuli provides evidence on the role of adrenaline in activation of the cortical centres of the analysers and its connexion with the reticular system mechanics. Simultaneous observation of E.E.G. and blood pressure changes revealed the presence of two distinct phases in this increased cortical activity, one due to arrival of neuronal impulses into the reticular formation and the other to adrenaline released into the blood stream, acting on the reticular formation and hypothalamus, and thus altering the functional state of the cortical cells (Bonvallet, Dell and Hiebel, 1954).

The importance of the neuro-humoral element in the complex control of sensitivity is also borne out by other observations. Stimuli applied to the visual receptors can effect the dark adaptation of the eye via the hypophysis cerebri and its hormones. The biogenic stimuli discovered by Filatov can also influence the sensitivity to light (Kravkov, 1948).

In this way the effects produced through humoral mechanisms are added to the direct effects of activity of the autonomic nervous system on the various parts of the analysers. This complex of elements which, when brought into operation, effects the tuning of the analysers can be appropriately termed "the neuro-humoral control system" (Bykov, 1947).

The relative significance of the various components of this diffuse autonomic reaction involving exteroreceptors, cortex and internal organs needs further consideration. Peripheral vasoconstriction associated with cerebral vasodilatation is one particular manifestation of this kind of diffuse autonomic reaction resulting from the application of a variety of stimuli. This redistribution of blood facilitates cerebral activity (Tarkhanov, 1889, Lazarev, 1947). It seems that certain elements of this diffuse reaction can, in turn, influence the functional state and activity of the analysers.

Reflex control within the analysers is effected therefore through:

1. The descending efferent fibres running in the sensory nerves.

2. The propriomuscular apparatus of the receptor.

3. The autonomic nervous system, the following elements of which may be involved:

    a. The sympathetic (and parasympathetic) nerve supply to the receptors.

    b. The effects of the sympathetic nervous system on the functional state of the cortex.

    c. The neuro-humoral control system.

    d. The indirect, secondary action of autonomic reactions on the internal organs, particularly the vascular system, and consequently on the excitability of nervous tissue.

Whenever a stimulus is applied to a receptor, the results include, in addition the local changes in the receptor and corresponding changes in the respective centres, a reflex change in the functional state of the receptor in question and of all other analysers. In this way, as a result of the involvement of a great number of reciprocal influences, the effects of the action of a stimulus on the corresponding receptor are constantly changing, while the actual process of perception proceeds as a series of reflex acts.

B. Unconditioned Reflexes and the Tuning of Analysers

The biological significance of the various mechanisms involved in the reflex control of analysers has not been so far discussed. The alterations of the functional state of the analysers is but one aspect of the adaptive reactions of the body as a whole. Each such reflex is a complex functional system (Anokhin, 1949) and includes a variety of control mechanisms which provide for the suitable tuning of analysers.

Studies of the autocontrol of analysers, from the point of view of the biological significance of the reflexes involved, point to defence, orientation and adaptation reflexes as being those of the greatest importance.

The orientation reflex is the first response of the body to any type of stimulus. It tunes the corresponding analyser to ensure optimal conditions for perception of the stimulus (Pavlov, 1947). The conception of the orientation reflex as an important adaptation reaction is historically connected with the teaching of Sechenov on reactions adapting the sensory apparatus for the perception of objects (Sechenov, 1952). In its wider sense, however, this concept was formulated by Pavlov in 1910, in his Moscow lecture in connexion with the foundation of a laboratory for the study of higher nervous activity (Pavlov, 1949).*

The orientation reflex involves muscular activity resulting in specific movements of eyes, lids, ears, head and trunk, which together give the animal "the power to meet chance dangers" (Pavlov). At the same time it inhibits other unconditioned and conditioned reflexes (Pavlov, 1949, 1947). Thus the orientation reflex manifests itself in the stimulation of some and the inhibition of other systems in the body. This inhibitory effect of the orientation reflex on other activities of the body has been a prominent feature in research in the form of external inhibition (Pavlov, 1949). Ivanov-Smolenskii (1927) has made a special study of the orientation reflex in man.

Another phenomenon, very similar to the orientation reflex, the "concentration reaction", was studied by Byekhterev and his collaborators—Shchelovanov and Myasishchev (1926). This reaction of concentration has been studied in pathological states, and special attention has been given to its ontogenesis (Figurin and Denisova, 1949).

The collaborators of Byekhterev made an important step forward in the study of the orientation reflex, when they succeeded in identifying its autonomic components (Milyavskaia, 1930; Feoktisvova, 1929; Myasishchev, 1929, 1945; and others). The application of graphic methods to the studies

---

* By orienting–investigatory reflex we mean the series of reactions bringing the animal into contact with the object, and tuning the analysers of animal or man, so that perception of the stimulus takes place in the most favourable conditions. This definition of the orienting–investigatory reflex is, however, too wide. The orientation reflex in the restricted sense of the word, should be distinguished in the reflex as the non-specific reaction resulting in the tuning of the analyser when exposed to a new stimulus. This elementary reaction is quite distinct from the complex exploratory chain of reflexes, aiming at investigation of the object in detail and involving a whole series of conditioned orientation reflexes.

In this book the orientation reflex is analysed in the restricted sense.

of respiratory, pupillary and cutaneogalvanic reflexes allowed them to establish a link between the external motor manifestations and the autonomic components, of the concentration reaction.

A characteristic feature of the orientation reflex is its extinction when stimulation becomes repetitive (Popov, 1921; Chechulin, 1923; Rozental, 1929). This phenomenon resembles the inhibition of conditioned reflexes and suggests a cortical component in the orientation reflex (Pavlov, 1949, p. 341). At a later period, Orbeli put forward the view that extinction of the orientation reflex is due to spread of elaborated inhibition from higher to lower centres and that in this way the cortex inhibits the sub-cortical orientation reactions (Orbeli, 1949).

The close connexion between the orientation reflex and cortical inhibitory processes and the fact that an orientation reflex may develop in the decorticate dog indicate that "this reflex can be anchored, either to the cells of the hemispheres, or to those of the lower parts of the cerebrum" (Pavlov, 1947, p. 315).

An important factor in the production of an orientation reaction is the "newness" of the stimulus (Anokhin, 1941; Berlyne, 1954, 1955), and there is also direct dependence on the intensity of the stimulus (Chechulin, 1923; Rozental, 1930).

As an independent functional system (Anokhin, 1949), the orientation reflex has, in addition to its inhibiting and disinhibiting effects on conditioned reflex activity, its own stimulation mechanism, and comprises a number of reactions.

First of all there is the widely studied motor component of the orientation reflex which consists of turning movements of the eyes and body of the animal towards the stimulus, and movements associated with sniffing. There are also the secretory components, such as the orientational secretion of saliva as a manifestation of activation of the taste analyser (Robinson and Hunt, 1947). Autonomic reactions such as dilatation of the pupil (Smirnov, 1955; Liberman and Strel'tsova, 1952; and others), changes in the respiratory rhythm (Anokhin, 1949), change in the form of electrical activity of the brain (Gershuni, 1950) and cutaneogalvanic manifestations also belong to the complex orientation reflex.

According to some, the orientation reactions are but reflexes limited to the muscular apparatus of individual analysers, arising in opposition to vegetative reactions (Kvasov, 1955). Autonomic (e.g. vascular) reactions serve the same purpose as somatic reactions, and facilitate increase of analyser sensitivity. The orientation reflex is, therefore, a complex combination of somatic and autonomic reactions forming a complete functional system.

The autonomic components of the orienting reflex provide control of analyser sensitivity over a wide range. As with the motor component of the orientation reflex, the autonomic component participates in the tuning of receptors and in the realization of the ultimate aim of the orientation reflex as a whole, namely *increase of analyser sensitivity*. A serious defect in work done on the orientation reflex has been that its autonomic and motor manifestations have usually been studied quite apart from its most important function, the enhancement of analyser sensitivity (Stevens, 1951). The factual demonstration of the connexion between analyser sensitivity and the orienting reflex was a major contribution to the study of this reflex.

The connexion between the sensory significance of change in sensitivity and the orientation reflex was specifically pointed out by Snyakin (1948). Describing the experiments of Yakovlev (1940), who demonstrated increase of the field of vision as a result of auditory stimulation, he suggested the orientative nature of this reaction. Increased sensitivity of the organs of vision as a result of auditory, tactile or other stimulation, as well as of voluntary effort, was demonstrated by Semenovskaya (1946, 1947). In these experiments the increase of sensitivity was associated with alterations of the respiratory rhythm and a cutaneogalvanic reaction (C.G.R.). The results of the experiments were not analysed with the laws governing the orientation reactions in mind, but certain facts indicating the extinction of these reactions with repetition of the stimuli are described. Dobriakov (1947) obtained similar results, and also demonstrated the simultaneous occurrence of cutaneogalvanic reactions and changes in sensitivity. Gradual levelling out of the, at first increased, sensitivity of the visual analyser as a result of repeated thermal stimulation was observed by Kekcheyev (1947).

Despite this, however, investigation of the orientation reflex was still not directly linked with the mechanism for the reflex control of analysers. It was Snyakin (1948) and Gershuni (1949) who first raised the question of a possible connexion between change in analyser sensitivity and the orientation reflex.

Direct proof of this connexion was obtained by Maruseva and Chistovich in Gershuni's laboratory in 1951–1954. These workers registered simultaneously the electrical changes in the scalenus anterior muscles participating in movements of the neck, variations in the polarization current of the eye-ball resulting from the movement of the eye, both being components of the orientation reaction, and determined the threshold of auditory sensitivity. The subject was informed neither of the object of the experiment nor of the nature of the sounds to be used as stimuli. The threshold in these cases was found to be high, and the motor reactions registered showed a long latent period. However, as soon as the orientation reflex started operating in response to a stimulus, the threshold was lowered by 10–12 dB and the latent period of the motor reactions was shortened. It was thus demonstrated that, as a result of the operation of the orientation reflex, the threshold of analyser sensitivity was lowered and that the increase in the sensitivity of the analyser in respect of the stimuli applied was, therefore, a component of the orientation reflex.

In addition to orientation reactions initiated by any change of stimulus, there exist certain special analyser tuning reflexes arising in connexion with the quality and intensity of the stimulus in operation. The pupillary responses to light and darkness are good examples of such tuning reactions. Application of a light stimulus results in contraction of the pupil; the maintenance of the contraction depends then on reflexes which remain in operation for the duration of action of the optical stimulus. In darkness, the pupil is kept dilated in the same manner. Certain digestive reflexes also belong to this group of reactions, as their operation results in adaptation of the taste analyser to the individual properties of the specific stimulus. These specialized reflexes, which bring about adaptation of the analysers to the quality and intensity of the stimuli, can also be observed during the investigation of other activities of analysers and they can be appropriately termed "*adaptation reflexes*".

This term was first applied by Makarov (1955) to a special group of reflexes which result in adaptation of the functional characteristics of an organ, in this case adaptation of the visual analyser, to the prevailing external and internal conditions. They were discovered by him in the course of his studies on reflex changes of sensitivity within the visual analyser. In spite of much work on reflex changes in the sensitivity of analysers (Kravkov, 1948, 1950; Kekcheyev, 1947), the properties of the adaptation reflex as a distinct complex of reactions have not been investigated. This has been due to the fact that the adaptation processes were considered to be peripheral reactions confined to the receptors (Adrian, 1947; Lazarev, 1947).

When the intensity of the stimulus reaches a certain level *the defence reflex* enters into operation. This reflex shows certain properties similar to, and others quite distinct from, orientation and adaptation reflexes. The similarity of the adaptation and defence reflexes lies in their common object, namely limitation of the action of the stimulus. This object, however, is restricted to one analyser only in the case of the adaptation reflex and concerns the body as a whole in the case of the defence reaction. The defence and orientation reflexes are similar in that they bring into operation generalized reactions and are not limited to any given analyser depending on the nature of the stimulus. On the other hand, they differ in their ultimate object, this being the establishment of contact with the stimulus in the case of the latter and the breaking away from, or limitation of the activity of the stimulus in the case of the former (Montgomery, 1955). The defence reflex (general defence reflex of the body) can appear in two forms, active and passive. The passive defence reflex takes the form of complete immobilization of the animal. The active defence reflex is expressed by behaviour directed to the removal of or escape from the destructive agent. When the defence reflex is brought into operation, the relationship between the animal and the stimulus is altered and, consequently, the action of the stimulus on the analysers undergoes alteration. In man the defence reflex is closely connected with the sensation of pain. Its manifestations include withdrawal, alterations of the respiratory rhythm, vascular reactions and a number of hormonal changes. The appearance of the defence reflex influences not only the way in which the responsible stimulus is perceived, but also results in altered perception of the effects which follow. The defence reflex is closely linked with the orientation reflex and, by stimulating or repressing it, can influence the sensitivity of analysers.

From another point of view, the link between these two reflexes reminds one of the reciprocal relationship demonstrated by Head between fine (epicritic), and coarse, diffuse (protopathic), sensitivity. Any exclusion of fine tactile sensitivity results in intensification of the coarse pain sense and development of hyperpathia. In these conditions even a weak stimulus can result in unbearable pain associated with an intense defence reaction (withdrawal of arm, exclamation).

It was experimentally shown on cats in Orbeli's laboratory that after division of the tactile sensory path, the animal was incapable of fine specialized analysis and responded by a stormy defence reaction. Similar intensification of the defence reaction was observed after section of the posterior columns of the cord, partial destruction of the thalamus or decortication (Orbeli, 1949; Popov, 1953).

It is the participation of the cortical centres in the orientation reflex which makes it so different from the defence reflex. This is why the uninterrupted orientation reflexes observed in decorticate dogs have the appearance of defence reactions. In spite of their similarity at a subcortical level, defence and orientation reflexes show fundamental differences in their cortical mechanisms.

It should be mentioned, however, that in a number of experiments on animals, a certain inhibitory effect of the orientation reflex on the defence reactions could be observed. For example, rats investigating their new compartment got through an electrified grill (Voitonis, 1949).

At the same time the defence reflex can, by stimulating the orientation reaction, have a positive effect on the sensitivity of analysers. In man, a painful stimulus resulting in a defence reaction causes a temporary lowering of visual sensitivity. However, this soon returns and is then maintained on a higher level than originally (Zagorul'ko, Lebyedinskii, Turtsayev, 1933).

C. Conditioned Reflexes and Analyser Control

Modern conceptions of the unconditioned reflex assume the participation in one form or another, of the cortical centres in every unconditioned reaction (Dolin, 1936, 1955; Kupalov, 1951; Asratiyan, 1955). This conception is also wholly applicable to the three reflexes under consideration—orientation, adaptation and defence—and to the associated reflex changes in the functional state of the analysers.

The effect of cortical activity is either inhibition or stimulation of the orientation reflex. It can be assumed, therefore, that the signal significance of the applied stimulus exerts an important effect on the orientation reflex. Stimuli which give rise to specific reactions (sexual, digestive, defensive), bring about persistent orientation reactions. This can be explained by the fact that correct perception and differentiation of the signal is an essential condition for the development of an adequate reaction. The stimuli producing persistent orientation reactions are specific for each species of animal, e.g. the rustling of paper for hares, splashing of water for waterfowl (Biriukov, 1952), and visual stimuli for monkeys (Butler and Harlow, 1954; Harlow, 1955).

The orientation reflex, being intensified in response to signal stimuli, manifests itself more clearly whenever the conditioned connexions in question undergo change. Soloveichik (1928), and Narbutovich (1938), brought the orientation reflex into operation by manipulating the established pattern of stimuli and the intervals between them. The degree of intensification of the orientation reflex was connected with the degree of change in this pattern.

In man the orientation reflex becomes enhanced in response to signal stimuli. Myasishchev, (1926) demonstrated that the elaboration of a conditioned (combinative) reflex, led to restoration or intensification of cutaneogalvanic reactions which could be regarded as a component of an orientation reflex. Experiments on the pupillary component of the orientation reflex gave similar results (Smirnov, 1952; Glezer, 1952, 1953). The experiments of Musyashchikova, (1952), Zimkina, (1957) and Mushkina, (1956) point to a longer persistence of orientation reactions in response to signal than to indifferent stimuli.

The role of the orientation reflex in the production of conditioned reactions is best shown by experiments demonstrating the connection between intensification of the orientation reaction and analyser sensitization. As soon as auditory stimuli assumed the significance of signal stimuli for the subject of the experiment, the sensitivity threshold was noticeably lower. (Maruseva and Chistovich, 1951, 1954; Maruseva, 1955; Chistovich, 1955). The sensitivity of the auditory analyser is greatly modified by the verbal stimuli usually used in experimental work on the physiology of the sensory organs (Gershuni, 1955; Maruseva and Chistovich, 1954). Gyuradzhan, (1953) demonstrated changes in the sensitivity of the auditory and visual analysers when a stimulus became a signal for a pain reaction. These changes in sensitivity are inherent in an orientation reflex developed in response to a signal stimulus, and it is suggested that the intensification of the reflex to a signal stimulus is connected with the production of a conditioned orientation reflex to the reinforcement. This may be investigated by observing the combined effects of two indifferent stimuli. In this respect the experiments of Narbutovich and Podkopayev, (1936) are of very great importance. These workers demonstrated that an orientation reflex can be developed as a conditioned reflex. Two stimuli were used in combination in experiments on dogs: light from an electric lamp was followed immediately by a sound. Linkage between the light and the sound began to be observed in the process of combining the two non-signal stimuli. The appearance of the light resulted in turning of the head towards the source of the sound and vice versa. Repeated application of the combined stimuli was found to be an indispensable condition for the maintenance of the connexion between them. During similar experiments carried out by Zelenyi, (1928) who employed a great number of indifferent stimuli, the orientation reaction was extinguished and no connexion could be established. The results of the study of connexions between indifferent (non-signal) stimuli in various species of animals have confirmed the basic contention that conditioned orientation reflexes can be elaborated (Voronin, 1948; Rokotova, 1952, 1954).

The special study of the conditioned orientation reflex in man, first embarked upon by Ivanov-Smolenskii and his co-workers, (Ivanov-Smolenskii, 1927), has facilitated investigation of the formation of conditioned orientation reflexes in children. Thus, although they have not yet been studied to their full extent, the effects of the conditioned orientation reflex seem to occupy an important place in the reflex control of sensitivity.

The conditioned adaptation reflexes provide another mechanism for the cortical control of sensitivity. These reflexes, the operation of which results in reflex tuning of the sensitivity of analysers in accordance with the intensity of the acting stimulus, have also been insufficiently investigated. The first evidence of the conditioned reflex control of sensitivity was provided by Dolin, (1936). As unconditioned reinforcement he employed a light stimulus which reduced the sensitivity to light of the dark-adapted eye. The sound of a metronome, which does not usually reduce sensitivity to light, was used as the conditioned stimulus. After reinforcement of the metronome by the unconditioned stimulus—light—the former also acquired the capacity of reducing sensitivity to light.

Discussing Dolin's results, Pavlov (1949) suggested that as a result of a cortical synthesis by the cells of the visual and auditory analysers, the sound began to evoke the change previously produced by the light and apparently altered the content of visual purple in the retinal photoreceptors. Conditioned reflexes of this kind were therefore named "*photochemical conditioned reflexes*". As light normally produces contraction of the pupil, it has been suggested that the conditioned pupillary reaction was the factor reducing sensitivity. Rozhdestvenskaya (1954) experimenting with an "artificial pupil", succeeded in demonstrating that conditioned lowering of sensitivity also takes place when the diameter of the pupil remains constant. Transient (Makarov, 1952), and more prolonged (Kravkov, 1948; Kekcheyer, 1947; Sniakin and Anisimova, 1955), changes of sensitivity as a result of the operation of conditioned reflexes have been studied by numerous workers.

Bogoskovskii (1936) investigated conditioned reflex changes in the functional state of the more centrally placed parts of the visual analyser. While measuring the electrical sensitivity of the eye (sensitivity to electrical current which, when passing through the retina and optic nerve, produces a sensation of a flash of light—phosphene) he succeeded in producing a conditioned reflex to the moment of illumination of the eye kept in darkness. Light is an unconditioned stimulus which normally increases the electrical sensitivity of the eye. It was found that after a number of applications of this stimulus, always at the same time, the electrical sensitivity of the eye was increased at the set time even in the absence of the light flash. The increased electrical sensitivity of the eye, resulting from the light, was apparently due to the action of the more centrally placed parts of the analyser, and was not connected with any change in the concentration of the visual purple, which at that moment was actually reduced. Therefore, the description of this kind of reflex as photochemical would be entirely wrong.

Further investigations have clearly shown that conditioned reflex changes of sensitivity conforming to the general rules of conditioned reflex activity are characteristic of all analysers. Consequently all such changes are termed "*sensory conditioned reflexes*" in the literature (Kravkov, 1948).

The publication of data on conditioned reflex changes in the sensitivity of the visual analyser attracted the attention of a number of electrophysiologists. Jasper and Shagass (1941), using the electroencephalograph (E.E.G), succeeded in producing a conditioned reflex depression of α-thythm for the duration of a light stimulus. The blockage of α-rhythm was found to coincide in time with the onset of illumination. Correlation of these results with the findings on the conditioned reflex increase of electrical sensitivity in the eye leads to the assumption that the α-rhythm block is connected with increase in the sensitivity of the visual analyser. It should be pointed out, however, that further study of the conditioned reflex depression of α-rhythm became detached from the problem of conditioned sensory reflexes (Beritov and Vorobyev, 1943; Livanov, 1952; Laptev, 1949 etc.). Furthermore, the name of conditioned sensory reflex, can hardly be applied to a α-rhythm block in the occipital area, unconnected with any actual change in the sensitivity of the analyser. All the conditioned reflexes just described, concerned with changes in the functional state of analysers and developed by their correlation with unconditioned adequate stimuli, can be grouped under the term "*conditioned adaptation reflexes*". This group would include conditioned contraction of the pupil and conditioned lowering of sensitivity to light, conditioned increase of the electrical sensitivity of the eye and conditioned changes in the electrical activity of brain.

The conditioned defensive reactions are much more widely known. The widespread use of defence reinforcement (usually in the form of electrical stimulation of the skin) in experimental work involving the elaboration of conditioned reflexes in man and animals, confirms the fact that the defence reaction, including its somatic and autonomic components, can be reproduced in conditioned reflex form. The role of these reflexes in producing changes of sensitivity in analysers and their influence on the processes of perception in man have not, however, been sufficiently studied. It is well known, nevertheless, that a non-signal stimulus can, after correlation with a painful stimulus, reproduce a complex reaction including perception of pain or a sharp increase in pain sensitivity. Pshonik's experiment (1952) is of major interest in this respect. This worker demonstrated that repeated application of painful stimuli to one point on the skin of the hand in man rendered a weak stimulus, subsequently applied to the same point, capable of evoking a sensation of pain and vascular reactions of defensive type.

D. Intra-analyser and Inter-analyser Connexions

The processes involved in the perception of a particular stimulus cannot be understood on the basis of either the conditioned reflex activity alone or the unconditioned reflex activity produced solely by the stimulus. The transformation of a stimulus in an analyser is a combination of conditioned and unconditioned reactions, appearing as a "unitary reaction" *sui generis*, to use the term coined by Krushinskii in 1948. Interaction of conditioned and unconditioned elements takes place after the simplest unconditioned stimuli and to single out the conditioned reflex components at first sight seems almost impossible.

Each analyser is, in fact, a combination of several afferent systems, differing in their properties. For example, the cutaneous analyser includes touch, temperature and pain components. Their thresholds of sensitivity and their speeds of impulse conduction are different. Consequently, an unconditioned stimulus acting on the skin for even a short period of time reaches the central nervous system in a complex form.

Anokhin concluded from his morpho-physiological and electrophysiological investigations that "the complex nature of an unconditioned reflex is already apparent in its receptor part" (Anokhin, 1949, p. 47). Laptev, (1949) made a special study of the breakdown, in micro-intervals of time, of an unconditioned stimulus into its components by virtue of the different properties of the afferent systems concerned in its perception. By registering the action potentials in the lingual nerve of the dog, he demonstrated that a food stimulus produces, at first, rapidly travelling tactile impulses, followed by those of temperature and, finally, the impulses of chemical stimulation.

Analysing these results, Anokhin drew attention to the possible development of conditioned reflexes in the analyser as a result even of unconditioned stimulation. In view of the time intervals, each antecedent stream of impulses can possibly serve as a conditioned stimulus for the impulse immediately following. Tactile impulses, which have the shortest latent period and the highest speed of transmission, can serve as signals for the subsequent chemical impulses. In this way certain aspects of an unconditioned stimulus can serve as signals of its other qualities. The principle of signalling between different afferent systems can be further developed and supplemented by the principle of signal relationships within a single afferent system, developing at various intervals of time during the action of an unconditioned stimulus on this afferent system. This means that every moment in continuous impulse formation can become a signal of intensification or weakening of the impulses immediately following. In this way the moment of application of the stimulus can apparently become a signal of its own duration, intensity and time of extinction.

The formation of conditioned reflexes within a single analyser system, as a result of the repetition of an unconditioned stimulus, and their role in the control of sensitivity, has not been specifically discussed in the literature. The numerous experiments described in connexion with conditioned sensory reflexes have only studied the mechanism by means of which a conditioned stimulus, e.g. sound, can reproduce the effects of an unconditioned stimulus, e.g. light, normally acting on another analyser. At the same time, the hypothesis that any, even the simplest unconditioned stimulus, acting only on one afferent system, is in fact a complex of stimuli, allows the explanation of its mechanism of action to be based on certain general principles for the development of conditioned reflexes with simultaneous and successive complexes and chains of stimuli acting on various analysers (Voronin, 1948; Kravkov, 1948). The view that every unconditioned stimulus is of complex nature suggests that the development of intra-analyser conditioned connexions is possible. It may also be suggested that the unconditioned adaptation reflexes set up within the analyser by an unconditioned stimulus become more complex and undergo changes after repeated application of the stimulus as a result of the elaboration of intra-analyser *conditioned adaptation reflexes*. Conditioned adaptation reactions can also develop in response to signals from other analysers. Inter-analyser connexions controlling analysed sensitivity have been experimentally investigated in great detail. For example, it has been demonstrated in a number of experiments that tactile, auditory, olfactory and verbal stimuli can become signals for conditioned reflex changes in sensitivity to light (Kravkov, 1948).

In reckoning the degree to which orientation, adaptation and defensive reactions involve various analysers, one can distinguish two types of connexion, embracing both conditioned, and the unconditioned reflex mechanisms, for control of the sensitivity of analysers, and manifesting themselves through these types of reaction. The two types of connexion are *intra-analyser* and *inter-analyser* connexions.

An important example of inter-analyser connexion, influencing the sensitivity of an analyser, is that formed on elaboration of an ordinary conditioned motor reflex. There is a need for special study of the changes occurring in the sensitivity of an analyser on transition from perception of a non-signal stimulus to perception of an agent which has become the signal for a conditioned reaction. This was not done when the interrelationship of analysers was investigated by Kravkov, (1948) and the problem has not been considered again until recently (Gershuni, 1955, 1957).

It can be assumed that in man the closure of conditioned reflex connexions results in changes in the perception of both the conditioned stimulus, and the unconditioned reinforcement. The reinforcement acts on the analyser receiving the conditioned stimulus and conversely, the conditioned stimulus influences the sensitivity of the analyser receiving the reinforcement.

Another example of inter-analyser connexions is the change in sensitivity of a signal-receiving analyser under the influence of organs participating in the corresponding reaction. When the role of return afferentiation from the motor apparatus during the production of any reflex is considered (Anokhin, 1949, 1955), it must be assumed that impulses arising in the motor apparatus can influence the exteroceptors. This assumption seems to be confirmed experimentally by the changes in sensitivity to light associated with muscular contraction (Kekcheyev, 1947; and others).

Furthermore, there is the fact that the response developed is connected with the uninterrupted flow of signals from the organs participating in the response reaction to the stimuli perceiving analysers.

Inter-analyser connexions capable of influencing the sensitivity of analysers are linked with the simultaneous or successive action of various exteroceptor stimuli. This group of inter-analyser connexions, concerned in the reception of stimuli, has been studied in great detail (Kravkov, 1948).

The complex transformation of signals received leads to the development of various adaptation reactions safeguarding the existence of the subject in the prevailing environmental conditions. The fact that the final result of this complex process is an appropriate and adequate adaptation reaction leads to the assumption that the reflex mechanism of action of the reinforcement on the activity of the analysers is of decisive importance.

The processes of perception of stimuli cannot be divorced from the reflex adaptation reactions of the organism as a whole and thus, perception of even the simplest stimulus is based on processes involving conditioned and unconditioned reflexes which participate in the control of the sensitivity of the analyser acted upon by the stimulus in question.

CHAPTER 2

Measurement of the Functional State of Analysers

A. Sensitivity and Its Measurement

The reflex changes taking place within the analyser, as a result of stimulation call for specific quantitative evaluation, and measurement of sensitivity is the most widely accepted method of assessment of its functional state.

In psycho-physiology, "sensitivity", is usually taken to imply the ability of the analyser to respond to the first application of a stimulus of minimum intensity capable of evoking the appropriate sensation (Krakov, 1946). The sensitivity is inversely proportional to the threshold, i.e. the lowest intensity of a stimulus acting for a sufficiently long period capable of producing sensation.*

The usual method of measuring sensitivity is determination of the threshold, based on subjective perception of a given stimulus of increasing or diminishing intensity. This subjective method has been widely used since the work of Fechner (1889) and, though by virtue of the powers of differentiation and the exactitude of the verbal and motor reactions of a normal healthy subject it is sufficiently reliable in certain cases (Vavilov, 1950), it cannot be used for all the investigation necessary for more accurate assessment of the sensitivity of analysers. It is in fact only suitable for the measurement of one kind of sensitivity, namely sensitivity to stimuli which in the case of man assume signal significance as a result of the preliminary verbal instruction usually given in this type of experiment. It cannot be used for the measurement of sensitivity to stimuli which are non-signal for man, or if the subject consciously misinterprets his sensations. Finally, although the method might be reliable in the case of healthy adults, it is quite unsuitable for use with small children or in the presence of pathological conditions associated with sensory disturbances, or of motor disturbances involving speech and movements. The question arises, therefore, of making use of reactions which, by transforming

---

* The inclusion of the time factor in the definition is essential, as in the case of stimuli of short duration, the threshold value depends on the duration of their action (Hoorweg–Weiss law). The threshold is only independent of the time factor when the stimuli are of sufficiently long duration—over 3 seconds (Makarov, 1952; Pieron, 1952).

the pre-arranged verbal or motor response of the subject, help to assess the functional state of the analyser (Gershuni, 1950; Tato, 1954; Perl, Galambos and Gloring, 1953; Hardy and Bordley, 1952; and others).

The reactions which can be used to determine sensitivity include changes which take place either directly in the receptive system stimulated, or reflexly in other organs;

(a) Local peripheral reactions occurring in the receptor and the nervous elements immediately concerned (cochlear reaction, electroretinogram, action potentials in nerves). These reactions can also be produced from preparations of the auditory and visual organs (Granit, 1947; Wever and Lawrence, 1954; and others), but they do not reflect the sensitivity of the analyser as a whole, and do not provide any indication as to the possible utilization of these stimulations in reflex acts.

(b) The reaction of the cortical ends of the analysers, manifested as electrical activity, (primary cortical response) in the cortical projection areas of the analyser concerned as a result of stimulation of its peripheral end. This reaction, however, can be registered only in acute experiments against the background of a generalized inhibitory state and with the leads directly applied to the cortex of the animal. It can not, as a rule, be recorded in conscious man with leads applied to the scalp.

(c) Orientation reflexes characterized by widespread excitation (ocular and head movements, peripheral vasoconstriction, galvanic skin reactions), and arising with the participation of either cortical or subcortical centres. The orientation reflex is the first response of the body to any new stimulus. It would seem therefore that this reaction would provide the most accurate guide as to the sensitivity of the analyser but its tendency to become extinguished with repeated stimulation makes it unsuitable for the purpose.

The extinction of the orientation reflex raises a new problem not touched upon in the classical physiology of sensory organs. This is that the threshold of sensitivity, which has been assumed to be constant and has been usually determined by statistical analysis of the results of a great number of experiments, is in fact variable and depends on the very number of the measurements carried out. The threshold, as determined by the orientation reaction. rises as the number of measurements increases (Gershuni, 1955).

(d) Specialized adaptation reflexes based on the analyser undergoing stimulation, operating at various levels of the central nervous system and concerned with the adaptation of the analyser to the stimulus (pupillary light reflex, tonic changes in the muscles of the tympanic membrane resulting in adaptation of the auditory receptor). The great advantage of adaptation reactions is their stability in face of repeated stimulation which makes them a more accurate measure of the threshold of sensitivity. The fact that they can be brought into operation only by an adequate stimulus is a disadvantage.

c

A special reaction has to be selected for measurement of the sensitivity of each analyser, and this makes the adoption of any universal method very difficult.

(e) Defence reactions brought into operation, when the intensity of the stimulus reaches such proportions that it threatens the integrity of the body (withdrawal reflex, dilatation of the pupil etc.). These, as well as the orientation reactions, can be produced by a variety of stimuli of sufficient intensity. The general tendency to withdraw, and the sensation of pain in the ear occurring as a result of intense auditory stimulation are examples. The usefulness of the defence reactions for the purpose under consideration is strictly limited. It can be applied only to determination of the threshold of pain and not to measurement of sensitivity at lower levels.

(f) A great variety of conditioned reflexes formed by the combination of indifferent with painful or other specialized stimuli can be used. If they are employed for the determination of sensitivity, it is the sensitivity of the analyser as a whole, including its central endings, which is measured.

Since the work of Pavlov, (1947, 1949) conditioned reflexes have been widely adopted as constituting an objective method for investigation of sensitivity in animals, (Andreyev, 1935) and in man, (Bekhterev, 1928; Myasishchev, 1929; Gershuni, 1949, 1955, 1957; Samsonova, 1953), and can be used for measurement of the sensitivity of analysers of all kinds. However, a problem arises, similar to that presented by the orientation reflex as an index of sensitivity. Whereas the threshold as determined by means of the orientation reflex rises with increase in the number of estimations, the threshold as estimated by means of a conditioned reflex tends to fall to a certain limit with increase in the number of combinations of the conditioned stimulus and its reinforcement (Maruseva, 1955; Gershuni, 1955). Consequently, whenever a conditioned reflex is used for the purpose of estimation of sensitivity, one should not forget that even a deliberately supra-threshold stimulus will not be capable of producing the expected reaction if the conditioned link is not sufficiently strong. Any temporary inhibition of the link will have also a negative effect on the threshold of sensitivity. Thus sensitivity is not only determined by the properties of the analyser, but also by those of the reaction registered. Gershuni concludes that the analyser sensitivity (E) which always gives a definite reaction R should be expressed as E_r. Sensitivity, therefore, cannot be discussed in general terms, but only after consideration of the types of reaction used for its estimation. Sensitivity as determined by the verbal reactions connected with sensation is a special form of sensitivity. The threshold values as obtained by the recording of different reactions may differ from one another. Thus, sensitivity measured by verbal response, can in some conditions be lower than sensitivity as defined by orientation or defence reflexes. This is because weak stimuli remain subsensory; they are unrecognized by the subject, although they can give rise to orientation or defence reflexes.

Although estimation of thresholds is based on the recording of one or another reaction (verbal, conditioned, motor, orientation etc.) the problem of the essential intrinsic sensitivity of the analyser remains unsolved. A distinction must be made between the threshold for one or other reaction and the excitation threshold of the analyser concerned in producing the reaction. These two thresholds may be the same or may differ in value. In order to arrive at an accurate value for the threshold of excitability of an analyser from the threshold for the reaction, knowledge of the properties of the reaction and the nature of its relationship with the analyser under consideration is essential.

It is necessary to explain that the *threshold of reaction* is taken as the lowest intensity of stimulus capable of producing a just noticeable reaction, whether conditioned or unconditioned. The *threshold of excitability* of an analyser is the lowest intensity of stimulus, which has to be applied in order to excite the analyser as a whole including its cortical endings, "analyser" being considered as an integral system of peripheral and central mechanisms essential for the transmission and perception of information on the properties of the stimulus. It is also evident that the analyser threshold differs from the receptor threshold, as the latter defines the sensitivity of the peripheral part of the analyser only.

The difference between the threshold of discrimination (the lowest noted alteration of the stimulus) and the differentiation of conditioned reflexes, can serve as an illustration of the distinction made between the analyser and the reaction thresholds.

Usually, the ability to differentiate necessitates the ability to remember (Teplov and Borisova, 1957); it is complicated by a conflict between the inhibitory and excitatory processes within the conditioned reflex activity, and it does not always reflect the full potentialities of the analyser to detect minimal change in the stimulus.

Although the analyser threshold and the reaction threshold do not always coincide, one can, from study of the reaction, draw conclusions as to the degree of sensitivity of the analyser concerned. Comparison of the thresholds of various reactions becomes an important method for estimation of the true analyser threshold. In the case of man, however, the objective, direct registration of the specific cortical reactions of analysers is difficult with present investigational techniques. One must therefore select and use indirect equivalents which will give reliable indications of the excitability thresholds of analysers.

Much care is needed when the analyser threshold is assessed from reaction thresholds. The nature of the relationship the reaction bears to the analyser under consideration, and the level of analyser activity with which the reaction is connected must be considered. The fact that the analyser can still carry on its function in its simple form in spite of certain lesions involving its central parts, should also be kept in mind. It is thus a wise practice to define the level of the analysing mechanism involved in the reaction under consideration. The connexions between various reactions and the various levels of activity in the same analyser assume major importance in a number of cases. This point can be illustrated by a pupillary reflex evoked by light directed on the blind spot of the retina in the presence of cortical hemianopia. In such a case the subject does not see the light, the sensitivity of the analyser as a whole is diminished, and the pupillary reflex is the result of the operation of the sub-cortical centres of the analyser and is a measure of the latter's sensitivity. It follows that a comparison of different reactions may help in localizing the level of a lesion in an analyser, or in defining the level at which its function is disturbed (Gershuni, 1955).

To sum up, by distinguishing between reaction thresholds and thresholds of analyser excitability, we avoid oversimplified conclusions as to the threshold of the analyser based on measurements of the threshold for a particular reaction.

B. Reactivity and Lability

The threshold of sensitivity fails to provide any reliable indication as to the ability of the analyser to respond to supraliminal stimuli. There are cases in which raised threshold (diminished sensitivity) is associated with a more intense reaction to stronger supraliminal stimulation. This ability of the analysers to respond to supraliminal stimuli can, with advantage, be described as reactivity, the measure of which is the magnitude of the reaction produced. Therefore the measurement of reactivity always involves registration of reactions (conditioned, orientation etc.).

A distinction must be made between the reactivity of an analyser and the reactivity of a reflex arc which includes the analyser and is concerned in the production of the reaction in question. The two values can be identical or different. A full knowledge of the properties of the reaction produced is essential for assessment of the value of the reactivity of the analyser from that of the arc. A reliable assessment of reactivity cannot be based on the results obtained with a stimulus of one supraliminal intensity. The effects of a wide range of stimuli of various supraliminal intensities on the magnitude of the reaction must be studied. The amplitude of the reaction is thus a quantitative measure of reactivity or the capacity to respond to exogenous, supraliminal stimulation. Other features of the reaction, such as its duration and its latent period, also contribute to a full picture of reactivity. In the case of man, analyser reactivity in relation to various stimuli may be indicated by scaled assessments of the strengths of these stimuli. An arbitrary numerical scale of intensities is arranged and the subject gives the "number" corresponding to his subjective appreciation of the strength of the stimuli (Stevens, 1951).

The reactivity of the reflex arc is not constant. It may change as a result of repeated applications of a stimulus. The depression of α-rhythm in the occipital area in response to a supraliminal auditory stimulus diminishes when the stimulus is applied repeatedly. If α-rhythm depression is taken as evidence of the state of the cortex we may speak of decline in its reactivity with repetition of supraliminal auditory stimulation.

Changes of reactivity as a result of supraliminal stimulation can be demonstrated during the elaboration of conditioned reflexes, in which, as a result of reinforcement, an agent, previously indifferent in relation to a particular function, becomes active and there is increase of reactivity in relation to the now conditioned stimulus.

Thus the reactivity of any conditioned or orientation reflex, is not at any given moment a direct measure of the reactivity of the analyser. Only detailed analysis of the features of the reaction can lead to reliable conclusions as to the real reactivity of the analyser.

Changes in reactivity manifest themselves not only as variations in the amplitude of the reaction as measured objectively, but also as variations in the intensity of the stimulus as assessed by the subject. Comparison of both will give a more reliable indication as to the reactivity of the analyser.

When the properties of the reactions recorded are known, and the reactivity of the analyser has been assessed from these reactions, the intrinsic capacity of the analyser to react to this particular stimulus can be defined. Just as in the case of sensitivity determinations, the distinction already made between the analyser reactivity and the reactivity of the reflex arc prevents any hasty conclusions on the reactivity of the analyser based on the latter.

An important problem in any investigation of the processes of perception is that of the connexion between sensitivity and reactivity. The absolute sensitivity of the analyser is, to a certain degree, an index of its reactivity or its capacity to respond to supraliminal stimuli. The general logarithmic dependence of sensation on stimulus intensity as expressed in threshold units, is well known (Fechner, 1889; Lazarev, 1947). This law also governs the objectively recorded reactions of an analyser. Thus, the contraction of the pupil is proportional to the logarithm of the light intensity (Pieron, 1952). The amplitude of the microphonic cochlear effect is proportional to the logarithm of the pressure exerted by the sound wave (Wever and Lawrence, 1954). A similar relationship can also be observed in the case of a single nerve fibre, in which the frequency of impulses increases in proportion to the intensity of stimulus (Hartridge, 1950).

The regularity with which the magnitude of reaction increases with intensity of stimulus may be upset and then the absolute sensitivity value bears no relation to the response to supraliminal stimuli. An example of such interference and the resulting disparity between reactivity and sensitivity, is seen in the irregular increment of loudness (recruitment) in certain diseases of the auditory apparatus, when despite a higher absolute threshold of sensitivity, the loudness of middle and high intensity sounds is for the patient the same or sometimes higher than in the normal ear (Huizing, 1952). At the same time there may be lowering of the pain threshold so that a sound, readily tolerated by the healthy ear, will give rise to a sensation of pain in the affected ear. In this case the increase of the absolute threshold, which is the evidence of diminished sensitivity, is not accompanied by any comparable lowering of reactivity, which on the contrary can even be slightly raised for stimuli of medium or high intensity. Despite being linked to absolute sensitivity (Fechner's law), reactivity may, therefore, be altered in such a way that the relationship becomes disturbed.

The orientation reaction may reveal even greater differences between reactivity and sensitivity. For example, after the reaction to very intense sounds has ceased, the reaction can continue to appear in response to weaker sounds, which means that, in this case, reactivity to strong stimuli, is lower than that to weak stimuli.

One of the important parameters of the functional state of an analyser is its lability, as determined by the greatest number of stimuli which can be registered by it in a unit of time (Vvedenskii, 1952, Ukhtomskii, 1951). The concept of lability has now been extended to higher, including cortical, centres (Rusinov, 1957). The interest aroused by measurement of the lability of various analysers is therefore understandable (Lebedinskii, 1958; Semenovskaia and Struchkov, 1953).

As in the case of sensitivity and reactivity, the lability of an analyser should not be confused with the lability of the reflex arc of which the analyser forms part. It is clear, for instance, that the lability of the arc of the cutaneogalvanic reflex is extraordinarily small, and if the frequency of auditory stimuli is increased to several a minute, the reflex ceases to operate. The lability of the auditory apparatus is obviously much higher. The distinction between the lability of reaction and analyser lability is not, however, always as clear as this. How far a reaction reflects the actual lability of an analyser is a particularly difficult question in the case of the electrical reactions of the cortex, the nature of which has not yet been sufficiently elucidated. The best known method for the determination of the lability of an analyser is observation of the stimulus frequency at which fusion takes place. In the case of the visual analyser, this occurs when the frequency of flicker reaches its critical value, or the critical frequency of electrical stimulation results in the disappearance of phosphene (Kravkov, 1950). The critical or fusion frequency of intermittent light is the best measure of the lability of the visual analyser.

In addition to the maximum frequency of stimulation still perceived by the analyser, lability can be described in terms of the oscillatory processes which are representative of the basic activity of the analyser. The frequencies of the "spontaneous" oscillatory electrical activity of the brain range from 0·5 to 60 c/s.

According to modern conceptions, the oscillatory rhythms arising from exogenous and endogenous stimuli are connected with cycles of excitation developing in the chains of cortical or thalamo-cortical neurons (Brazier, 1955, Smirno, 1956). Eccles, (1953) found a direct connexion between the frequency of the "spontaneous" cortical potentials on the one hand, and the refractory period and excitability of the cortical cells on the other. On the basis of his study of motor neurones, he states that a cortical cell discharges approximately every 100 msec, during which time its excitability is renewed. This would correspond to a rhythm, of the order of 10 c/s, which is within the α-rhythm band. With increased intensity of stimulation some of the neurons discharge during the period of relative refractoriness i.e. at less than 100 msec intervals, and this gives rise to a higher frequency. The cortical rhythm, the level of stimulation remaining constant, is thus determined by the rate of recovery of the nerve cells. The frequency of the rhythm is an expression of the number of excitation cycles completed in a unit of time and depends on the average rate at which a majority of cortical neurons recover their excitability; the predominant frequency can therefore be taken as a measure of lability of the cortical part of the analysers (Golikov, 1956; G. D. Smirnov, 1956; Rusinov, 1957). There are thus two ways of investigating lability. One is the use of interrupted afferent stimulation and determination of the highest frequency reproduced by the cerebral rhythm; the other is the study of "spontaneous" electrical activity and its predominant rhythms. These two methods are employed together in the study of electrical changes produced in the brain by rhythmic (generally photic) stimulation of varied frequency. Adrian, (1947) and other workers have shown that the electrical activity of the brain is changed by a repetitive light stimulus in such a way that the same frequency pattern or a multiple thereof can be reproduced. The technique of automatic frequency analysis (Walter, 1953) extended the scope of this method.

C. **Poly-Effector Reaction Recording (Electropolygraphic Technique)**

Knowledge of the inter-relationship of the reflexes participating in the control of sensitivity and, consequently, in the determination of the efficacy of the stimulus is essential for an understanding of stimulus perception. Extensive data from only one reaction to a stimulus is, however, insufficient for investigation of the numerous aspects of analyser activity. Only *combined* recording of a number of reactions or their successive investigation under identical conditions will reveal the relationships between the various reflexes participating in such activity. The importance of the combined recording of a number of somatic and autonomic reactions in the investigation of conditioned reflex activity has been pointed out by a number of authors. The principle of poly-effector recording was enunciated by Myasishchev (1949), who in the course of his investigations on man, came across a considerable amount of divergence between the autonomic and motor components of various reactions. As a result of experiments on animals, Anokhin, (1949) also came to the conclusion that the combined, simultaneous recording of secretory and motor components of the conditioned, (salivary) reflex is of prime importance. The poly-effector recording technique provides both quantitative and qualitative data, and consequently, a better insight into the mechanism of the processes observed. The responses of the body always appear in the form of complicated reactions exhibiting both inhibitory and stimulatory influences. Inhibition of an external conditioned motor reaction, for example, may be the outcome of a major intensification of autonomic activity, indicative of the development of an excitatory process (Anokhin, 1955).

The reactions selected for recording should serve to distinguish and demarcate orienting, special adaptional and defensive reflexes so that the complex reflex acts which produce changes in the excitation of analysers can be differentiated and analysed as completely as possible. Correlation of the data provided by electroencephalography (E.E.G.) with directly obtained indices for the elaboration, establishment and variation of conditioned reflexes is one of the important modern lines of research on the dynamics of nervous processes (Motokawa and Huzimori (1949); Maiorchik and Spirin (1951); Mushkina (1956); Mukhova (1956); Gastaut, Roger, Dougier and Regis (1957)). The advantages of such combined studies of a number of indices have been demonstrated in a number of investigations. They include Gershuni's work (1949), in which combined recordings were made of conditioned motor reactions, cutaneogalvanic reflexes, eye deviation as part of an orientation reaction, and E.E.G. changes during the completion of a conditioned reflex in man. Peimer and Faddeyeva (1956), obtained simultaneous electroencephalographic, electrocardiographic and electromyographic tracings which enabled them to speak of dynamic relationships between cortex and subcortex during the production of conditioned reflexes in man. With suitable data units the electroencephalograph can be used for the recording of pupillary (Atayev, 1955), vascular (Babskii, 1954) and motor (Alekseyev, 1953) reactions, and in the investigation of sensory processes (Gershuni, 1955) as well as for the recording of electrical activity in tissues. One great advantage of the electropolygraphic technique which has not been adequately stressed should be noted. It may be difficult to establish the true nature of a reflex by means of one reaction. For example, the pupil can dilate as a result of darkness, or in response to sound or pain. The dilation of the pupil by itself, therefore, does not give any indication as to which reflex actually has been brought into operation. Simultaneous registration of a number of reactions allows of differentiation between the activities of separate functional systems although each particular reaction may be involved in several systems. With this method, mistakes can be avoided. Comparison of the values obtained with various reactions helps to establish the real value of the threshold for a complicated systemic reflex, and to differentiate the thresholds of excitability for orientation, defence and other specialized reactions. This in turn leads to more reliable conclusions regarding the sensitivity and reactivity of an analyser.

This electropolygraphic technique was employed in several phases of the work to be described; more particularly, for registration of the latent period and motor reaction in connexion with the galvanic skin effect of Féré; for the plethysmographic recording of the vascular reactions of the head and hand, combined with recording of motor reactions; for complex tracings of the electrical activity of the brain and the muscles of the hand; and in the recording of eye movements, and respiration, pulse and blink reflexes. In addition, the pupillary reactions to infra-red rays were registered by means of a Ciné-recorder, and the light sensitivity by means of an automatic monochromatic adaptometer producing a continuous record (Sokolov, 1955). With intermittent "impulse" stimulation, used for the determination of sensitivity, it was possible to measure all parameters of the reaction produced (latent period, amplitude, duration), in addition to the threshold of excitability. The duration of each stimulus was usually 5 sec. If no response resulted, the stimulus was considered subliminal in respect of the reaction in question. It should be pointed out that, as far as measurements of sensitivity are concerned, this form of stimulation gives the most accurate and the least variable results, as shown by audiometric studies (Tsireshkin, 1953). The threshold was usually determined by the technique of minimal changes (the "limiting method"). Stimuli, subliminal at first, were applied every 30–60 sec. As soon as a reaction was observed, the stimulus intensity was then reduced gradually. If the thresholds, as indicated by the various indices, differed, the thresholds for individual reactions were determined. Parallel with the determination of the excitability thresholds of various analysers, and investigation of the influence of variation in the conditions of the experiment on such threshold, a study was made of the nature of the reflexes produced by subliminal stimuli.

PART TWO

THE PERCEPTION OF
NON-SIGNAL STIMULI

Vascular and cutaneogalvanic components of orienting, thermoregulatory and defensive reflexes

A. Vascular Reactions in Various Reflex Acts

In this chapter the reflex mechanisms of perception, as observed by the vascular and cutaneogalvanic reactions of man, are discussed.

Investigation of the processes of perception, carried out in terms of the classical psychophysiology of the sensory organs, involved on the part of the subject, a performance of a verbal or motor reaction in accordance with pre-liminary instructions. Such a reaction would denote the perception of the stimulus, which in the meantime, had acquired the significance of a signal. The problem of perception of the stimuli *not* accorded this significance could not be studied in these conditions.

If the perception of true non-signal stimuli is to be investigated, no such preliminary instruction, which links in advance a definite group of stimuli with the response of the subject, should be given.

One method which can be adopted is to question the subject at the end of the experiment, but the drawback here is that the results are necessarily dependent on the subject's memory.

Another method is to record objective reactions which are produced by the stimulus, and which are themselves intimately connected with the process of its perception. The difficulty here is that we are not in possession of sufficiently reliable data linking the reactions with the act of perception of the stimulus.

Before further consideration of non-signal stimuli, the term "*indifferent stimulus*" requires closer definition. Strictly speaking, "indifferent stimulus" is a contradiction in terms and does not exist. Every stimulus is unconditioned at least in respect of the analyser on which it acts. In addition, however, to its direct action on the receptor and its associated centres, every stimulus also sets into operation certain reflexes.

Depending on its intensity, quality and "novelty", a stimulus gives rise to reflex activity which involves different organs in different degrees. The said stimulus remains indifferent or becomes indifferent with continued use only in relation to the activity of certain organs. Reflex adjustments taking place in the analyser under the influence of stimulation are of varied significance. Some are concerned with adaptation of the sensitivity of the analyser to the intensity of the stimulus (*adaptation reflexes*). Such are the thermo-regulatory reflexes developed as a result of thermal stimulation and aiming at the limitation of the effects of this stimulation by means of such reactions as sweating, or the dilatation of the surface blood vessels. Enhancement of sweating and peripheral vasodilatation resulting from exposure to heat, and inhibition of sweating and peripheral vasoconstriction in response to cold, regulate the exchange of heat with the environment, and prevent overheating or excessive chilling of the body. Other reflexes bring about increased sensitivity during listening, sniffing and watching, and in this way facilitate a more intimate knowledge of the object (*orientation reflexes*). In the vascular system these reflexes manifest themselves as vasoconstriction of the limbs. When the intensity of the stimulus reaches certain limits and threatens the integrity of the body, a qualitatively different defence reaction is brought into operation, which is associated with the sensation of pain. The *defence reflex* also produces constriction of the vessels of the limbs. If only the peripheral vasomotor reactions were considered, various reflex acts could not be distinguished. Sound, pain, cold, all produce peripheral vasoconstriction. Heat is the only exception and produces peripheral vasodilatation. The problem of differentiation of these undoubtedly functionally distinct reflexes arises and careful analysis of each as an isolated specialized entity is necessary.

The reactions of the peripheral and cerebral vessels have been selected for differentiation of the vascular manifestations of orientation, thermoregulation and defence reflexes.

As shown by Pshonik (1952), Rogova (1951), Musyashchikova (1952) and others, any new stimulus gives rise to peripheral vasoconstriction which becomes weaker and ceases with repetitive stimulation. Painful stimuli, and the application of cold, give rise to similar reactions which do not disappear with repetition. Reaction to heat consists of peripheral vasodilatation and is less stable. Istmanova (1885) recorded plethysmographic changes in the living brain (in a case of head injury with a bone defect), and demonstrated cerebral vasodilatation following the application of a variety of stimuli. Bentelev (1956) made similar observations. Further confirmation can be found in Klossovskii's (1951) direct observation of cerebral capillaries during experiments on animals, and in electrical measurements of the volume of cerebral vessels as obtained by Kedrov and Naumenko (1954). The cerebral vaso-dilatation reaction is similar to peripheral vasoconstriction in all its properties except in the sign of the reaction. It depends on the intensity of the stimulus and dies out with repetition. At the same time the cerebral vessels show a specific reaction to thermal stimuli, which becomes particularly clear in the vasoconstrictor response to cold. The method adopted for differentiation of orientation, thermoregulation and defence reflexes (Sokolov, 1955; Vinogradov and Sokolov, 1957), namely the simultaneous recording of vascular changes in the hand and head, is based on the reciprocal relationships observed between the cerebral and peripheral vessels during the action of various stimuli producing orientation reflexes, and *concomitant* changes in these vessels in response to thermal stimuli. There is little opportunity, however, for the direct observation of the cerebral vascular reactions in man and special methods had to be devised (Kedrov and Naumenko, 1954). We measured the volumetric changes in an area supplied by the temporal artery, which are thought to reflect closely those of the cerebral circulation. In addition, we introduced into the external auditory meatus an olive-shaped device, closely fitting and connected by air-transmission to the plethysmograph. This allowed us to record the changes in the air volume of the auditory meatus—which served as an index of the volume of the vessels of the head. The study of vascular reaction is an important part in laboratory and clinical investigations. Since the work of Istomanov (1885) plethysmography has been widely adopted as a method for the recording of volumetric vascular changes. Water plethysmographs of various types are in common use (Pshonik, 1952; Rogov, 1951) but they are bulky and cumbersome. Recently a pneumatic finger plethysmograph has been introduced. It provides for photographic recording of vascular reactions on the ciné-camera principle. Babskii (1954), has been using wire recording units for the registration of information on variations in pressure. Kedrov and Naumenko (1954) devised a method of recording vascular reactions based on variations of tissue resistance to high frequency alternating currents, and this method has been found useful in laboratory practice. Animal experiments involving the use of an artificial transparent skull provided an opportunity for direct observation of cerebral vessels (Klossovskii, 1951).

Indirect methods for the recording of vascular changes include such techniques as the measurement of infra-red radiation, surface temperature, and light reflected by the skin, but on the whole they are not always reliable as far as the measurement of vascular changes proper are concerned. For instance, in the state of high nervous tension created in the subject by the frightening effect of an electrical spark, the reactions include peripheral vasoconstriction, increased skin temperature and acceleration of the pulse rate. The rise in skin temperature in this instance, contradicts the accepted view that vasoconstriction is associated with a fall in temperature, and it seems that it is an independent element of the emotional reaction (Barker and Taylor, 1954).

In our experiments we have made use of the Watchall–Filippovich finger plethysmograph. Essentially this consists of a special, highly sensitive, metal capsule with mirrors attached in such a way that their angles of reflection change as a result of variations of the air pressure in the capsule. The capsule is connected by rubber tubing to a glass tube into which fits a finger of the subject. The air in this closed system transmits all variations in the volume of the finger, and these variations thus become converted into changes in the position of the mirror on to which a beam of light is directed from an illuminator. The movements of the reflected beam are recorded on standard photographic film moving at standard speed. Two plethysmographic tracings, time intervals, and moments of application of the stimuli, are all recorded on the film. In the experiments the subject's reaction, motor or verbal, was recorded on the same film or noted in the written record of the experiment in relation to the lighting of an indicator lamp connected to the reaction key operated by the subject.

Pure tones from an audiometer, of strictly predetermined intensity, photic stimuli and tactile stimuli were used. Electrodermal stimulation was produced with constant current impulses, 2 msec in length and 100 c/s, from a square wave generator, applied for 5 sec at a time to the skin on the back of the hand. Vessels filled with water at various temperatures served as thermal stimuli. A heated ceramic source of infra-red radiation provided thermal stimulation without tactile component. The advantage of infra-red radiation as a thermal stimulus is the absence of any involvement of tactile receptors, which is unavoidable if other methods of thermal stimulation are employed.

As a variety of stimuli with the exception of heat, give rise to similar vasoconstrictor reactions in the limbs, it became imperative to devise a method which would provide means for differentiation of the various types of reflex. For this purpose the vascular reactions of the head were recorded, in addition to those of one or two phalanges of one of the fingers of the left hand. A small capsule, covered with thin rubber, similar to that described above, was fixed in the area of the bifurcation of the temporal and frontal arteries by means of a head piece. It was closely applied to the surface and was connected to a plethysmograph. This device provided for uninterrupted recording of the volumetric changes of the vessels of the head occurring simultaneously with the changes in the limb vessels. During the experiment the vascular reactions could be followed through a small window in the apparatus on which the beams of light from both capsules were reflected. During an experiment the subject was seated in a comfortable armchair and was separated from the investigator by a screen. The record of the vascular reactions included the latent period, the rate of decrement, the duration from onset to return to the base line, and the amplitude of change. In a number of cases the reaction coefficient—the product of duration and amplitude—was calculated. The data obtained from the temporal area were found to be closely comparable with those recorded directly from cerebral vessels in cases with skull defects. Cerebral vasodilatation also coincided with similar change in the retina, associated with the increased cerebral supply.

Simultaneous recording of vascular changes in the head and hand in healthy man served to distinguish the agents capable of giving rise to orientation, thermoregulatory and pain reactions respectively. The existence of a link between the cerebral and temporal vascular changes provided an opportunity for the study of the dynamic relationships between adaptation (thermoregulatory), orientation, and defence reflexes in adults and children in relation to the perception by man of stimuli of various kinds and intensities.

B. Vascular reactions in the Course of the Application of Stimuli Evoking Orienting Reflexes

The activities of stimuli of various kinds and intensities were compared by recording cephalic and peripheral vascular changes. The stimuli were usually applied for 10 sec, but in certain instances this period was extended to 30–40 sec. The first application of many different stimuli—heat (hand warmed to 40°C by means of infra-red rays), cold (glass of ice water 0°C), sound (metronome, 60–120/min, or pure tones), light, tactile (touching the skin with a small brush), proprioceptive (bending a finger), electrocutaneous (constant current 2-msec square wave pulses, 100 c/s.)—was found to give rise to the same kind of *reciprocal reaction*, namely vasoconstriction in the finger and vasodilatation of the cephalic vessels [Figs. 1(*a*) and 4(*a*)]. The only exceptions were strong electrocutaneous stimuli giving rise to a sensation of pain, and loud, unpleasant sounds, both of which produced immediate responses in the form of cephalic and peripheral vasoconstriction. Further study of various stimuli has showed that this reciprocal vasomotor reaction varied with the nature and intensity of the stimuli. With repetitive stimulation the reaction ceased to appear and showed all the features of the gradual extinction of an orientation reflex.

The vascular component of the orientation reflex, manifesting itself as a gradually increasing vasoconstriction in the limbs, appears with a latent period of 2·5–5 sec, and a characteristic feature is the return of the volumetric curve of the vessels to its original level while the stimulus is still in operation. The reaction lasts 15–20 sec and reaches its maximum in the seventh second from the time of application of the stimulus. It can also be brought about by a change in the intensity of the stimulus in either direction and, in this case, the intensity of the reaction corresponds to the extent of the change. The "novelty" of the stimulus is of decisive importance, and it depends on the original background upon which the stimulus acts. Extinction of the vascular component of the orientation reflex is seen as diminished volumetric change

D

in the vessels, with a quicker return of the volume curve to the base line, an increased latent period and, finally, complete cessation of the reaction. Extinction of the cephalic reaction proceeds in a different way from that in the hand; the former is extinguished first [Fig. 1(*a*), (*b*)].

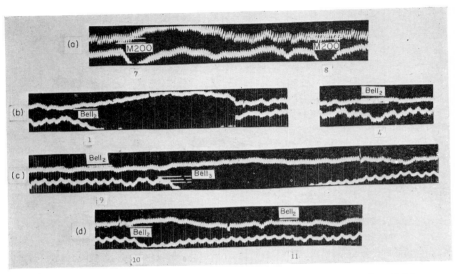

Fig. 1.   Vascular reactions in the head and hand to acoustic stimuli. (*a*)—Subject
G.P., April 1955. (*b*), (*c*), (*d*)—Subject G.A., April 1955.

Figure 1(*a*) shows cephalic vasodilatation and peripheral vasoconstriction in response to sound (metronome-200/min). Repetitive stimulation gives rise to a reaction, which grows weaker in time. First, the cephalic reaction is extinguished (M-200; 7–8). The duration of reaction diminishes. Figure 1(*b*), (*c*) and (*d*) show the gradual extinction of the response to a bell of medium intensity (Bell$_2$—1, 4, 9). Extinction is observed first in the case of the cephalic reaction. The reduced duration of the reaction and the reduced fall of the tracing together with the prolongation of the latent period, can all be clearly seen. When a new strong stimulus (Bell$_3$), giving rise to a similar reaction is applied, the inhibition of the vasomotor reactions to Bell$_2$ is temporarily removed only to return soon (10, 11).*

Extinction of the vasomotor reactions to sound, light, tactile and weak electrocutaneous stimuli, as well as extinction of the motor elements of the orientation reflex, and the extinctive inhibition of conditioned reflexes, are

* In all Figures, the upper curve represents cephalic, and the lower curve peripheral vessels. Vasoconstriction is shown as deflection downwards and vasodilatation as deflection upwards.

characteristically undulant. The reactions on the verge of extinction show episodes of intensification, without any noticeable cause, before final extinction (Vinogradova and Sokolov, 1955). Chronic extinction from one experiment to another can be seen, when a stimulus fails completely to produce a reaction immediately following its first application.

Differences between the process of extinction as observed in the vasomotor reactions of the hand and head respectively correspond to the vasomotor background activities in those two anatomical areas. The vasomotor curve for the hand tends to be labile and more easily influenced by endogenous or exogenous agents. The temporal area curve is more stable and shows practically no third order waves or spontaneous oscillations which are frequently seen in the case of the hand vasomotor curve. Evidence of respiratory interference, however, can also be found in the case of the cephalic curve, especially if the subject is tired. Cases occur in which respiratory interference affects only one of the curves [Figs. 1(a) and 3(d)].

There is a marked difference between the vasomotor responses of the head and hand to external stimuli. The cephalic response has a longer latent period, is longer in total duration and the corresponding curve is smoother and declines more slowly (Fig. 1).

A characteristic feature of the reciprocal reactions of the head and hand, and at the same time an important point in favour of the orientative reflex nature of those reactions, is the re-emergence of the reaction in response to a new stimulus, and temporary disinhibition of the reactions to a previously-used stimulus as a result of the action of a new agent. Disinhibition by a new stimulus occurs more readily in the case of the vasomotor reactions of the hand [Fig. 1(c) and (d)]. The absence of any specific stimuli for the reciprocal reaction is also in favour of its orientative nature. It can be produced by any sufficiently new stimulus, no matter which analyser is actually involved. Vasomotor as well as motor elements of the orientation reaction are governed by the law of strength. A stronger stimulus produces a stronger response. Characteristically, however, the vasomotor components of an orientation reflex are often more intense in response to the first application of a very weak, liminal stimulus, than to strong and clearly perceived stimuli (Vinogradova and Sokolov, 1955). The existence of an intimate connexion between the reciprocal vasomotor reactions of the head and hand on one side, and the orientation reflex on the other, is further confirmed by the development of responses to all changes in the stimulus,—its application, removal, intensification, weakening, or change of nature. A vasomotor reaction to sound develops when the stimulus is applied, fades away while its action continues and reappears when it ceases (Sokolov, 1954). It is therefore obvious that this reaction develops as an element of an orientation reaction in response to a change of stimulus, and not to its absolute intensity or, any special quality.

To summarize:
1. both cephalic and peripheral reactions are extinguished by repetitive stimulation, in the same way as an orientation reflex;
2. both reactions are temporarily disinhibited by new stimuli;
3. any change affecting the stimulus becomes a stimulus for both reactions.

It can be concluded that the stimuli so far considered (sound, light, touch, weak current) bring about the vasomotor responses as part of the orientation reflex. The result is a redistribution of blood in such a way that the blood supply of the central ends of the analyser is improved at the expense of that to the skin (Lazarev, 1947). The biological significance of this blood redistribution as a mechanism for increase of the sensitivity of analysers in general, and of the visual analyser in particular, is revealed by the linking of the vasodilatation in the temporal area with dilatation of the cerebral and retinal vessels (Granit, 1955).

If it is correct that the vasomotor component of the orientation reflex is a mechanism for control of the excitability of the central nervous system and not just an autonomic concomitant of the somatic reactions, it should follow that extinction of these vascular components of the orienting reflex as a result of repeated application of the stimulus will be associated with a general lowering of the analyser's reactivity and sensitivity.

Extinction of the orientation reflex and the associated inhibition of the vasomotor reaction lead, to changes in the reactivity and sensitivity of the orienting reflex arc as a specialized functional unit in addition to general reduction of cerebral reactivity. During the process of extinction, increasingly strong stimuli are required to reproduce the reaction. This applies to all kinds of stimuli. In the case of electrodermal stimulation, the reduction of sensitivity as measured by the intensity of the orientation reaction produced, is proportional to the number of times the stimulus has been applied. Diminution of reactivity, as measured by the intensity of the vasomotor component of the orientation reflex produced, shows as a diminished intensity of the "reciprocal" type reaction particularly noticeable when comparisons are made in relation to the first applications of electrodermal stimulation. It can be stated, therefore, that weakening of the reaction (*diminished reactivity*), is associated with raising of the threshold (*diminished sensitivity*).

C. Vascular Reactions to Thermal Stimulation

The stimuli examined so far give rise only to orientation reflexes. Heat and cold also produce reciprocal type reactions in response to the first application of the stimulus [Fig. 2(*a*) and Fig. 3(*a*)], but with repeated applications, the reactions become concomitant and there is vasodilatation in response to heat and vasoconstriction in response to cold, in both areas [Fig. 2(*b*) and Fig. 3(*b*)].

Extinction of the vasomotor reactions of the head and hand, in response to
cold or heat, coincides with the extinction of the orientation reactions to
sound, light, etc. Against the background of the fading orientation response,
another, specialized vascular *thermoregulatory reaction* develops, which was
not produced by other stimuli evoking orientation reactions only.

Reflex contraction of surface capillaries under the influence of cold, and
their dilatation as a result of the application of heat, are the basic mechanisms
of thermo-regulation maintaining the internal temperature of the body.

When heat or cold is first applied one can observe a complicated reaction
pattern resulting from interaction of the orientation and the thermoregulatory reflexes. The general principles governing the course of the orientative
type responses to temperature change are the same as for the other stimuli.
An application of an extraneous stimulus results in temporary inhibition of
thermoregulation and re-emergence of the orientation reciprocal reflexes.

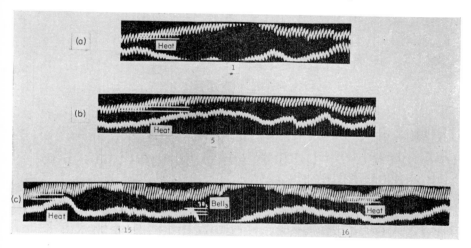

FIG. 2. Vascular reactions in head and hand to heat. (*a*), (*b*)—Subject V.L.,
April 1955. 1st and 5th applications of heat. (*c*)—Subject V.I., April 1955

For example, the sound of a bell producing a strong orientative reciprocal
reaction, alters the response to the thermal stimulus immediately following.
Application of heat, for instance, gives rise once more to a reciprocal reaction, which betrays its character as that of an orientation reflex, instead of
the concomitant vasodilatation, which would be the proper thermoregulation
response (Fig. 2). This Figure shows the general pattern of change when, as
a result of the repeated application of heat, the initial orientative reciprocal
reaction (Fig. 2(*a*)) is replaced by the concomitant reaction (Fig. 2(*b*)). When
the latter is well established an extraneous stimulus (the sound of a bell) leads

to reappearance of the reciprocal vasomotor response (Fig. 2(*c*)) i.e. finger vasoconstriction to the succeeding heat stimulus.

The differences in rate and duration between vasomotor reactions of thermoregulatory and the orienting type are considerable. While the orientation reflex produces a descending curve, with a relatively rapid recovery, the vasodilatation reaction which follows the application of heat produces an ascending curve, with the ascent maintained for the total duration of stimulation and for a considerable time thereafter.

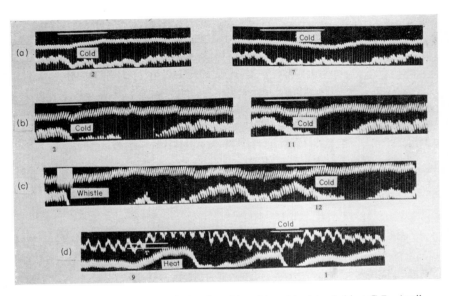

Fig. 3. Vascular reactions in head and hand to cold. (*a*)—Subject G.P., April 1955. 2nd and 7th applications of cold. (*b*), (*c*)—Subject V.L., March 1955. 6th application of cold (2, 11, 12). (*d*)—Subject A.M., March 1955. 9th application of heat and 1st application of cold.

A similar relationship can be observed between the responses to cold and the orientation reflex. The initial typical "reciprocal reaction" becomes, with stimulus repetition, a concomitant vasoconstriction. Further, as with heat, extraneous stimuli causes temporary reappearance of the reciprocal reaction, in this case, cephalic vasodilatation to the succeeding cold stimulus.

Figure 3(*a*) and (*b*) shows the replacement of the reciprocal by the concomitant vasomotor reactions. The reappearance of the reciprocal reaction to cold after the application of an extraneous stimulus (a whistle), is shown in Fig. 3(*c*). Figure 3(*d*) shows the concomitant thermoregulation reaction to heat and the reciprocal orientation reaction to cold. The differences between their action, as shown, becomes self explanatory when the number of times each stimulus has been applied is counted. In this particular case heat (9th application) gives rise to a thermoregulatory and cold (1st application) to an orienting reaction. It is obvious that the reaction as a whole cannot be sufficiently described in terms of a single vasomotor response recorded either in the hand or in the head separately. Cephalic vasodilatation can be a part of either an orientation, or a thermoregulation reaction. Hand vasoconstriction can also be an element of either. It is the simultaneous recording of both vascular reactions which makes the objective differentiation between the types of reflex possible.

Interaction of orientation and thermoregulatory reflexes explains a number of phenomena which have frequently been incorrectly ascribed to the variable initial state of the subject. For example, the seemingly paradoxical effects of the application of heat on the vessels of the limbs, produced regularly by any change in the course of the experiment, become understandable in terms of the reactivation of the orientation reflex.

Obviously, the orientation reaction replaces the thermoregulation reaction whenever any of the qualities of the heat or cold stimulus undergo alteration. For instance, displacement of the agent to a different area of the skin of the arm, stimulates the reciprocal head and hand reaction which is a part of the orientation reflex. Subsequent stimulation again gives rise to a concomitant thermoregulatory reaction. Thus the influence of the orientation reflex on the specialized thermoregulatory reaction explains the instability of vasomotor reactions in response to cold.

While gradual extinction is the characteristic feature of the reciprocal reaction, the specialized thermoregulation reaction, appearing against the background of extinction of the orientation reaction, becomes intensified and increasingly stable in the face of repeated stimulation. While any change affecting the stimulus gives rise to an orientation reaction, the thermoregulation reaction can only be produced by the specific thermal qualities of the stimulus. The reaction to heat or cold persist as long as the stimulus remains in operation. The transition from orientation to thermoregulation reaction during the action of any particular stimulus can be well observed by extending its action. The initial reciprocal reaction becomes transformed into the concomitant reaction, and persists for the total stimulus duration. Removal produces a reciprocal reaction once more, followed by the return of the curves to the base line (thermoregulation reflex connected with removal of stimulus).

Thus, the same stimulus (heat) can give rise first, to an orientation, and then to a thermoregulation reflex. It could be argued that the orientation reaction is caused by the tactile element of the heat stimulation but infra-red rays give rise to this pattern of reaction without any possibility of tactile stimulation. This objection cannot therefore be sustained.

To sum up, thermal stimulation can give rise to both orientation and specialized thermoregulatory reflexes, the relationship between them depending on the conditions of the experiment.

No special investigation of the sensitivity and reactivity of the thermoregulation reflexes was made. In view of the stability of these reactions in the face of repeated stimulation, however, it would appear that the sensitivity and reactivity of the underlying apparatus to heat and cold, as measured by the vasomotor components of the thermoregulation reflexes, are of a high order.

D. Vascular Reactions to Painful Stimuli

Very strong electrical stimulation of the skin and sounds of very high intensity give rise to a reaction in which cephalic and hand vasoconstriction are prominent features. In addition, with very strong stimuli, a jerking movement of the whole body can sometimes be observed and, at the same time, the subject experiences pain or an unpleasant sensation. This combination of reactions constitutes a defence reflex.

There is a definite difference between the cephalic—hand vasoconstriction appearing as a component of the defence reaction, and that developing in response to cold. The former is characterized by a short latent period, a sharp descent of the curve and a quick return to the original level when the painful agent is removed. The response to cold is more protracted and has a long latent period.

In spite of the vasoconstriction in the hands, which occurs in both the orientation and the defence reactions, the vasomotor reaction as a whole in each case appears as a distinct functional unit. The defence reflex includes cephalic vasoconstriction in contrast to the cephalic vasodilatation, characteristic of the orientation reflex. Differentiation of the two types of reflexes thus becomes possible (Vinogradova and Sokolov, 1957). Their individual character, so far as vasomotor reactions are concerned, is shown by their influence on each other in a reciprocal direction. For instance, a sound giving rise to a strong orientation reaction, leads to the re-emergence of a reciprocal vasomotor reaction characteristic of the orientation reflex, instead of the concomitant pain reaction, in response to a subsequently applied painful electrocutaneous stimulus.

Where the intensity of the stimulus is high, but not high enough to produce an immediate defence reaction, a complicated combination of orientation and defence reactions develops. The initial reaction shows the features of the orientation reflex (Fig. 4(a)). With repetition of the stimulus, this is displaced by the defence reflex (Fig. 4(b)), and the stimulus, which initially produced cephalic vasodilatation and hand vasoconstriction now gives rise to vasoconstriction at both sites.

A change of site of stimulation (Fig. 4(c)), from index finger (14), to thumb (1), results in reappearance of the reciprocal vasomotor reactions pointing to re-emergence of the orientation reflex, temporarily displacing the defence reflex. Figure 4(d) shows a repeated electrodermal stimulus (T 7),—having given rise first to an orientation reaction—then produces a defence reaction (43). An increase in its intensity (T 9·5 units, 1—first application), results in

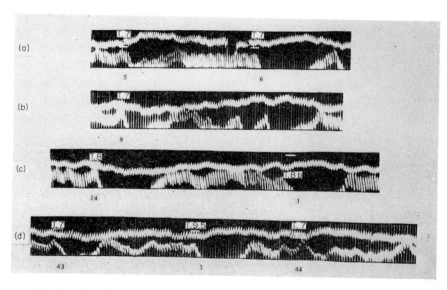

Fig. 4. Vascular reactions in head and hand to electrodermal stimulation. (a), (b)—Subject L.D. (c), (d)—Subject A.S. The intensity of the stimulus is shown in arbitrary units (T 7, T 8 etc.).

the reappearance of the orientation reaction. The next stimulus (44), lowered to the original level (T 7), now produces an orientation reaction, although the preceding one of this strength (43), produced a defence reaction. Thus, inhibition of the defence reflex and a reappearance of the orientation reflex is also a result of a change in the painful stimulus itself. Similar phenomena can be observed during the application of strong auditory stimuli. Figure 5(a) shows repeated sounds of high intensity (70, 80 dB), giving rise to the con- comitant defence reaction. Then, a weaker one (60 dB), produces an orien- tative reciprocal reaction. In another experiment undertaken after an interval, a loud sound (100 dB), produced a reciprocal reaction (Fig. 5(b)), which be- came replaced by a concomitant reaction (Fig. 5(c)), while the stimulation was maintained. Unexpected reduction in the intensity of the sound (to 90 dB) gave rise to a reciprocal, orientation reaction again (Fig. 5(d)).

In addition to the reciprocal relationship between the defence and orientation reflexes, leading to the displacement of one by another, instances can be encountered when the orientation reflex is actually reinforced by the defence reaction. This positive link is a result of stimulation of the orientation reaction by the defence reflex. A strong stimulus, for instance, disinhibits the orientation reflex to weaker stimuli. The increased magnitude and stability of the orientation reaction in response to stimuli of intensity near to pain threshold, is also an example of reinforcement of the orientation reaction by the defence reflex.

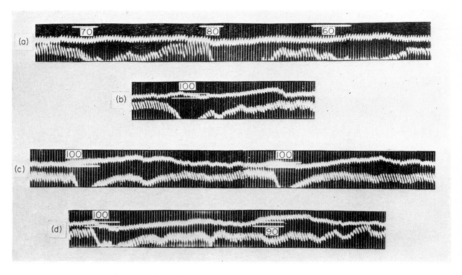

Fig. 5. Vascular reactions in head and hand to loud acoustic stimuli. (*a*)— Subject V.L. (*b*), (*c*), (*d*)—Subject E.S. Acoustic stimuli of 1024 c/s and 70, 80, 60, 100 and 90 dB above audibility threshold.

Stimuli which prove sufficiently strong on repetition to give rise to defence reactions, produce stable orientation reactions in the immediately preceding period; weaker stimuli unlikely to give rise to a defence reaction, and which in time cease altogether to excite any reaction, give rise to much less stable orientation reflexes. It is obvious, therefore, that within limits, the stronger the stimulus the more stable is the consequent orientation reaction. A further increase in the stimulus intensity brings about the emergence of the defence reflex, associated with the inhibition of the orientation reflex. At the same time the defence reflex proves very stable and resistant to attempts at suppression.

The defence and orientation reflexes are similar in that they develop in

dominant defence focus which does not become suppressed until the fifth application of the sound of the bell, and even then only partially (Figs. 8(*c*), 3, 4 and 5).

The factor of dominance produces further changes in the inter-relationship between the orientation and defence reflexes and, consequently, in the sensitivity and reactivity of the analysers, as measured by these two reactions. This becomes apparent when sub-threshold stimuli become capable of producing the defence reflex, though normally producing an orientation reaction only.

Elucidation of rules governing the inter-relationship of the vascular components of the orientation, thermoregulation and defence reflexes, provides the means for investigating the sensitivity of analysers in respect of stimuli devoid of signal significance.

The methods for measurement of the sensitivity of analysers described above are of great practical importance, especially in connexion with the determination of pain threshold and also in the investigation of the traumatic effects of strong auditory stimuli and industrial noises.

F. The Galvanic Skin Component of Orienting Reflexes

The galvanic skin reaction (C.G.R.—also known as the G.S.R. or P.G.R.) helps in differentiating orienting from defensive and thermoregulatory reflexes, and occupies an important place in psychological and psychophysiological research.

Two types of galvanic skin change as a result of stimulation are recognized. One, Tarkhanov's phenomenon (1889), is the development of electrical potentials at various points of the skin, and the other, Féré's phenomenon, change in the electrical resistance of the skin to the passage of a constant current. Both phenomena are manifestations of a single reflex reaction (Kozhevnikov, 1955). Alekseyev and Arapova (1949), using weak stimulation, were unable to demonstrate the existence of any constant reflexogenic zone and found that the reflex can develop as a result of stimulation of any analyser. The relationship between the galvanic skin reflex and motor reactions was studied by Byelyavskii and Khvilivitskii (1930). Asafov, Zimkina and Stepanov demonstrated a link between the galvanic skin reaction and respiratory and motor reactions, such as movements of the head (1955). Sakhiulina's findings (1944) are of great importance, as she succeeded in demonstrating the major significance of the novelty factor, and of proprioceptive stimuli as agents giving rise to galvanic skin reactions. The reaction has been studied by Ur'yeva (1936) in the conditions of various types of manual work.

Many authors have concluded that the galvanic skin reaction depends on the difficulties encountered in carrying out conditioned reflex activity. Thus, Vlasova (1954) demonstrated a considerable increase in galvanic skin activity when the subject met with difficulties in the differentiation of stimuli. Merlin (1953, 1954) studied galvanic skin reactions in the complicated conditions of conflict.

The similarity of the process of extinction of the cutaneo-galvanic reaction and of the orientation reflexes, has been demonstrated in man by a number of experiments. Musyashchikova's (1952) investigation of the process of extinction of this reaction has shown beyond any doubt the cortical nature of its inhibition, and the close relationship between this process and the orientation reflex. According to Mundy–Castle and McKiever, the galvanic skin response is essentially a manifestation of the orientation reflex.

Much research has been done in relation to various types of galvanic skin responses.

Regelsberger (1952) noted the connexion between the galvanic skin reaction and the food reflex. Gorev (1939) described various types of the reaction depending on the site of stimulation.

The link between the sensitivity to light of the eye and the manifestations of the galvanic skin response as observed by Semenovskaya (1947) and Dobriakova (1947) is of great importance. Those workers succeeded in demonstrating the similarity of certain aspects of the variations in sensitivity to light to galvanic skin reactions. In recent years research in this connexion has been carried out by Gershuni (1950), Maruseva and Chistovich (1954), Samsonova (1956), Myasishchev (1945), Merlin (1954) and others. According to Gershuni (1950), and certain other authors, the C.G.R. is but a component of the complex orientation reaction.

There are many methods for automatic registration of the electrical resistance of the skin in current use (Woodworth, 1950; Stevens, 1951). The majority are based on the Wheatstone bridge principle, with the skin of the subject as one of its elements, or on the determination of the intensity of the current traversing the body of the subject (Regelsberger, 1952).

The latter method has been used in the experiments to be described and continuous records of the intensity of the current and its variations, depending on changes of skin resistance, have been obtained. In man, the record of galvanic skin responses was superimposed on the tracing (also automatically obtained), of the latent periods of particular motor conditioned reflexes (Sokolov, 1955, 1956).

The galvanic skin reflex was recorded from the skin of the palm of the hand. Skin resistance was measured by means of the electronic, automatic potentiometer, type EPP-09, fitted with a direct-writing device. The apparatus, usually used for continuous temperature recording, is based on the principle of compensatory potential measurement by means of a potentiometer bridge. In the electronic potentiometer, the handle of the rheostat is moved automatically by an electric motor. Changes of potential, measured in relation to the rheostatic potential of the apparatus, are transformed into alternating current, and this after reinforcement is fed to an asynchronous device, which, by controlling the rheostat, equalizes the rheostatic potential with the measured one. The same device also transmits the movement to the recording element and a continuous record is thus obtained.

The current used for the measurements of skin resistance was supplied from a battery of known resistance, in series in the circuit. Changes of potential across the known resistance were obviously due to the corresponding changes in the resistance of the skin and were duly registered by the device described above. The scale of the apparatus was graduated in kilohms depending on the various potentials used. This allowed for investigation of a wide range of changes of skin resistance without any additional calibration of the apparatus.

The following features of the cutaneo-galvanic reaction were recorded: latent period, amplitude (the maximum alteration of the resistance during the reaction in question), duration (from the onset of change to the point where the original level was reached once more or a new level established). Similar features of motor responses were registered at the same time.

Silver lamellae, 12 mm in diameter, wrapped in cotton wool soaked in saline, were used as electrodes and were attached to the palm of the hand by means of rubber bands. In certain cases the record of the resistance of the skin of the back of the wrist, forehead and sole of the foot was similarly also obtained.

Light, sound, temperature, tactile, proprioceptive and other stimuli of various intensity and duration were used. The subject was placed in a light-proof, sound-proof chamber or, if thermal stimulation was involved, he sat in the same room as the investigator, with his eyes covered. All stimuli, as well as the subject's responses, were noted by the investigator on the tape of the recording apparatus.

The experiments demonstrated the similarity of the galvanic skin response to the vascular component of the orientation reflex. This similarity consisted of the appearance of the reaction in response to stimulation and the return to the original level while the stimulus was still in operation. Furthermore, just as with the vasomotor component of the orientation reflex, the galvanic skin reaction underwent gradual extinction with repetitive stimulation, whether tactile, auditory or proprioceptive. The general type of changes is illustrated by Fig. 9A and B.

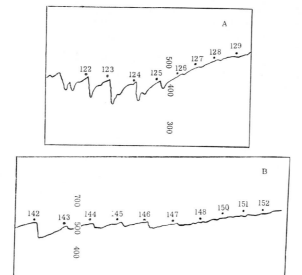

Fig. 9. Extinction of cutaneogalvanic reactions to tactile and proprioceptive stimulations. Subject L., March 1954. Ordinate: resistance (kilohms).

E

The figure shows that after visual and auditory stimulation, tactile stimuli —touching a finger—give rise to galvanic skin responses which become weaker and disappear (122–129). If at that moment, proprioceptive stimulation is substituted—bending the finger—the reaction reappears only to become extinguished once more with repeated stimulation (142–152).

It is interesting to note that motor stimulation shows the same potentialities in relation to the galvanic skin reaction as other stimuli. The process of extinction of the reaction obeys the same laws as that of the orientation reflex.

Finally, just as with the vasomotor component of the orientation reflex, the extinguished galvanic skin reaction can be temporarily disinhibited by an extraneous stimulus. It seems, therefore, that the main laws governing the galvanic skin reactions are identical with those described in connexion with the orientation reflex.

When the effects of light, sound and proprioceptive stimulation are compared, however, it becomes clear that the extinction of the galvanic skin reaction, appearing in response to the proprioceptive stimulation, develops more slowly. It often needs 15–20 passive movements of the finger to suppress the reaction, while 5–10 applications of sound or light are usually sufficient.

In order to demonstrate further similarities between the galvanic skin and vasomotor reactions, records were obtained of the resistance of the skin of the forehead, sole of the foot and back of the wrist. The characteristics of change of skin resistance of the forehead turned out to be similar to these characteristics for the dorsal surface of the wrist. It was found that the resistance of the skin of the forehead and of the back of the wrist fell during the course of the experiment; when these values fell, there was no sign of response reactions to stimulators from these areas of skin. Conversely, the resistance of the palmar skin and of the sole normally increased during the experiment and the application of stimuli caused a marked drop in this resistance. (Fig. 10). It seems, therefore, that the galvanic skin component of the orientation reflex can be brought into operation in certain skin areas (the palm of the hand and sole of the foot), and in these areas its properties are similar to those of the vasomotor component of the orientation reflex.

It can be assumed that the phenomena of depolarization, as observed during the orientation reaction in the glabrous areas of skin devoid of hair— follicle sensitivity, are due to sensitization of tactile receptors. According to modern data, depolarization potential plays an important part in the excitation of the photoreceptors of the eye and of the pressure receptors (Granit, 1955). It is possible that the cutaneo-galvanic reflex is but one of the processes —resulting in sensitization of the skin analyser—in the wider process of the orientation reaction.

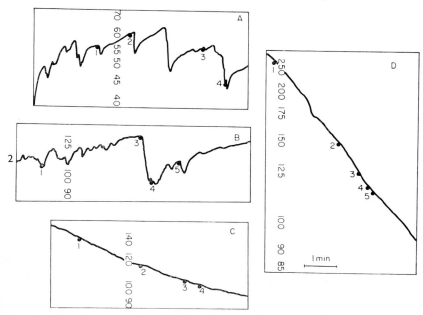

Fig. 10. Galvanic skin reactions on the palm, sole of the foot, forehead and back of the hand. Subject U., December 1954. A—Resistance of the skin of the palm. 1—"Attention!". 2—Bang. 3, 4—Start and finish of rhythmic clenching of the hand. B—Resistance of the skin of the sole of the foot. 2—"Attention!". 3, 4—Start and finish of rhythmic clenching of the hand. C—Resistance of skin on forehead. 1, 2—"Attention!". 3, 4—Start and finish of clenching of the hand. D—Resistance of the skin on the dorsum of the hand. 1—"Attention!". 2—Bang. 3, 4, 5—hand movements. Ordinate: resistance (kilohms).

The tracings obtained for the palm of the hand with the use of thermal stimuli did not differ from those given by other kinds of stimuli. The galvanic skin reaction developed as soon as the stimulus was applied (Fig. 11A 1). and the curve returned to the base line while the stimulation was continued. Cessation of stimulation produced another reaction (Fig. 11A 2). Similar tracings were obtained whether hot or cold stimuli were applied.

With repetitive stimulation, the reactions on application and on removal of heat became extinguished in accordance with the general laws of the orientation reflex (Fig. 11B). Extraneous stimulation resulted in disinhibition. In order to exclude the element of touch, the heat was applied by infra-red irradiation of the skin of the other hand up to 40°C.

Comparison of the tracings of the galvanic skin reactions of the palm of the hand with those of the vasomotor reactions, show that the former appear as a component of the orientation reflex but do not accompany the vaso-motor changes of the thermoregulation reaction. The galvanic skin reaction, therefore, only accompanies those vasomotor reactions which themselves develop as a component of the orientation reflex.

This confirms the view that an apparent similarity of vascular reactions can mask the basic differences between the processes of which they are but one element. The differences between the orientation and adaptation reflexes, and the connexions between the galvanic skin reactions and orientation reflexes, thus found experimental confirmation.

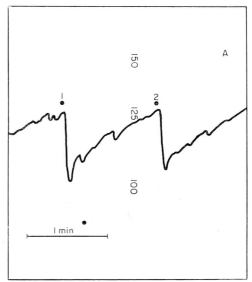

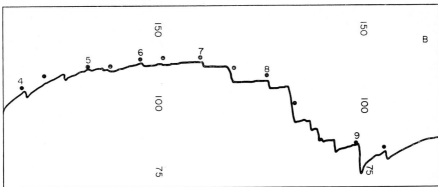

Fig. 11. Changes in the resistance of the skin of the palm produced by heat. Subject B., September 1954. 1, 2 and 4–9—Application of heat from a ceramic heater to the back of the hand on the side opposite to that on which the recordings were made. The times at which the heater was switched on and off are indicated by dots.

Thermal stimulation produced the evidence of a connexion between the galvanic skin reaction and the defence reflex. Prolonged exposure of the body to infra-red radiation does not produce any change in the electrical resistance of the skin so long as the heat gives rise to no unpleasant sensation. As soon as the threshold of pain is reached, a sudden and powerful cutaneo-galvanic reaction develops (Fig. 11B). The reaction, in the early stages of the defence reflex often shows spontaneous oscillation, persistent after-effects and a much greater than usual amplitude.

The transition, therefore, from the thermoregulation to the defence reflex, manifests itself as a strong galvanic skin reaction and then the orientation reaction in response to heat reappears. The C.G.R. tracings (Fig. 11) also confirm the stimulating effect of the defence on the orientation reflex, as demonstrated before by means of vasomotor reactions.

Figure 11A shows the galvanic skin reactions in response to application (1) and removal (2) of the thermal stimulus. Figure 11B shows that during the period of stimulation (4, 5, 6) the skin resistance gradually increases and the orientation reaction to heat becomes extinguished. It becomes disinhibited (9), when the intensity of stimulus reaches the threshold of pain (7–8).

Responses to heat undergo extinction in the same way as to other stimuli. At the same time, the general level of electrical resistance of the skin increases. When the pain threshold is reached, the resistance falls sharply (7–8), spontaneous fluctuations appear and the response to application or removal of the heat stimulus re-emerges once more. The development of the defence reflex can result in the formation of a pain dominant focus in connexion with the stimulated skin area. Therefore, once the heat stimulus has produced a defence reaction, the succeeding cold stimulus, which previously was only capable of giving rise to a weak orientation reaction, now produces the sensation of pain (Fig. 12).

The figure shows also that against a background of steadily declining resistance cold, the first application of which (1) results in slight fall of the resistance, ceases to produce any effect (2, 3). Sounds and speech (4, 5) result in a fall in resistance at their onset. Increase of heat to 60°C brings about the pain reaction (6), as above, with sharp fall in resistance and spontaneous fluctuations (6 to 7). Cold applied to the same area of the wrist to which heat was applied immediately before, produces a burning sensation, a fall in resistance and its spontaneous fluctuations (7).

The problems arises, therefore, as to what degree the galvanic skin reaction, developing as a result of painful stimulation, is a manifestation of the defence reaction, and to what extent does it reflect the orientation reaction connected with qualitative change in the action of the stimulus on the skin receptors. This problem arises from the fact that, while the painful stimulation of the skin is maintained, the galvanic skin response, in some cases, grows weaker and may be completely extinguished. This process of extinction is slow but still does take place and is in some respects more similar to the (albeit quicker) process of extinction of the vasomotor component of the orientation reaction, than to the defence reaction which replaces the former and which persists.

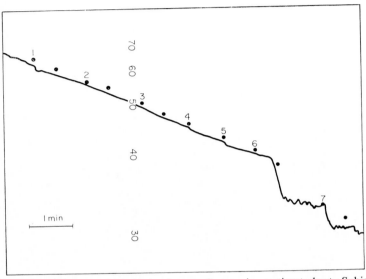

FIG. 12.   Development of pain dominance after a pain reaction to heat. Subject M., August 1954. 1–3—Cold. 4—Bang. 5—"Attention!". 6—Heat. 7—Cold. Ordinate: resistance (kilohms).

A study of the effects of strong, repetitive thermal, electrocutaneous and auditory stimulation has shown that when the threshold of pain is reached, the galvanic skin response to change of stimulus is accompanied by an orientation reflex which becomes extinguished with repetition and is not a direct outcome of the defence reaction. When heat reaches the pain threshold, the reaction grows weaker while the sensation of pain actually becomes more intense. Figure 13 shows the diminishing amplitude of galvanic skin responses to repetitive, painful stimulation by means of heat. A similar weakening or even complete extinction of the reaction can be observed in response to repetitive, painful electrocutaneous and sound stimulation which, nevertheless, continue to give rise to a sensation of pain. It needs pointing out, however, that the galvanic skin reaction usually undergoes extinction with difficulty and, in some cases, escapes it altogether. This is in accordance with the persistence of the response to pre-painful agents as observed in the case of the vasomotor orientation reaction.

During the action of painful stimuli, the galvanic skin reaction becomes intensified by all the same factors which bring about the intensification of the orientation reaction, (e.g., change of stimulus, change of site of the application of current, alternation of stimuli of different intensity). In some cases, when the galvanic skin reaction to strong pain has become extinguished, one can observe its re-emergence in response to a moderate, but unexpected, stimulus.

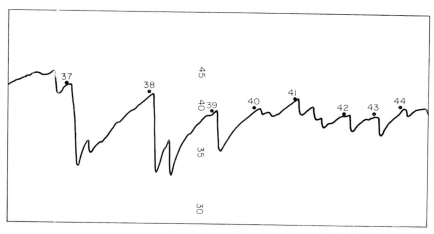

Fig. 13. Attenuation of the response to a painful stimulus. Subject K., October 1954. Heat from a ceramic heater (60°C) applied for 5 sec (stimuli 37–44). Ordinate: resistance (kilohms).

The threshold of the C.G.R. increases with repetitive stimulation in the same way as observed during the recording of vasomotor reactions. Consequently, the reaction is brought about by stimuli of increasing intensity, which is especially obvious during experiments involving the application of 20; 50; 70 and 80 dB sounds in succession. After five applications of 20–70 dB sounds, the reaction ceases but, at that point, an 80 dB sound not only gives rise to the reaction but also results in its re-emergence in response to weaker stimuli (Fig. 14).

The existence of a link between the C.G.R. and the orientation reflex is confirmed by the fact that a range of liminal stimuli give rise, in a number of cases, to intensified galvanic skin responses. Such intensification is characteristic of the orientation reaction. As far as the connexion between the magnitude of the C.G.R. and the strength of stimulus is concerned, the "Law of intensity of stimulus" begins to operate, starting with stimuli of medium intensity.

The difference between the C.G.R. and the cephalic vasomotor response may be found in their behaviour in the face of new stimuli, which inhibit the defence reflex and therefore weaken its vasomotor component. The novel stimulus intensifies the orientation reflex and *eo ipso*, weakens the vasomotor component of the defence reaction (cephalic vasoconstriction), and intensifies the galvanic skin reaction as a component of the orientation reflex.

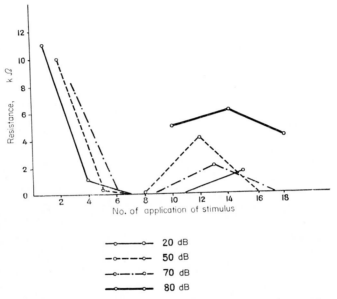

No. of application of stimulus

—o———o— 20 dB
—o————o— 50 dB
—o—·—·—o— 70 dB
—o———o— 80 dB

Fig. 14.   Changes in the threshold of the galvanic skin reaction produced by sounds of various intensities. Subject L., May 1955.

Intensification of the reaction in response to liminal stimuli is not a result of any special phase of the C.G.R., but is a manifestation of the orientative nature of the reaction which, with other components of the orientation reflex, constitutes a functional system instrumental in bringing about an increase in general sensitivity. Intensification of the galvanic skin reaction to liminal stimuli gives place to its weakening in response to stimuli of medium intensity. Intensification is again observed in the high intensity range, where the "Law of Intensity" enters into the picture.

This general tendency in any particular case becomes masked by various degrees of suppression or disinhibition of the orientation reflex. A special method is employed with the purpose of levelling out these fluctuations in the magnitude of the reaction. It consists of the application of auditory stimuli of 1000 cps. at 10 (or 20), 50; 70; 90 (or 100) dB, in a certain order until the reaction becomes extinguished. In view of the fact that the speed of extinction is different for stimuli of different intensity, the extinction is not considered complete until no reaction is forthcoming in response to any of the stimuli. The amplitude of change in resistance to each stimulus is noted, and the sum of the total responses to all applications of the stimulus of the given intensity and thus, the average amplitude of the change in response to a single application, are calculated. The data are obtained for various subjects and expressed in percentages (Fig. 15). It will be seen that the size of the reaction is somewhat greater in the range of weak stimuli than the medium ones, after which it steadily increases with the intensity of stimuli.

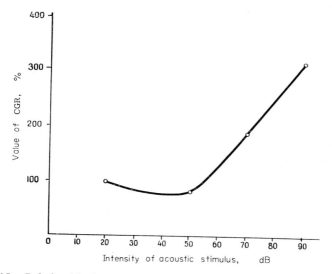

Fig. 15. Relationship between the galvanic skin reaction and intensity of acoustic stimulation. Average values for 15 subjects. May 1955.

Studies of the galvanic skin reaction show that its behaviour is similar to that of the reciprocal vasomotor reaction appearing as a component of the orientation reflex. The recording of the C.G.R. in its "pure form" allowed us to single out one of the components of the orientation reflex brought into operation by an alteration of the stimulus, and remaining distinct from the adaptation and defence reflexes. Whatever the stimulus, the occurrence of a C.G.R., as registered on the palm of the hand, reflects the participation of the orientation reflex in the resulting response. This again confirms the need for the establishment of a dividing line between the orientation and the defence reflexes as shown by experiments involving the recording of vasomotor reactions.

A change in the conditions of application of painful stimuli leads to intensification of both the vasomotor component of the orientation reflex and the galvanic skin reaction.

G. Interrelationships between the Orienting, Thermoregulatory and Defensive Reflexes

The study of galvanic skin responses and vasomotor reactions of the head and hand, at various phases of action of stimuli of diverse nature and intensity, led to differentiation of the following reflexes:

1. *Orientation reflex*—a non-specific reaction to a great variety of stimuli of low or medium intensity and consisting of cephalic vasodilatation, vasoconstriction in the hand, and a fall in the palmar skin electrical resistance.

2. *Specific adaptation (thermoregulation) reflex*—a reaction preparing the body for the action of thermal stimuli and consisting of cephalic and hand vasoconstriction in response to cold, and vasodilatation in response to heat, not accompanied by any change of the electrical resistance of the skin.

3. *Defence reflex*—a non-specific reaction to a great variety of stimuli of sufficiently high intensity, consisting of cephalic and hand vasoconstriction and a fall of the palmar skin electrical resistance.

Fig. 16.   Relationship between orienting, adaptational and defensive reflexes during heat stimulation. Subject N., May 1956.

The relationship between these three types of response can be studied in the vascular system by means of a single long-acting thermal stimulus. Thus, heat, as any new stimulus, produces cephalic vasodilatation and vasoconstriction in the hand. Soon this gives place to the thermoregulation reaction, consisting of concomitant vasodilatation. Finally, with the stimulus still acting, and the sensation becoming one of pain, this thermoregulation reaction is replaced by concomitant vasoconstriction in the head and hand. With removal of the stimulus, the curves of vasomotor reaction return to normal (Fig. 16). In this way, depending on the characteristic sequence of orientation, thermoregulation and defence reflexes, continuous thermal stimulation can give rise to a reaction passing through the same stages as does the response to repetitive stimulation.

A characteristic feature of the orientation reflex is its universality. It is the response of the body to all changes in the environment, a response which mobilizes all its resources for the perception of the new stimulus.

In certain conditions, the orientation reflex, developing in response to a sufficiently novel stimulus, can temporarily inhibit the specific thermo-regulation reflexes developing in response to cold or heat and even the defence reactions to strong stimuli. This inhibitory influence of the orientation reflex depends, however, on the physiological intensity of the stimulus. If this is high, the defence and not the orientation reaction is produced.

With continued stimulation, the orientation reaction undergoes extinction and its inhibitory effect on the specific thermoregulation and defence reaction weakens. That is why heat, cold, electrical current, or other painful stimuli, give rise, in time, to their specific reactions. The orientation response to sound, light and tactile stimuli of low or medium intensity also becomes extinguished in time. As these stimuli do not give rise to any specific vaso-motor or galvanic skin changes, extinction of the orientation reflex means that all vasomotor and galvanic skin responses are suppressed.

Thermal stimulation gives rise to simultaneous orientation and thermo-regulation reactions, which involve the same vasomotor effector and therefore become superimposed on one another. In the initial phase of the reaction, the orientation reflex dominates the picture. With its gradual extinction, the necessary conditions develop for the emergence of the thermoregulation reflex and the vasomotor reactions undergo change towards concomitant, vasoconstriction in the case of cold, and vasodilatation in the case of heat. At the same time, the C.G.R. playing no part in the thermoregulation re-action, becomes extinguished whether the stimulus is thermal, auditory, visual, or in fact of any other nature.

The difficulties encountered in the course of recording the vasomotor reactions to heat—their stability and their tendency to end in vasoconstric-tion—are due to the development of the orientation reflex, and the associated peripheral vasomotor reaction of opposite sign in response to any change in the stimulus. On the other hand, the ease with which the vasomotor response to cold is obtained, is the result of the peripheral vasomotor reaction to cold being identical with the orientation reflex as recorded for the peripheral vessels.

Intense stimuli frequently give rise initially to the orientation reflex, which becoming extinguished, results in intensification of the action of the agent as a painful stimulus. The similarity of the orientation and defence reactions in this respect consist of the ease with which a sufficiently strong stimulus can bring them about whatever the analyser stimulated.

Confirmation of the fact that the described changes in vasomotor and galvanic skin reaction are connected with a definite interaction between the orientation, thermoregulation and defence reflexes, can be found in the changes occurring in these reactions as a result of extraneous stimulation (a loud whistle, bell, etc.). This, as is well known, can disinhibit the orientation reflex, and result in the re-emergence of the orientation reactions to sound, light and touch which have been hitherto extinguished, and in the temporary displacement of the specific reflexes to cold, heat or painful stimuli. The explanation lies in the intensification of the orientation reaction and the resulting inhibition of the specific reflexes.

The appearance of the orientation reflex produces only a temporary dis-inhibition. After one, two or three applications of the new stimulus the orientation reflex again enters into an inhibitory phase, light, sound or touch of low or medium intensity produce no vasomotor response whatsoever, and where relevant, the specific thermoregulation or defence reflexes, reappear.

In this way, hand vasoconstriction, or cephalic vasodilatation, which present all the features of identical reactions, can in fact develop as the components of distinct functional mechanisms, can have various biological significance, can differ in their dynamics and can interact in different ways with other reflexes. A scheme of the inter-relationship of these diverse functional mechanisms is presented in Fig. 17. This Figure shows the relationship between the reciprocal vasomotor reactions of the head and hand and the galvanic skin reaction of the palm of the hand and of the forehead. They become extinguished and re-emerge in unison. With continued stimulation, the orientation reaction tends to weaken and its influence on the specific reflexes diminishes, which leads to their intensification.

These experiments helped to define certain principles governing the inter-relationship of the orientation, specific and defence reflexes brought into operation by non-signal stimuli. It can be assumed that these changes in relationship between the various reflexes affect the efficacy of the action of the stimulus on the analyser and, eventually, the actual perception of the stimulus. This effect is frequently reflected in the subsequent verbal account of the sensation.

Although the change of sensitivity in respect of various reflexes (in particular the orientation and defence reflexes), can not be taken as an index of sensitivity and reactivity of the skin analyser, it can, however, be accepted as a sufficiently accurate guide to the direction in which its sensitivity and reactivity change. The general effect of these changes is the intensification of the action of strong, painful stimuli and the weakening of the action of stimuli of low or medium intensity. Thus, the recording and subsequent analysis of the various types of reflex response to the stimuli used, helps in objective assessment of the various aspects of perception of non-signal stimuli.

The pattern of interaction of the orientation and specialized reflexes as demonstrated in the course of experiments, confirms the data obtained by Lagutina (1955), who found that the first few applications of a cortical

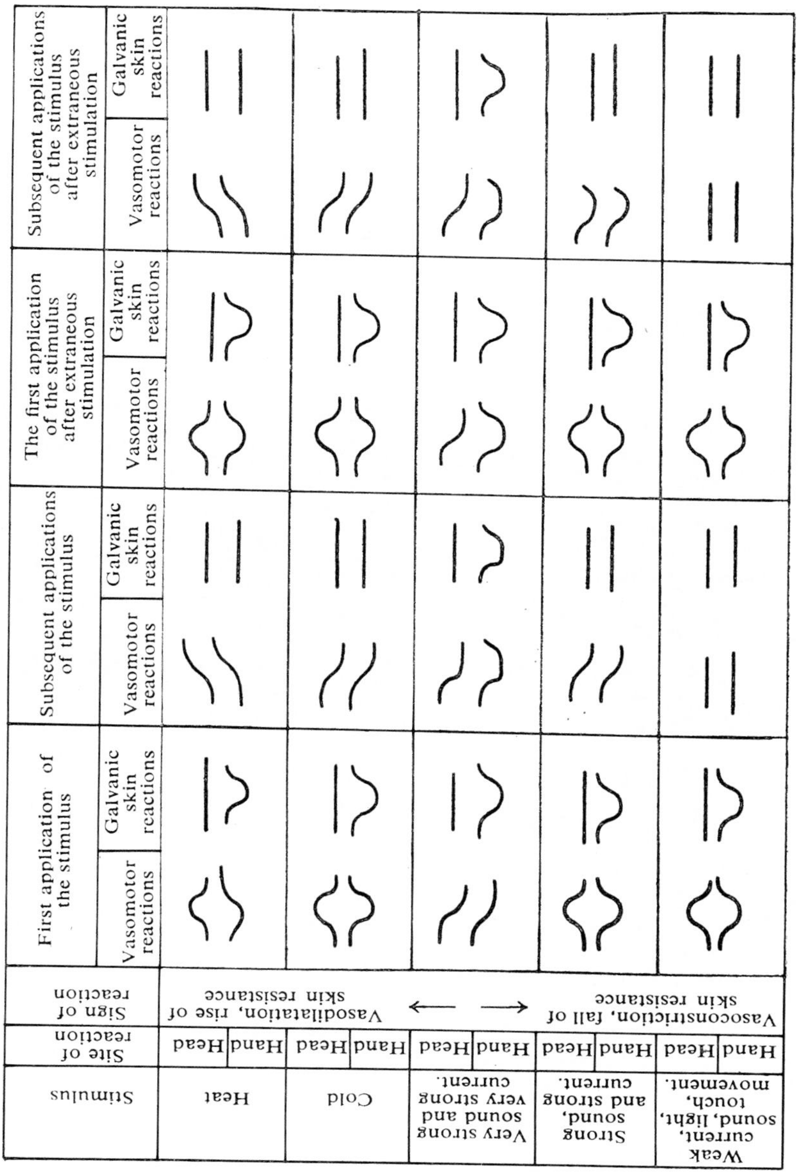

FIG. 17. Relationship between vascular and galvanic skin reactions to various non-signal stimuli.

electrical stimulus in animals (dog and monkey, by means of implanted cortical electrodes) result in the displacement of the orientation reaction by a specific reflex, such as the digestive. Increased intensity of stimulation brings into operation the defence reflex which now replaces the orientation reaction.

The complex nature of a stimulus, certain aspects of which, such as quality,

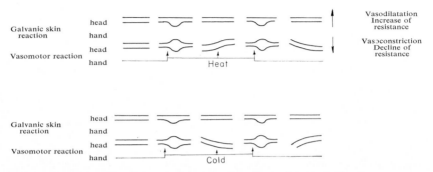

FIG. 18.   Schema of the complex effects of thermal stimuli.

intensity and novelty, influence the type of the reflex response, explains the variation in the body's reaction to repetitive stimulation by the same agent. Let us consider the effects of heat and cold from this point of view. At the onset of stimulation of any kind, non-specific paths seem to be brought into operation and, consequently, only the very presence of the stimulus is signalled. With maintenance of stimulation, the specific stimulus is signalled and specific reactions—vasoconstriction in response to cold; vasodilatation in response to heat—replace the orientation reflex. In the case of the C.G.R. as a component of the orientation reflex, those changes connected with the specific nature of the stimulus do not develop. The moment of removal of the stimulus again gives rise to the orientation reflex, followed by the return of the thermoregulation reactions to the original level (Fig. 18).

This figure shows the identical complexes of non-specific reactions observed at the beginning and at the end of the action of the stimulus, whatever its nature. In between the stimulus, brings into operation specific responses in accordance with its special properties.

The displacement of the orientation reflex by a specific reaction is a result not only of the inhibition of the former, but also of the development of a kind of conditioned reflex. Production of the latter could conceivably take place in the short period of repetitive stimulation between the first application of the stimulus and the point when the specific reaction appears. This hypothesis is quite close to the views expressed by Anokhin (1949), with regard to the complex nature of non-conditioned stimuli.

While with repetitive stimulation the orientation reaction becomes extinguished, the first application of the stimulus probably becomes the signal for the specific reaction. In favour of this hypothesis is the fact that repeated application of a painful stimulus gives rise to the specific reaction even if the quality of the stimulus is suddenly changed (dominant focus). Cold or sound, applied after a strong, painful heat or electro-cutaneous stimulus, also produce reactions associated with pain. It is possible that, in this case, the mere application of the stimulus became a signal for slow, pain impulses.

The impulses produced by the onset of stimulation act as signal for either a specific, or the defence reflex. The latent period of the specific reaction is shortened and the reflex involves the cortical centres. The biological significance of these connexions is the shortening of the time lag in the onset of the specific or defence reflexes.

Any alteration affecting the stimulus leads to an increased level of excitability in the orientation apparatus, and inhibition of the connexions between the impulses produced by the start of stimulation and the specific reaction apparatus. Consequently, at the start of its action a stimulus gives rise to the orientation reaction. The specific reflex either develops after a considerable latent period or is inhibited altogether.

When this line of thought is developed further, it gives us a link between the efficacy of the stimulus and the interaction of the resulting non-conditioned reactions which are dependent on the development of temporary connexions. The physiological intensity of various non-conditioned reflexes varies with the repetition of the stimulation. The changes affect the analysers and thus, the perception of the stimuli in operation.

Non-specific nerve fibres discovered by Laurente de Nö (1943, see Fulton, 1951), seem to provide the anatomical basis for the impulses concerned in the production of the non-specific orientation reaction. It can be assumed that vasomotor and galvanic skin reactions of an orientative nature involve the reticular formation, which participates in the transmission of non-specific excitation and in maintaining a certain level of cortical excitability. Wang, Stein and Brown (1596), have demonstrated that in cats, the development of the galvanic skin reaction is connected with the reticular formation of the thalamus, hypothalamus and brain stem and also, to a large extent, with the sensory-motor area of the cortex. The hypothalamic reticular formation is the main activating element in the reaction. Experimental division of the hypothalamus from the thalamus and cortex in cats, by removing the inhibitory influence of higher centres of the more central portion, resulted in purely hypothalamic reactions with typically strong galvanic skin responses, showing wide fluctuation and no tendency to extinction.

The connexion between vasomotor reactions and the activity of the reticular formation was shown in the experiments of Bonvallet, Dell and Hiebel (1954). Stimulation of the reticular formation resulted in electrical activation of the cortex, vasoconstriction in the limbs and dilatation of the pupil, all occurring simultaneously.

The characteristic features of the orientation reaction (diffuse nature, lack of specificity) can be explained, therefore, on the basis of the non-specific paths of the impulses concerned and the part played by the reticular formation.

CHAPTER 2

Manifestations of Orienting and Adaptation Reflexes in the Visual Analyser

A. Adaptation and Orientation reflexes in the Visual Analyser

The pattern of interaction of the orientation, adaptation and defence reflexes, changing with different phases of the action of non-signal stimuli, can be recognized, and in fact plays a decisive part in the activity of the visual analyser, especially in the positioning of the body in space.

The differentiation of orientation from specific adaptation reactions in the visual analyser is difficult. What is the significance, for instance, of the depression of α-rhythm in the occipital area observed during the action of a light stimulus? Is it an expression of the orientation reaction in the same way as in the case of auditory or other stimulation, or is it a manifestation of the specific response of the visual analyser to light?

In certain cases it is also difficult to distinguish dilatation of the pupil appearing as an orientation reaction, from the same occurring as a response to darkness—a specific stimulus of the visual analyser. Yet, such distinction must be made if the mechanism of visual perception is to be properly understood.

A study of the properties of the blink reflex helps in the differentiation of the various components of orientation and adaptation reflexes in the visual analyser. In contrast to the generalized defence reaction produced by strong, painful stimuli, the blink reflex can be considered as a special defence reaction for the eye. In this way, it becomes more akin to adaptation reactions such as contraction of the pupil in response to light. At the same time, however, the blink reflex as a specific reaction may be brought about not only by a strong light, but also by stimulation of the cornea with a jet of air. This latter method of stimulation helps to exclude a great number of reflexes produced in the visual analyser by the action of light on the photoreceptors. A study of the eyelid reflex by this means provides the necessary criteria for differentiation of the specific adaptation and general orienting reflexes.

In this chapter the connexions between the electrical reactions of the brain and various reflexes participating in the adjustments of sensitivity are considered. For correct interpretation, the electrical reactions are correlated with clear-cut components of the orientation reflex such as the galvanic skin and respiratory reactions. Changes in the respiratory rhythm as a result of novel stimulation belong to the group of orientation reactions (Anokhin, 1949; 1956; Asafov, Zimkina, Stepanov, 1955; Vlasova, 1954). The patterns of change in respiratory reactions follow the features of change in the other components of the orientation reflex. The respiratory component itself is probably akin to the sniffing movements so clearly seen in animals.

It should be pointed out that the connexion between the cerebral electrical reactions and what are termed acts of attention had already been noted by the early investigators in the field of electroencephalography (Berger, 1933; Adrian, 1947; Jasper, 1949; Shpil'berg, 1940; Durup and Fessard, 1936). In the course of his studies on the depression of α-rhythm in response to auditory stimulation, Gershuni (1949) came to the conclusion that this is a reaction of orientative nature, and this concept was further developed by Kozhevnikov (1951), Peimer and Faddeyeva (1956), Kratina (1956) and others.

We have generally used a direct recording, 4-channel electroencephalograph [the technique has been described many times (Chugunov, 1950)] for the simultaneous recording of changes in the visual analyser, locomotor-apparatus and the body as a whole.

Bipolar leads were used, the inter-electrode distance being 2 cm. The subject's head was covered with a headpiece made of strips of rubber and metallic electrodes, wrapped in saline-soaked gauze, were placed under this headpiece. In some cases "stick-on" electrodes were used. The subject was kept in a light-proof, screened chamber for the period of the experiment. Depending on the aim of the particular investigation, the device was used for recording cerebral potentials, galvanic skin responses, action potentials of muscle and other electrical phenomena arising primarily within the visual and motor analysers. The Tarkhanov galvanic skin reaction was also recorded. This consists of the sudden development of a difference of electrical potential between two points on the skin—usually the palm and the dorsum of the hand. In some cases records were made of the C.G.R. of the foot, and the scalp.

The electrodes were placed on the two points chosen and the variations in the difference of potential were recorded by the electroencephalograph. In spite of deformities of the tracings resulting from the employment of an AC amplifier, the beginning of the reaction and the relative amplitude were recorded clearly. The records were confirmed by comparison with tracings obtained with a DC amplifier (Kozhevnikov, 1955).

A time constant of 2 sec was used in a number of experiments involving the recording of respiratory reactions. The respiratory movement recording device consisted of a rubber tube, filled with saline and containing two electrodes connected to the input of the amplifier. The tube was placed tightly round the chest of the subject and its length, and thus its diameter, varied with respiratory movements. The changes of potential resulting from these variations in length and diameter, were amplified and recorded by the electroencephalograph simultaneously with other reactions.

Continuous recording of respiratory movements correlated with the E.E.G. tracing was of advantage, for it allowed the discovery of insignificant stoppages of respiration by the alteration of shape of one or even two waves of the tracing.

Electromyographic tracings were obtained in the usual manner with two flat electrodes applied to the skin over the group of muscles to be investigated. In some experiments, the addition of a piezo-electric device, placed under a finger of the subject, helped in distinguishing the potential changes of active movement from artefacts. Any pressure on this device was recorded simultaneously with the electromyogram and other reactions.

Eye movements were recorded using a method described in the literature, the recording of changes in potential between fixed electrodes placed in the polarization field of the eyeball, the movements of which cause changes in the position of this field. Eye movements of as little as 3°, whether in the vertical or horizontal plane, were successfully recorded with two pairs of electrodes, one pair placed over the supra-orbital ridge and on the cheek, and the other on the temporal edges of the orbits.

The blink reflex was recorded by means of electrodes placed over the supra-orbital ridge and the lateral corner of the eye. The tracing of this reflex was different from that of the eye movements. The reflex was stimulated by means of a puff of air directed into the eyes from a rubber bulb.

Depending on the aim of experiments, the reactions were recorded in various combinations. The usual combination consisted of the E.E.G. from the occipital area, the cutaneo-galvanic reaction (C.G.R.), an electromyogram (E.M.G.) and electro-oculogram (E.O.G.). In the analysis of the tracings, latent period, duration, and amplitude of every reaction were noted.

In addition to the usual light and sound stimuli, rhythmic optical, auditory and tactile stimulations with frequencies of from 3 to 50 c/s were used. The stimuli were provided by a special apparatus built in our laboratory by Ilyanok (1953), and capable of delivering optical, auditory and tactile stimuli of the same or different frequencies.

The weak light stimuli used in the measurement of light sensitivity were provided by a Kravkov's adaptometer. This projected light on to a white screen placed at a distance of 0·7 m from the subject, the latter being assisted by a red fixation spot of the type usually used in physiological investigation.

Cerebral potentials were studied with a Walter analyser (1946 model), producing an analysed record of the electrical potentials of the brain in the range from 1·5 to 30 c/s for each 10 sec period of investigation. The frequencies are isolated in this device on the resonator principle. The energy of oscillation at any given frequency is fed into a corresponding resonator during 10 sec, and then a capacitor, collecting the load with the help of a mechanical commutator, discharges into the automatic recording device. The extent of the deviation of the stylus is proportional to the energy stored in the capacitor during the preceding 10 sec, in respect of each of the investigated frequencies. As the analysis is being carried out continuously, the changes in the whole spectrum of bioelectrical rhythms which take place as a result of stimulation during the experiment can be discovered. The analyser is of particular assistance when intermittent stimulation is employed, for the latter results in an alteration in the dominant frequency of the cerebral potentials. For this reason 10 sec epochs of light flicker at 4–30 c/s were used. The tracings so obtained were compared with the basic range of frequencies before and after stimulation.

In addition, Walter's analyser permits of isolation and continuous simultaneous recording of one of the analysed frequencies. One of the resonators is connected through a special commutator to the electroencephalograph. The analyser was modified to permit selection and simultaneous recording of any frequencies and as a rule, three or four frequencies were thus registered in the experiments. This technique proved to be especially important when intermittent stimulation was employed, for by adjusting the analyser, "driven" cortical rhythms of the same frequency as the flicker rate could be isolated, as well as associated harmonic rhythms, which remained simple multiples of the basic frequency. Usually frequencies of 9, 18 and 27 c/s were thus isolated, and Fig. 19A shows such a tracing obtained with the analyser.

It can be seen (A) that a flicker rate of 9 c/s and 10 lux on a white screen, leads to the emergence of the basic frequency of 9 c/s as well as of the harmonics of 18 and 27 c/s. Neither before nor after flicker stimulation could these frequencies be observed.

The results can also be presented in graphic form (Fig. 19B). It becomes clear that the frequency spectrum before stimulation (continuous line) does not coincide with the spectrum during flicker (interrupted line). The difference is due to a slight diminution in δ- and θ-wave activity* and, in particular, to an increase in amplitude of the 9, 18 and 27 c/s wave activity. The high degree of selectivity in the alteration of the range of cerebral rhythms when "driven" by interrupted stimulation is of great interest.

---

* In this book cerebral rhythms, irrespective of site, are denoted as follows: 1–3·5 c/s–δ, 4–7 c/s–θ; 8–13 c/s–α; 14–30 c/s–β; over 30 c/s–γ.

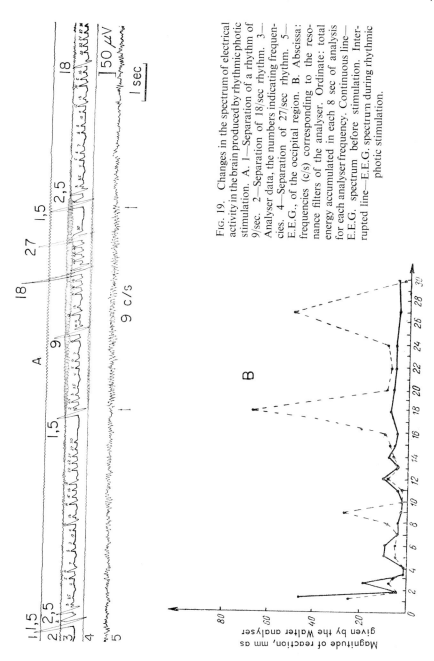

FIG. 19. Changes in the spectrum of electrical activity in the brain produced by rhythmic photic stimulation. A. 1—Separation of a rhythm of 9/sec. 2—Separation of 18/sec rhythm. 3—Analyser data, the numbers indicating frequencies. 4—Separation of 27/sec rhythm. 5—E.E.G., of the occipital region. B. Abscissa: frequencies (c/s) corresponding to the resonance filters of the analyser. Ordinate: total energy accumulated in each 8 sec of analysis for each analyser frequency. Continuous line—E.E.G. spectrum before stimulation. Interrupted line—E.E.G. spectrum during rhythmic photic stimulation.

In addition to analysis, integration of potentials was carried out at the same time with a thermo-electric integrator. The output of the electroencephalograph was fed to a valve (LT-2), consisting of a heat source and thermocouple. The temperature of the former varied with the intensity of current flow through it, and in turn influenced the intensity of the current produced in the thermocouple. The latter was connected to an automatic ink-recording EPP-09 potentiometer. The time constant of the integrator, determined by the properties of the heat source and the degree of vacuum in the valve LT-2, was 45 sec. As the intensity of current produced in the thermocouple was proportional to the square of that reaching the heat source, the result obtained with the device were indicative of the actual energy of the cerebral electrical activity. The tracings obtained in this way were of particular value for the investigation of slow changes in the electrical activity of the brain taking place during the periods of adaptation to darkness and to light.

The blink reflex was recorded simultaneously with the E.E.G. from the occipital area and Tarkhanov's galvanic skin reflex by an ink-recording oscillograph. The C.G.R. provided the means for the study of the orientation reflex, and the occipital E.E.G. was the object of special attention in connexion with both the specific and the orientation reactions. It was found that, at first, a puff of air into the eyes produced a galvanic skin reaction, depression of the α–rhythm and blinking. Gradually, however, the α-rhythm depression and the galvanic skin reaction were inhibited, while the blink reflex persisted, as is shown in Fig. 20A.

Auditory stimulation produces no ocular defence reaction, and, when repeated, results in progressive inhibition of all the components of the reaction, as shown in Fig. 20B. A sound of 1,000 c/s and 70 dB, giving rise at first to slight depression in α-rhythm and C.G.R. (2), later ceases to produce any reaction (5). At the same time, as a result of repeated sound stimulation, the depression reaction and C.G.R. to the puff of air become disinhibited.

Figure 20C shows exactly the same effect in the form of disinhibition of the α-rhythm depression and C.G.R. responses to sound produced by the simultaneous action of sound and air stream stimulation. As the C.G.R. is intimately associated with the orientation reflex, it can be assumed that the puff of air on to the cornea gives rise to an orientation reflex, which also includes α-rhythm depression and the special blinking defence reflex, all occurring simultaneously.

The characteristic feature of the C.G.R., as stated before, is that it occurs only as a result of a new stimulus or at the moment of change in any stimulus. As the orientation and blink reflexes are recorded from different effectors, it can be assumed that they develop simultaneously and there seems to be no inhibition of the specific reflex by the orienting reflex in contrast to that observed when vasomotor reactions were recorded. With repetition, the C.G.R.

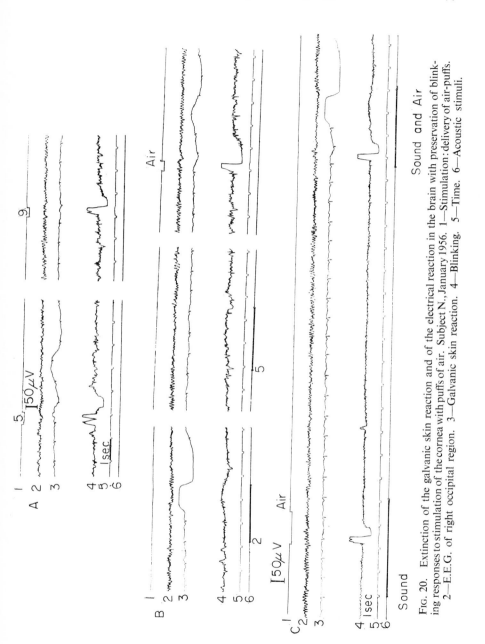

FIG. 20. Extinction of the galvanic skin reaction and of the electrical reaction in the brain with preservation of blinking responses to stimulation of the cornea with puffs of air. Subject N., January 1956. 1—Stimulation: delivery of air-puffs. 2—E.E.G. of right occipital region. 3—Galvanic skin reaction. 4—Blinking. 5—Time. 6—Acoustic stimuli.

rapidly diminishes and becomes extinguished. Depression of α-rhythm also diminishes with inhibition of the orienting reaction, and disappears at the same time as the C.G.R. The blink reaction to a puff of air into the eye, being a defence reflex, persists. It is therefore possible to isolate this specialized defence reflex and to establish its relationship with the bio-electric components of the orientation reflex, namely depression of α-rhythm and the C.G.R. Records of the electrical activity of the cortical cells of the visual analyser shows that stimulation of the eye, which does not involve the photoreceptors, in not reflected in these cells in the form of a specific persistent eye reaction, but only as a component of the orientation reflex proceeding to extinction with repetition, as occurs with auditory stimulation.

The orientation reflex produced by a puff of air into the eye can be reactivated in the same way as in the case of the vascular and galvanic skin components of the orientation reflex. Reinforcement by extraneous stimulation is necessary, after which the air stream is again capable, for a time, of producing α-rhythm depression and a C.G.R. This disinhibition of the orientation reflex is, however, temporary and, after one or two applications, extinction recurs and again only the specific defence reaction, the blink reflex, continues to appear.

An interesting feature of the action of extraneous stimulation is the fact that the depression of the α-rhythm and the galvanic skin reaction are affected in the same way. This tends to confirm the close connexion between the bio-electrical cerebral reaction and the orientation reflex, a connexion already indicated by their simultaneous appearance and then extinction, in the first instance.

B. The Electrical Manifestations of the Orienting Reflex in the Cortex

A number of authors, (Berger, 1933; Jasper, 1949 and others) have noted a connexion between changes in E.E.G. tracings and acts of attention, and Gershuni (1949) pointed out the association with the orientation reflex.

The series of experiments described, clearly shows the close relationship between cortical occipital activity and orientation reactions. For example, auditory stimulation, when applied for the first time, gave rise to depression of the α-rhythm, arrest of respiration, a C.G.R., and eye movement, frequently supplemented by movement of the head. Various other stimuli also produced, to start with, eye movement, a C.G.R. and depression of the α-rhythm, which became progressively extinguished with repetitive stimulation.

Inasmuch as the eye movement is a well known proprioceptive component of the orientation reflex, its association in time with the other reactions recorded confirms their orientative nature, The simultaneous occurrence of oculomotor, respiratory and galvanic skin reactions and depression of α-rhythm, lead to the conclusion that the last denotes an increased level of cortical excitability.

However, the orientation reflex can be associated with an enhancement of α-rhythm as well as its depression. In the drowsy phase during the onset of sleep, the α-rhythm begins to disappear and slow wave activity is seen. Novel stimulation of any kind intensifies the α-rhythm and this is again associated with a C.G.R. and eye movements.

This intensification of α-rhythm, occurring with an orientative galvanic skin reaction and movements of the eyes, now indicates a swing towards a generalized increased excitatory state with α-rhythm replacing the slower cortical rhythms of sleep.

It has therefore been demonstrated experimentally that, depending on the functional background, the orientation reflex can manifest itself either as depression or as intensification of the α-rhythm, both changes being associated with an increased level of excitation.

Finally, there are cases in which the orientation reaction finds no reflection in the E.E.G. This occurs with subjects in a state of cerebral excitation characterized by the appearance of β-waves against a general flat background of depression. Nevertheless, even then the oculomotor and galvanic skin reactions can be noted. Thus, although the orientation reflex is being brought into operation, no change in cortical activity is noted. According to Kozhevnikov (1955), however, even then certain changes—increased β- and γ-wave activity —can be demonstrated with a high frequency analyser.

An explanation for this variability in the cortical manifestation of the orientation reflex within the visual analyser, can be found in the connexion between the level of excitation of the cortex and the predominant frequency in the E.E.G. The lowest levels of the former, characteristic of drowsiness and sleep, are associated with θ- and δ-rhythms. The condition of rest is associated with medium levels of excitation and the appearance of an α-rhythm. Finally, high levels of excitation are accompanied by depression of the α-rhythm and often, by rapid β- and γ-wave activity.

The ultimate significance of the orientation reflex is a swing towards a state of increased excitation, which coincides with a generally increased frequency in the E.E.G. (with δ-waves being replaced by the α-waves and the latter by β-waves or with intensification of γ-wave activity).

C. General and Local Orienting Reactions

In addition to the general orientation reaction which includes the activation of the cortical ends of various analysers, a local, narrower form of the orientation reaction must be distinguished, involving mainly the analyser actually stimulated.

The difference between generalized and local orientation reflexes may be demonstrated by comparison of the effects of vibration, light and sound on various components of the orientation reaction, as shown in Fig. 21. Initially (21B), tactile-vibratory stimulation gives rise to a widespread, generalized orientation reflex. With repetition, the effects of this type of stimulation on various components of the reaction become differentiated. Depression of the occipital α-rhythm disappears while the galvanic skin response continues to be produced. On the other hand, light (21A) soon ceases to evoke a C.G.R., but the α-rhythm depression persists even after tens of applications of the stimulus. Auditory stimulation (21C, D), not linked directly with the activity of the motor or the visual analysers, quickly ceases to give rise to a C.G.R. or to depression of occipital α-rhythm (Novikova and Sokolov, 1957). This may be observed after only 3–6 applications of the auditory stimulus. The galvanic skin response to vibration is stronger than that to either sound or light, although the α-rhythm depression is rapidly inhibited.

Thus, the orientation reflex is more persistent in the analyser specifically acted upon by the particular stimulus. It can be postulated that the more persistent depression of the occipital α-rhythm in response to light is connected with the local orientation reaction of the organ of vision to an adequate light stimulus.

A study of the local and general orientation reflexes within the motor analyser is of particular interest. The manifestation of the orientation reaction in this case, consists of a *sui generis* state of increased preparedness, which is reflected in the electrical activity of the muscles. This phenomenon has been termed by Kvasov (1952) a "what is to be done?" reflex, by analogy to the "what is this?" reflex in the case of exteroreceptors' adaptational reactions. At the same time, the propriomuscular apparatus of the analyser, which participates in the orientation reaction, ensures the maintenance of sensory preparedness (Kvasov, 1956).

The orientation reaction does not, however, end with the tuning of the peripheral muscular apparatus. An important change is the activation of the cortical end of the analyser. Gastaut and his collaborators (1952, 1957), demonstrated the occurrence of rolandic fissure rhythm in the motor area of man corresponding in frequency to α-rhythm but giving rise, in a number of cases, to a characteristic waveform (*MU rhythm*) and showing a selective reactivity to proprioceptive stimuli. Repetitive proprioceptive stimulation leads to replacement of the generalized reaction—which appears as cortical depression including depression of the activity in the occipital and motor areas—by a local reaction consisting of rolandic rhythm depression.

The study of reaction to light or proprioceptive stimulation has shown that the first application of a proprioceptive stimulus results in blockage of the rhythms in the occipital and motor areas and, a C.G.R. With repetition, first the depression of the occipital α-rhythm fails to develop and then, the

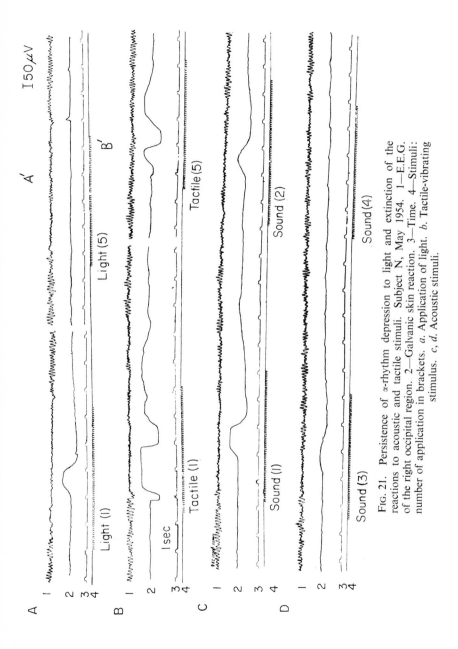

Fig. 21. Persistence of α-rhythm depression to light and extinction of the reactions to acoustic and tactile stimuli. Subject N, May 1954. 1—E.E.G. of the right occipital region. 2—Galvanic skin reaction. 3—Time. 4—Stimuli: number of application in brackets. *a.* Application of light. *b.* Tactile-vibrating stimulus. *c, d.* Acoustic stimuli.

C.G.R. disappears. However, the depression of the rolandic rhythm continues to appear and to make it disappear, not less than 30–50 applications of the stimulus are required.

The light stimulus, when first applied, also produces generalized depression in the occipital and motor areas and a C.G.R., but the depression of the rolandic fissure rhythm and the C.G.R. disappear after 2–5 applications. The depression of the occipital α-rhythm continues for hundreds of applications of the light stimulus. This reaction can be suppressed only with difficulty—in a number of cases its complete suppression could not be achieved (Roger, Voronin and Sokolov, 1958).

Figure 22 shows the effects of the 1st application (*a*) and 7th application (*b*) of a proprioceptive stimulus. Figure 22(*c*), shows the compared effects of the 8th application of the proprioceptive stimulus, and 1st application of the light stimulus. Figure 22(*d*), shows the effects of the 14th application of the light stimulus. The displacement of the generalized cortical reaction by a local reaction in the analyser primarily concerned can be clearly seen.

The fact that local bio-electrical reactions belong to the group of orientation reactions is confirmed by the close similarity between the laws governing local reactions and those governing such typical orientation reactions as the C.G.R., which can also undergo extinction in various ways, depending on the nature of the light or proprioceptive stimuli in operation.

Intensification of the local reaction, or re-emergence of the generalized reaction following any change affecting the conditons of the stimulation, are manifestations of this close similarity. The effects of extraneous stimulation are also highly typical; depending on its intensity and degree of "novelty", it produces either a local or a generalized orientation reaction, with a variable number of other components.

The local orientation reactions—characterized by activation of local potentials in response to, for any given analyser, adequate stimuli—are very similar to specific reactions in as far as their persistence and selectivity is concerned. A characteristic feature of the specific adaptation reflexes in contrast to orientation reactions—which reflect any change affecting the stimulus—is the change in the sign of the reaction with application and removal of the stimulus.

The effect of darkness, an adequate stimulus for the visual analyser, was studied in order to differentiate between the generalized and local orientation reactions appearing in the occipital E.E.G. in response to light stimulation. It can be assumed with a high degree of probability that darkness, being a change in the conditions of illumination, will give rise to a generalized orientation reaction, usually expressed as depression of the α-rhythm. In addition, darkness, by suppressing practically all visual input and thus the local orientation reaction, should lower the excitability of the cortical end of the visual analyser i.e. should lead to intensification, or re-emergence of the

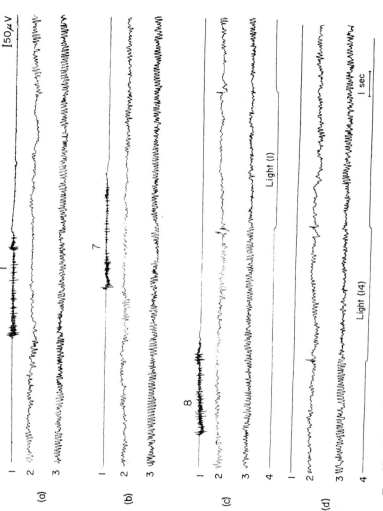

FIG. 22. Changes in the effects of light and proprioceptive stimulation on the E.E.G.s of the occipital and motor areas in the course of repeated application of the stimuli. Subject M., October 1956. 1—E.M.G. of the extensor muscles in the right forearm. 2—E.E.G. of left motor area. 3—E.E.G. of the left occipital region. 4—Light stimulation.

previously depressed α-rhythm against the background of a generally increased state of excitation of the subject (Sokolov, 1955).

It is well known that the effects of darkness on the occipital E.E.G. are opposite to those of light. In addition, darkness leads to diminished electrical sensitivity of the eye, which is an index of excitability of the central end of the visual analyser (Kravkov, 1948). This diminution of cerebral excitability in darkness is confirmed by various observations made in the course of the study of conditioned reflex activity (Faddeyeva, 1955). On the other hand, light leads to increased electrical sensitivity and increased excitability, as also shown by studies of conditioned reflex activity (Pressman, 1955).

The assumed differences between the generalized and local orientation reactions, as shown by means of occipital E.E.G. changes, were confirmed by experiment. The application of darkness as a stimulus in a previously well-lit room, leads at first to the blockage of the α-rhythm, i.e. produces the same effect as sound, light and all the other stimuli. However, after 2–5 applications, only the onset of darkness gives rise to the depression of the α-rhythm, or no such reaction can be recorded at all. During the remaining period of stimulation by darkness the α-rhythm is actually being activated. Transition to the previous level of illumination again produces depression of the α-rhythm. It must be added that the depression of the α-rhythm observed at the onset of darkness is accompanied by a galvanic skin reaction in the same way as is the onset of light stimulation, an association indicating the operation of a generalized orientation reaction.

Figure 23, (a), (b), (c), (d) show these varying effects of darkness. It can be seen that the first application (1), replacing the illumination of 43 lux (on a white screen), leads to depression of α-rhythm. With repetition (2; 3; 8), the duration of the depression becomes shortened, and the duration of the periods of activation of the α-rhythm increases.

Simultaneous recording of C.G.R. and E.E.G. has shown that eventually the phase of α-rhythm and C.G.R. depression, which precedes the phase of intensification in response to darkness, becomes extinguished. Thus the difference between the effects of light and darkness on the functional status of the cortex of the hemispheres can be seen in the α-rhythm response to such stimulation—decreased amplitude to light, increased amplitude to darkness, both effects being equally persistent. The dynamics of these changes in the occipital E.E.G. can be expressed as the summation of the generalized and local orientation reactions, which are of the same sign in the case of light and of the opposite sign in the case of darkness. The depression of the α-rhythm associated with a C.G.R. is a change towards a state of increased excitation. This change can be a part of various reflex complexes—such as the non-specific generalized orientation reflex—which may be brought into operation by any stimulus including the onset of stimulation by light or darkness, or,

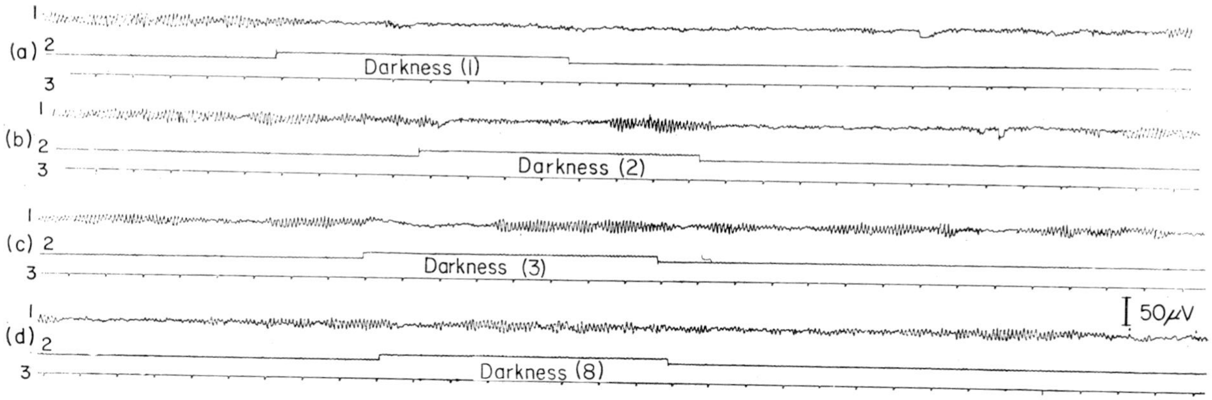

FIG. 23. E.E.G. manifestations of extinction of the orienting reflex on repeated application of darkness. Subject P., April 1956. 1—E.E.G., of right occipital region. 2—Stimulus. 3—Time.

of the local orientation reflex, when it is the expression of increased excitability at the central end of the visual analyser in response to stimulation by light.

Intensification of α-rhythm can also develop as a component of either generalized or local orientation reflexes. It may develop as a result of the subject emerging from a drowsy state, when it appears as a component of the general orientation reaction and signifies an increase in the state of excitability.

If the assumption is correct that the frequency of the basic electrical rhythms determines the nature of the electrical manifestations of the general and local orientation reactions, it would be of a special interest to study the effects of darkness during the transition into sleep. In these conditions the development of the general orientation reaction in virtue of increased excitability should result in intensification of the α-rhythm, while darkness leading to lowering of excitability should result in increased amplitude of the slow waves.

These assumptions found experimental confirmation. Stimulation by darkness during drowsiness leads to intensification of the α-rhythm at the beginning and end of its period of operation, with the deepening of the slow waves in between. Stimulation by light in similar conditions results in an intensification of the α-rhythm throughout the period of stimulation as both general and local orientation reactions in this case include increased excitability.

It thus appears that darkness, at the moment when it replaces light, gives rise to two reflexes, general and local, which differ in the sign of the excitability change. Conversely, replacement of darkness by light is associated with change of excitability, whether a component of the general or local orientation reaction, of the same sign. By measuring (1) the latent period of the reaction of intensification of the α-rhythm in response to darkness, (2) the duration of that reaction during the period of operation of the darkness as a specific stimulus, and (3) the duration of the period of depression of the α-rhythm in response to transition from darkness to light, one can study the dynamics of both the general and the local orientation reaction in one experiment. During the experiment, the latent period of the α-rhythm intensification reaction in response to darkness becomes shorter, the duration of the reaction increases, while the intensity of depression produced by passage from darkness to light diminishes.

Furthermore, with repetitive, adequate stimulation by light, the experiments show the gradual extinction, within the visual analyser, of the general orientation reflex and its replacement by the local reaction.

Experiments to show the effects of extraneous stimulation on the intensification reaction produced by the action of darkness, confirm the interaction of the orientation reactions of the same or opposite sign, resulting from the operation of light and darkness. An extraneous stimulus reinforces the generalized orientation reflex and increases the effects of light on the E.E.G. tracing where the general and local reactions are of the same sign. The same stimulus weakens or alters the effect of darkness as the general and local orientation reactions are in this case of opposite sign so far as the electrical potentials of the cortex of the visual analyser are concerned (Fig. 24).

The diagram shows how the duration of α-rhythm depression produced by a 10 sec period of darkness, replacing an illumination of 43 lux on white, diminishes with repetition. Similarly, depression produced by transition from darkness to light also diminishes with repetition. Auditory stimulation (a loud sound), increases the extent of depression in either case, but this increase is transient and becomes extinguished with repetition of the auditory stimuli, each succeeding stimulus having less influence on the reaction than the one immediately preceding. The nature of the reaction reveals the similarity between the effects of darkness on E.E.G. tracings under the influence of sound stimulation and the appearance of inhibition of the orientation reflex.

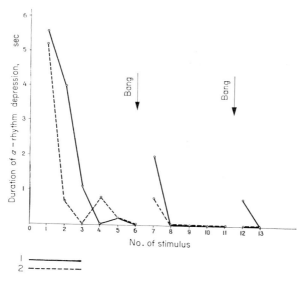

FIG. 24. Graphic representation of the extinction of the electrical reactions to the start and end of darkness and disinhibition of these reactions by an extra-stimulus (bang). 1—Duration of α-rhythm depression to the end of the stimulus. 2. Duration of α-rhythm depression during action of the stimulus.

It has been demonstrated experimentally that the degree of activation of the occipital area in response to light stimulation, is related to the general orientation reflex. This can be inferred from the following observations: firstly when in absolute darkness—a condition which normally leads to inhibition and to the development of slower rhythms—the subject's eyes are uncovered

G

and he attends visually so that a persistent α-rhythm depression is produced. The latter is particularly intense in cases where visual attention is concentrated on an object difficult to distinguish. Secondly, in the absence of visual attention even in bright illumination, the α-rhythm becomes re-established. This re-establishment of the α-rhythm becomes particularly clear if the eyes are kept shut and visual attention completely excluded.

Thus, in addition to the widespread irradiation of the general orientation reflex, the effects of light and darkness include the maintenance of a certain tone in the cortical activity of the visual analyser, depending on the degree of illumination of the eye. It can be assumed that in this mechanism the reticular formation plays the role of an intermediary on which the actual level of excitation of the cortical cells depends. These effects on the E.E.G. are mediated by the local orientation reaction depending on the activation of the visual analyser.

The effects of light and darkness depend on the orientation reactions of the visual organs, their excitation and inhibition, weakening or intensification and not on the actual physical intensity of the stimuli. The conclusion to be drawn from the observations made so far is that the bio-electrical reactions of the cortex, consisting of changes in the nature of its rhythmical activity, depend primarily on the operation of the orientation reflexes, both general and local.

D. **The Effects of Rhythmic Photic Stimulation**

The use of photic stimulation provides a new method for differentiating the specific and the orientation reflexes resulting from light stimulation of the visual analyser. The effects of intermittent stimulation of this kind includes the reproduction of the frequency of the flicker by the cortical end of the visual analyser for the whole duration of the stimulation, provided the illumination is of sufficient intensity (in the experiments to be described—up to 100 lux on a white screen placed at a distance of 0·75 m from the subject). Particularly distinct linkage of rhythm rate is obtained in man with flicker of 10–20 c/s. The development of cortical rhythms corresponding to the flicker frequency, or a simple multiple thereof—"driving"—shows the dependence of the electrical reactions of the cortex on the special features of the stimulus.

There are various schools of thought on the nature of photic driving. The view that it is a manifestation of primary responses in the cortex to light is the one accepted most widely (Smirnov, 1956). At the same time, a number of observations indicate that this phenomenon is of a quite different nature from primary cortical responses. The findings of Jasper *et al.* (1955) are of particular interest in this respect.

A problem arises concerning the part played by the generalized and local orientation reactions in this phenomenon of linkage. The orientation reflex produced by intermittent light stimulation, as in the case of other stimuli, includes a C.G.R. and α-rhythm depression in the occipital area. When the intermittent stimulation is continued, the generalized orientation reaction as manifested by the C.G.R. becomes extinguished, but the driving persists. Depression of α-rhythm in response to flicker is more persistent, but it also becomes progressively weaker. In time, the linkage between the rate of cortical rhythms and that of the intermittent stimulation also diminishes. This manifests itself in reduced amplitude of the imposed rate, first for a flicker rate of 20–30 c/s, and in the reappearance of α-rhythm from time to time during flicker stimulation. On the other hand, the effects of intermittent stimulation of low frequency are intensified.

How does this weakening of the effect of intermittent stimulation at high frequency, and strengthening of the effect of intermittent stimulation at low frequency, come about?

The E.E.G. analyser reveals that the effects of rhythmic photic stimulation are made up of blockage of the α-rhythm and the phenomenon of driving. In time, the C.G.R. undergoes extinction, depression of the α-rhythm is reduced and the intensity of rate linkage also diminishes. A connexion between the intensity of the driving effect in response to flicker of various frequencies and the degree of depression is thus revealed (Sokolov, 1957; Danilova, 1957). An extraneous stimulus, such as a loud sound, intensifies the depression and at the same time results in transient reinforcement of driving with high frequency stimulation. This is illustrated in Fig. 25, showing (*a*) the effects of flicker of 9 c/s after a number of applications and (*b*) the same with flicker of 18 c/s. The driving effects with the lower frequency are marked, but there is no driving with the higher frequency, though there is α-rhythm depression.

Figure 25(*c*), (*d*) shows the effects of flicker of 18 c/s, and 9 c/s after strong extraneous stimulation, which is seen to facilitate tuning to higher frequencies and reduce the response to lower frequencies. This intensifying effect of extraneous stimulation on driving with higher flicker frequencies, which is associated with a C.G.R., demonstrates the part played by the orientation reaction.

The response to a still higher frequency (27 c/s) is different. Before the orientation reflex becomes extinguished the amplitude of the reaction is high. With continued flicker, the reactions to the basic rate diminish in intensity and sub-harmonic rates of 9, 13·5 and 18 c/s make their appearance.

It can be assumed, therefore, that the development of inhibition of the orientation reflex affects the processes underlying the driving effect. This is associated with loss of higher harmonics in the case of low initial frequencies and the acquisition of sub-harmonics by higher frequencies. On the whole, there is swing of the driving mechanism towards slower cortical rhythms.

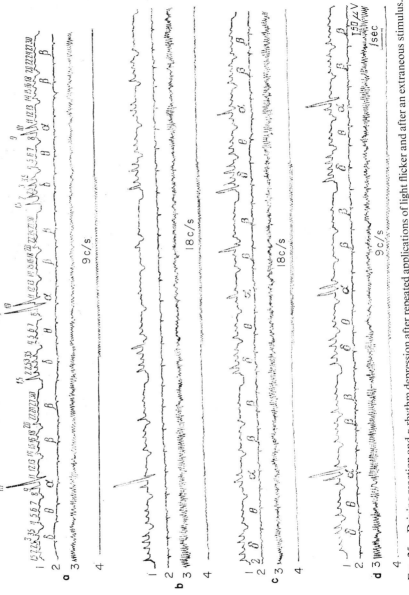

Fig. 25.   Driving reaction and α-rhythm depression after repeated applications of light flicker and after an extraneous stimulus. 1—Analyser.   2—Frequency band.   3—E.E.G. of right occipital region.   4—Stimulation.

This conversion of higher frequencies of stimulation into potential changes of lower frequency points to diminished lability of the cortical cells. An extraneous stimulus, giving rise to the orientation reflex, results in an alteration in the combination of harmonic frequencies, namely, the top harmonics developing in response to low frequencies are strengthened, sub-harmonics developed in response to high frequencies of flicker are suppressed (Fig. 26).

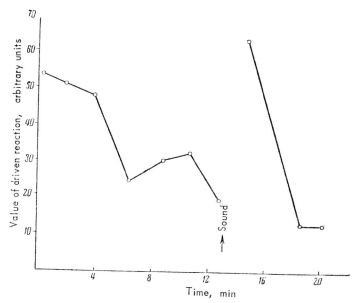

FIG. 26. Attenuation of the driving effect with continued flicker stimulation and intensification of driving after acoustic stimulation. Subject B., October 1956. Rate of light flicker 18/sec.

It appears, therefore, that the effects produced by intermittent light stimulation of various frequencies depend on the degree of extinction or re-emergence of the orientation reflex. A certain degree of reinforcement of the orientation reflex after its extinction is associated with a change in the tuning of the cortex to different flicker frequencies. If the lability of the cortical cells is, within limits, indicated by the ease with which the high frequency rhythms can be produced, it may be concluded that extinction of the orientation reaction coincides with reduction of cortical cell lability and its disinhibition with increased lability.

A connexion between the lability of the cortical cells and the orientation reaction is also indicated by observations on the ratio of high and low harmonics seen along with the basic rate in the human E.E.G. in response to rhythmic photic stimulation. The first application of flicker of 9 c/s does not result in tuning, as the orientation reflex has not yet become extinguished and no inhibition has developed. The basic rhythm is, therefore, associated with higher harmonics of 18 and 27 c/s. As flicker stimulation continues, still at 9 c/s, and there is progressive extinction of the orientation reflex, the transformation of the slower rate into faster rhythms ends and the cortex is tuned to the basic frequency. If flicker of sufficiently high frequency (20–30 c/s) is used, the connexion between attenuation of the driving effect and the usual dynamic changes associated with extinction of the orientation reflex can be traced.

The existence of a connexion between the phenomenon of photic driving and the complex of the orientation reflex is also confirmed by the following observations. All factors affecting the conditions of experiment in a way which makes the extinction of the orientation reflex more difficult, lead to intensification of the driving phenomenon. This is particularly clear in the case of change in the intensity of frequency of the stimulation: attenuation of the driving effect is delayed and may not be observed in the course of the experiment.

As demonstrated earlier, the effects of darkness on the occipital potentials (dependent on suppression of visual input) include lowering of the level of cortical cell excitation, which manifests itself by intensification of waves slower than those initially present. These findings have been confirmed by the use of rhythmic photic stimulation. After a 40-min period of dark adaptation, the driving effect of a high frequency was reduced. On the other hand, general illumination of the room after a period of dark adaptation intensified driving. It must be pointed out, however, that reduction of lability in darkness cannot be wholly attributed to the activity of the central parts of the visual analyser. Smirnov (1956), has demonstrated that the lability of the retina of an isolated eye is diminished in darkness, and this is reflected in the retinogram and action potentials of the nerve during photic stimulation. On the other hand, a return to the initial background level of illumination results in increase of retinal lability.

The weakening effects of darkness on cortical excitability can also be demonstrated by other means. The reduction of the electrical sensitivity of the eye in darkness is of particular importance (Kravkov, 1946). Electrical sensitivity, which reflects the level of excitation of neuronal elements of the visual analyser, is found to follow the cortical rhythm and also "tunes" in to the rhythmic photic stimulus. The effect of darkness, which suppresses visual input, is closely related to the passive inhibition of the cortex observed in Pavlov's laboratory animals (dogs), after destruction of several peripheral receptors. The results of suppressed input are similar to those of inhibition of the orientation reflex.

The positive effect of light on photic driving can also be observed in what, at first glance, appears a strange phenomenon. In darkness, attenuation of the reaction takes place more rapidly with occasionally applied flicker stimulation than if the applications are more frequent. More frequent stimulation leads to a general increase of cortical cell excitability and this increased level of excitability, whatever its cause—generalized orientation reflex or local orientation reaction in response to light—leads to an intensification of the photic driving reaction.

Our findings concerning the activation of the visual analyser in response to an adequate light stimulus are similar to observations made by Chang (1952). By electrical stimulation of the lateral geniculate body in the cat and recording the primary cortical responses, Chang discovered that the amplitude of the reaction, not great in darkness, increases progressively with illumination of the eyes and diminishes again when light is excluded. This increase of excitability radiates to other areas of the cortex, such as the auditory area.

The connexion between the increase of the lability of the cortical cells, as shown by the maximum frequency of the flicker which can be reproduced by the cortex, and increase of cortical excitability, has been demonstrated in our laboratory in experiments on rabbits. The administration of stimulating and inhibiting agents showed that intensification of the photic driving effect is linked with change in the optimum driving frequency, and depends on the level of cortical cell excitability. Caffeine intensified the driving effect, especially in the high frequency range (15–30 c/s). A similar but much weaker effect was observed as a result of the development of orientation and defence reactions. On the other hand, ether anaesthesia led to considerable weakening of the driving effect in the range of high frequencies, this coinciding with inhibition of orientation reactions to a variety of stimuli.

Thus, the use of flicker revealed a close connexion between the driving effect and orientation reflexes, local orientation reactions arising within the visual analyser having the greatest influence. There is some similarity between driving effects and the changes in the frequency of spontaneous rhythms produced by inhibition (appearance of slow waves) and disinhibition of the orienting reaction (their replacement by a faster rhythm). This similarity also extends to the effects of light and darkness. Darkness, by suppressing input, not only facilitates the development of a slower spontaneous rhythm but leads to such transformation of external intermittent stimulation that the resulting cortical rhythm is slower. On the other hand, light, by increasing cortical excitability, facilitates the development of quicker basic rhythms and intensifies the tuning reactions to higher frequencies of rhythmic stimulation. One can conclude, therefore, that the same mechanism underlies the control of both spontaneous and driven cortical rhythms and that both forms of rhythmical activity are connected with the level of excitability in the cortical cells.

E. Central and Peripheral Components of Adaptation Reflexes

Persistence of the reaction throughout the period of stimulation is a characteristic feature of the specialized adaptation reflexes. For instance, stimulation by heat produces a certain degree of vasodilatation which is maintained. In contrast, Shpil'berg (1940) has demonstrated the complete restoration of α-rhythm under continuous light stimulation, which confirms the orientative nature of the influence of light on the E.E.G. in man.

Further confirmation of this fact is found in experiments designed for the purpose, involving the use of an integrator of potential changes. The amplitude of the restored α-rhythm in the presence of light is somewhat lower, to start with, than in darkness. This difference reflects a generally increased excitability of the cortex under the influence of light. Transition to darkness leads to increased amplitude of the α-rhythm which is then fixed at a slightly higher level than in the presence of light. This change now reflects a lowered level of cortical excitability—an effect of darkness. With light and darkness alternating, the differences between the amplitudes of the α-rhythm become gradually reduced (Fig. 27).

Illumination (50 lux on a white screen) of the dark-adapted eye results, on first application, in prolonged depression of α-rhythm and some increase of activity at a slightly lower level towards the end of the period of illumination (Fig. 27(a)). Transition to darkness causes reappearance of α-rhythm of high amplitude. The second application of the stimulus has a similar effect, (Fig. 27(b)) and with continued illumination, the α-rhythm begins partially to re-emerge. The time lapse before the α-rhythm reappears is here shorter than after the first application of the light stimulus. Transition to darkness intensifies the α-rhythm. Figure 27(c) shows the effects of the third application of the light stimulus. The α-rhythm recovers completely with the illumination still continued and is intensified, but little, by the transition to darkness. With repetition of the long acting light stimuli, the reappearance of the α-rhythm becomes increasingly quicker.

A characteristic feature of the α-rhythm, re-emerging in spite of continuing illumination, is its irregularity. There is an alternation between the period of α-rhythm suppression and re-emergence with a general tendency to return to the original level of electrical activity. Finally, in spite of great differences between the degree of illumination of the eyes, there may be very little difference between the corresponding levels of α-rhythm.

One possible explanation for these findings may be based on the orientative nature of the visual analyser's reaction to light. There is, however, another important possibility. The fact that α-rhythm can reappear in spite of continuous illumination must be connected with the peripheral processes of adaptation. Adaptation results in a great reduction in the number of stimuli reaching the centres from the periphery. However, even absolute darkness cannot be compared with the suppression of all input following bilateral enucleation of the eyes in animal experiments. Granit (1955), demonstrated the spontaneous activity of the nerve elements in a dark-adapted retina and the tonic effect of this activity on the level of cortical activity reflected in the E.E.G. even in the absence of any illumination.

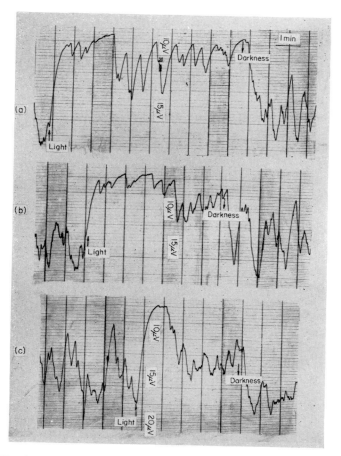

FIG. 27. Summation tracing of cerebral potentials on change from light to dark-ness and from darkness to light. Subject P., May 1956. Ordinate: amplitude of potentials (μV).

If it is true that the weakening of the cortical reaction to light and darkness is connected with the development of adaptation at the periphery, there should be strong evidence of this specific adaptation reaction in the peripheral parts of the visual system. Peripheral adaptation mechanisms include pupillary reflexes and photochemical changes in the retina. Pupillary reflexes can develop as components of either orienting or adaptation reflexes.

The features of pupillary dilatation as a component of orienting reflexes to new stimuli have been described by Kotlyarevskii (1935), and Brailovskaya and Levin (1953). K. S. Smirnov (1952), using a ciné-camera, demonstrated the connexion between dilatation of the pupil and development of an orientation reflex, and studied the development and extinction of those reactions. The findings of Glezer (1952, 1953), and Shakhnovich (1956), also pointed to a close connexion between pupillary and orientation reflexes. Liberman and Strel'tsova (1952), using various types of stimuli, have shown that the resulting pupillary reaction (dilatation) becomes extinguished with repetition. V. A. Smirnov (1955) made a detailed investigation of pupillary reactions.

Most authors have used cinematographic methods for the study of pupillary reactions. Those who have recently used this method are Glezer (1952, 1953), K. S. Smirnov (1952) and Shakhnovich (1956).

In our investigation of the pupillary reactions, we used a method of rapid cinematography (32–200 exposures per sec), developed in collaboration with members of the staff of the Scientific Cinematography Department, Pokrovskaya and Fradkin. The experiments were carried out after 15 min of dark adaptation and the light was switched on (this also served as the light stimulus) when the pupillary reaction to the noise of the apparatus was finally extinguished. The latent period of the pupillary reaction allowed pictures to be taken before the reaction set in, and, in this way, the complete course of the reaction could be studied in detail. Similarly, the noise of the ciné-camera served as the auditory stimulus. In this case the light was switched on first and the camera was started later. The latent period again allowed pictures to be taken before the pupil responded to the sound by dilatation, and the course of the reaction could thus be studied in its whole extent.

However, methods of this kind, recording pupillary reactions in the presence of illumination, suffer from a number of disadvantages. The effects of darkness as a special stimulus of the visual analyser cannot be studied. Bright illumination of the pupil makes the use of liminal light stimuli in conditions of dark adaptation of the eye impossible. Photo-electric recording involving the use of a photo-electric cell, as described by Mihama and Kotake (1954), is associated with similar disadvantages. The attention paid recently to the use of infra-red rays (Atayev, 1955) is not, therefore, surprising. The technique of recording pupillary reactions by means of infra-red cinematography has been described by a number of investigators (Clark, 1946; Young and Biersdorf, 1954 and others). We employed this technique using a special film with sensitivity in the range of 760 mμ. An incandescent lamp of 500 watts, incorporating several layers of infra-red filters, was used as the source of illumination of the subject's pupils and in this way we were able to proceed with cinematography in complete darkness.

The absence of any effect on the pupil of infra-red illumination, was confirmed in the following way. The pictures were taken after 15 min of dark adaptation, and infra-red illumination was switched on when any possible pupillary reaction to the noise of the apparatus disappeared. A study of the effects of the infra-red illumination on the diameter of the pupil showed an absence of any significant pupillary reaction. As only the sustained changes of the diameter of the pupil in response to light and darkness were of importance for the purposes of the investigation, the camera had been adjusted to take only 8 picture per sec. Later on, in order to study the manifold effects of various stimuli in time, the speed of 1·5 pictures per sec was employed. In the analysis of the pictures, the following parameters have been taken into consideration: the amplitude of the reaction, the latent period, the duration of the reaction and the speed with which the pre-existent conditions were re-established after the removal of the stimulus (after-effects).

This technique provided the means of studying the process of contraction of the pupil in response to light replacing darkness, as well as those associated with the dilatation of the pupil in response to darkness replacing the light, (Fig. 28). The dynamics of these reactions in the face of repetitive stimulation were also studied.

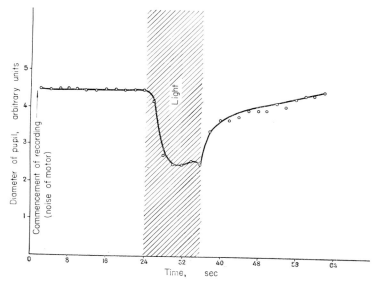

FIG. 28.   Pupillary reactions to light and darkness as revealed by infra-red photography. Subject V., April 1955. Light strength 25 lux.

The persistent pupillary reactions underlay the process of peripheral adaptation of the visual analyser and differed from the orientation dilatation of the pupil brought into operation by sound, tactile or painful stimulation. The orientative pupillary dilatation is similar to other reactions to new stimuli, inasmuch as it becomes extinguished with repetition (Liberman and Strel'tsova, 1952; Shakhnovich, 1955; Sokolov, 1955). The adaptation of the eye to the intensity of illumination is not exclusively dependent on the pupillary reactions alone. The adaptation of the retina, based on photochemical reactions, is also, in this respect, of major importance.

Further experiments involving the use of a pin-point source of light, capable of giving rise to adaptative reactions occurring only in one segment of the retina, were designed in order to study the place of the pupillary reflexes in the processes of peripheral adaptation.

It was found that the pupillary contraction which develops when the point source of light is switched on does not remain fixed at one level but in time gradually relaxes. It fails, however, to dilate to the initial level (Fig. 29). This figure shows that while in complete darkness the diameter of the pupil is stable, the result of stimulation with a pin-point source of light is a gradual return towards the previous size of the pupil through a series of irregular fluctuations.

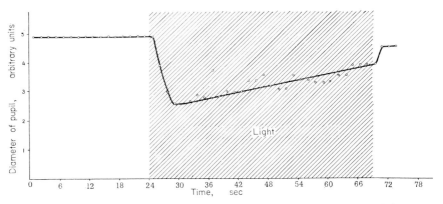

FIG. 29.   Restoration of pupil size on exposure to a weak point source of light. Subject L., March 1956.

It appears, therefore, that the re-emergence of the α-rhythm, in spite of continuous illumination cannot be explained on the basis of pupillary reactions, as the latter may also become weakened in these conditions. It can be postulated that both the re-emergence of α-rhythm, and the relaxation of the pupillary contraction are associated with the adaptive processes taking place in the retina. If that is true, then the stream of impulses, particularly strong in the first moment of light stimulation, would give rise to a marked depression of the α-rhythm and a strong pupillary reflex. The adaptation of the retina to the light would result in a weakening of the stream of the impulses, and, in turn, would lead to a weakening of the pupillary reaction and to a partial reappearance of α-rhythm.

In this way also, the variations of the diameter of the pupil, as observed during light stimulation of the eye, can be easily explained. If a pin-point source of light is used, the adaptation of various segments of the retina is not uniform. Any, even the slightest, movement of the eye brings a new, not yet adapted, segment of the retina under the action of the stimulus. In consequence, there develops another volley of stimuli and, as a result, depression of α-rhythm is increased and contraction of the pupil is intensified. This has been confirmed by simultaneous recording of cortical potentials and eye movements. The so-called "spontaneous" depression of α-rhythm in many cases coincides in time with eye movement, which, by upsetting the adaptation state of the periphery, results in an increased number of stimuli reaching the central end of the visual analyser, in the same way as does any increase in the intensity of illumination.

In order to confirm the importance of the non-uniform illumination of the retina and of the movements of the eye in the production of the "spontaneous" depression of α-rhythm during constant illumination, an experiment was carried out with uniform illumination of the retina. The subject's eyes were screened with frosted glass spectacles, which made the illumination of the retina uniform; the illumination of the room was non-uniform but of constant intensity. It was found that the α-rhythm returned more quickly and became regular in the same way as with the eyes closed. These findings agree with observations made by Gastaut and Bert (1954), in the course of their studies of α-rhythm during cinematographic presentations. While observation of moving pictures was associated with a persistent depression of α-rhythm, the uniform bright illumination of the screen led to its rapid return.

In contrast to vasomotor reactions in response to cold or heat (where the initial applications of thermal stimuli resulted in inhibition of the specialized reactions by the orientation reflex), the immediate response to the first application of the light stimulus consists of a specialized reaction—contraction of the pupil—which, at the same time, inhibits the pupillary manifestation of the orientation reflex—dilatation. Only on rare occasions can sudden light stimulation produce the orientation pupillary reaction in the form of dilatation. This distinguishes the pupillary response to light from the bioelectrical reactions where the orientation elements predominate.

It should also be pointed out, that change in the conditions of optical stimulation causes, first of all, contraction and not dilatation of the pupil

(Shakhnovich, 1956). This phenomenon could also be explained by the altered conditions of retinal adaptation, as a result of change of type or colour of the stimulus. Consequently, the intensity of the stimulation increases and the specialized reaction in the form of pupillary contraction is brought into operation.

As the, initially strong, pupillary reaction can in certain conditions become weaker in the face of continued light stimulation, other adaptation mechanisms must exist which would compensate for this weakening of pupillary reaction. These would limit the number of impulses reaching the visual centres.

The part played by peripheral retinal adaptation mechanisms in the partial re-establishment of the α-rhythm, and the weakened pupillary reaction during continued light stimulation, was investigated by continuous automatic recording of the light sensitivity of the eye. A number of investigators (Dolin, 1936; Gol'dburt, 1952; and others) endeavoured to study rapid changes of sensitivity to light by shortening the time interval between the individual measurements. This interval has been reduced to 10–30 sec but even that is not the limit, and further shortening opens the way to continuous recording of sensitivity to light. Vavilov (1950), succeeded in measuring the sensitivity once every second by recording the movements of the subject who pressed the key in response to any sensation of light perceived. Makarov (1952), described the method of receptography consisting of simultaneous recording on one tape of the apparatus, of the stimuli applied (for instance light), and, the motor responses of the subject. Another method of measurement of sensitivity was inspired by the constructor of the direct recording audiometer—Bekesy (1917). Here, the subject, by changing the direction of rotation of a motor, alters the position of the volume knob of the audiometer and in this way increases or diminishes the intensity of the sound used as the stimulus. The task of the subject is to achieve, by changing the direction of rotation of the motor, the appearance and the disappearance of a sound of liminal intensity. All the movements of the volume knob are registered automatically on the same tape of the apparatus and reflect the changes of auditory sensitivity.

A similar principle was employed for the purposes of continuous measurement of sensitivity to light during the process of adaptation. The terms used to describe the technique and the apparatus are "adaptography" and "adaptograph" respectively (Sokolov, 1954). A monochromatic adaptometer with a motor (Gurtavoi and Kravkov, 1950) has been used as an adaptograph. It consists of a source of light, a triangular prism producing a spectrum, a neutral light filter by means of which the intensity of illumination could be varied, and an opaque glass screen illuminated by the monochromatic light. Alteration of the position of the prism results in a change of the colour on the screen, which, in the conditions of the experiments to be described, was kept constant at 540 mμ. The neutral light filter brought into motion by the motor, and influencing the intensity of illumination, carried a pen producing a tracing on kymographic tape. The subject was asked to press or release pressure on the control button of the motor and in this way to switch the illumination on and off. The movements of the neutral light filter, the density of which could be thus changed in logarithmic progression, were automatically recorded on the same tape in the form of dashes which represented the range interval between the threshold of development and threshold of disappearance of the test spot. By adjusting the movement of the tape-carrying kymograph to that of the pen attached to the light filter, one could obtain a continuous curve which was a graphic representation of the sensitivity to light as thus measured. One measurement was obtained every 10 sec. By selecting a neutral filter of density increasing logarithmically, a relatively wide range of changes of sensitivity could be covered. These changes appeared in the form of oscillations incorporated into a curve, and, the effects of various stimuli could be studied. The amplitude and duration of the reactions, and the rate of change of the sensitivity, were considered.

A study of light sensitivity carried out with the help of the method described using specific (light, darkness) and non-specific (sound) stimuli has shown that the method is suitable for recording rapid changes of sensitivity (Golubyeva, 1955). In addition to the curve of sensitivity, the adaptogram also showed the moments of application of the stimulus. In a number of cases, simultaneous records were obtained of the skin resistance changes (Féré phenomenon), for the purposes of comparison of the C.G.R. and the variations of sensitivity to light. The skin resistance was recorded by means of an automatic recording potentiometer connected to silver-plate electrodes applied to the left hand of the subject. When a constant level of dark adaptation was achieved, the stimulus in the form of weak illumination (-0.2 lux on a white screen) was applied. The sensitivity to light was recorded with the help of an automatic recording adaptometer. It was found that stimulation of the dark-adapted eye by light results in a sharp fall in its sensitivity. In a number of cases, the sensitivity not only remained diminished but actually continued to fall while the illumination was maintained (Fig. 30).

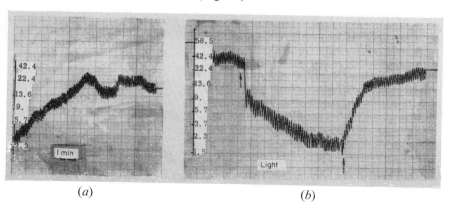

(*a*) (*b*)

FIG. 30. Reduction of light sensitivity as a result of exposure to light. Subject K., May 1956. Ordinate light sensitivity (arbitrary units). Each line represents the difference between the threshold for the appearance (lower end) and the point of disappearance (upper end) of the light in the test field of the adaptograph.

Figure 30(*a*) shows the end of the process of dark adaptation of the eye.
The gradual levelling up of the sensitivity curve can be noted. The onset of
weak illumination (Fig. 30(*b*)) leads to a sudden fall of sensitivity, and the
sensitivity continues to fall almost throughout the 5 min of illumination.
With the end of illumination, sensitivity gradually returns nearly to the
original level as a result of dark adaptation.

In this way, the comparison of cerebral bio-electrical reactions, pupillary
reactions and variations of sensitivity to light shows that the depression of the
central bio-electric and pupillary components of the adaptation reflex are
due to peripheral retinal adaptation.

F. Adaptation and Orienting Reflexes in the Control of Sensitivity

If we accept that any stimulus brings into operation both the orientation
and the specialized (adaptation) reflexes, it becomes clear that the degree of
sensitivity resulting from stimulation varies with the interaction of these
reflexes. The orientation reflex, by increasing the excitability of the higher
centres of the visual analyser, leads to its increased reactivity which manifests
itself in the tuning of the cortex to the rate of intermittent light stimulation,
and the intensification of α-rhythm depression.

Light and darkness, being specific forms of stimulation, have different
effects on the central and peripheral segments of the visual analyser. Darkness,
by bringing about dilatation of the pupil and, by increasing the concentration
of visual purple, increases the light sensitivity of the retina, but at the same
time, by diminishing the number of impulses arising at the periphery,
diminishes the excitability of the centre. Light, on the other hand, brings
about the contraction of the pupil and decomposition of rhodopsin, and in
this way lowers the sensitivity of the retina but simultaneously increases the
excitability of the centres.

The problem arises, therefore, as to the nature of the changes of sensitivity,
resulting from the combined action of the orientation and adaptation reflexes,
when their intensities and the parts played by them are unequal. In order to
study these changes, it is necessary to correlate data indicating increased
reactivity of the visual analyser (resulting from the operation of the orientation reflexes), with the results of direct measurement of associated changes
in sensitivity and for this purpose a non-specific stimulus, such as sound, must
be selected. The first applications of sound result in an increase of sensitivity
to light, which, with repetition, disappears in the same way as the galvanic
skin reaction and α-rhythm depression.

Extraneous stimulation disinhibits the C.G.R. to sound and the α-rhythm
depression, and at the same time restores the increased light sensitivity
response to auditory stimulation (Fig. 31). The diagram shows the changes
in light sensitivity of the eye with interrupted sound stimulation (73 dB).

The vertical lines correspond to the maximal differences between the thresholds during the 1 min before (continuous line) and the 1 min after (interrupted line). the onset of the stimulation. It can be noted that the sensitivity during the action of the stimulus, especially during its first few applications, is higher than the initial (pre-experiment), sensitivity. The increase is greater than could be accounted for by the maximum fluctuations of the initial

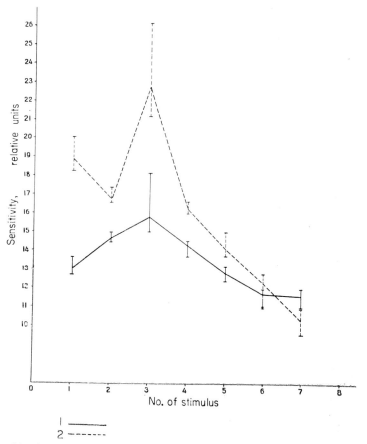

FIG. 31.   Increase of light sensitivity in response to acoustic stimulation. Subject K., April 1956. 1—Level of sensitivity before acoustic stimulation. 2—Level of sensitivity during period of acoustic stimulation.

sensitivity. With the interrupted sound stimulation continued, the difference between the initial sensitivity and the sensitivity during stimulation disappears, and a tendency to a lowered light sensitivity response to sound develops. It has been experimentally demonstrated that this increased light sensitivity

H

with interrupted sound stimulation coincides with increased central excitability (depression of α-rhythm), dilatation of the pupil, cephalic vasodilatation,
lowered resistance of the skin and is, in fact, the sensory component of the
orientation reflex. The inhibition of the increase in light sensitivity and α-
rhythm depression during repetitive sound stimulation, and their disinhibition
as a result of extraneous stimulation, are further proofs of the intimate
connexion of these reactions with the complex of the orientation reflex.
The increased sensitivity of the visual analyser to light cannot, it seems,
be attributed to the pupillary reaction to sound, as in darkness it remains
fully dilated (infra-red photography) and no further dilatation in response to
sound is possible.

It should be pointed out that a transition from weak and medium to high-
intensity sounds (90–105 dB) results in a fall of sensitivity replacing the increase. This was demonstrated in a series of specially designed experiments
(Steklova, 1957). It was observed that a loud sound, which at first resulted
in a rise of light sensitivity, with repetition started to give rise to its decrease.
Similar observations were made during the study of the effects of sound
stimulation on the cephalic vasomotor reactions when, as described before,
sound—the intensity of which was approaching the threshold of pain—gave
rise to cephalic vasoconstriction instead of vasodilatation. It is possible
that the fall of light sensitivity appears as the first stage of the response to a
painful electrocutaneous stimulus. This fall of sensitivity later becomes
replaced by increased sensitivity.

The increased sensitivity to light, as a result of sound stimulation, can also
be demonstrated in another way. The sound which gives rise to depression of
the occipital α-rhythm is capable of temporarily converting a subliminal
stimulus into a liminal one. As the α-rhythm depression disappears, the
increase of sensitivity due to sound tails off, and the above effect also disappears. The influence of sound stimulation on light sensitivity is basically
related to the orientation reflex and seems to be the outcome of the increased
excitability of the centres and its effect on the periphery.

Vasomotor change is one of the possible mechanisms for the increase of
excitability. The excitation wave produced by the action of the sound on
reaching the reticular formation, leads to sensitization of the cortical cells—
which manifests itself as an increase in rhythm frequency, and of the receptors—by increasing the lability of the individual receptive units and, by
lowering the threshold of their electrical responses. As shown experimentally
in Granit's laboratory (1955), the vasomotor changes taking place in the
retina as a result of excitation of the reticular formation, provide a possible
mechanism for such sensitization.

The action of a specific stimulus is much more complicated. As already
stated, the complexity results from the fact that stimulation by light

simultaneously brings into operation both the orientation and the specialized reflexes which are different so far as the centre and the periphery are concerned. The problem arises as to what is the final outcome, in the terms of sensitivity to light, of the interaction of these reflexes. The result of stimulation by light may be a lowering of sensitivity (at the first application) or, an increased sensitivity afterwards (Kravkov, 1950). Bronshtein (1946) and others, have described an increase of sensitivity to light as a result of specific stimulation. Dilatation of the pupil could be one of the factors concerned. However, absence of any dilatation of the pupil already maximally dilated has been demonstrated by infra-red photography in darkness during the application of light stimuli. Thus, the increase in the sensitivity to light as a result of stimulation by light, cannot be attributed to any change in the diameter of the pupil but seems connected with the general increase of tone in the visual analyser.

All observations on the sensitization of the eye as a result of stimulation by light have been based on verbal reactions to signal stimuli. The effects of light on the visual analyser, in conditions of non-signal stimulation, have been studied experimentally in terms of changes of sensitivity and reactivity of the eye, using the method of combined recording of the generalized and local orientation reactions. The study was carried out after complete dark adaptation (30–40 min). To start with, the threshold of sensitivity to light was determined by means of weak light stimuli, produced by an adaptometer, while a continuous E.E.G. record was taken. The threshold was determined in accordance with the reactive depression of the α-rhythm in response to supraliminal or subliminal, non-signal, light stimuli without any consideration being paid to whether the subject actually was, or was not, seeing the light. When a certain level of sensitivity was established, a light (43 lux on a white screen) was switched on for 10 sec.

In order to determine the changes of light sensitivity under the influence of sudden illumination of the dark-adapted eye, a method of "testing stimuli" was used. These were the near-liminal stimuli obtained with the adaptometer as above. At first, the test stimuli were exhibited before, and then 30 sec after, the illumination. It was found that illumination—after disappearance of the decrease of light sensitivity—gave rise to a phase of increased sensitivity with subliminal stimuli becoming liminal and with the duration of α-rhythm depression in response to previously liminal stimuli increasing.

In a number of cases after illumination, weak light stimuli gave rise to a C.G.R. (Sokolov, Danilova, Mikhalevskaya, 1957) which in some instances was also used for the determination of the threshold. Figure 32 shows that, after the illumination, the depression in response to all test-stimuli is extended in time. In addition, the stimuli, previously subliminal and producing no depression, now become liminal. This lowering of the threshold and intensification of depression in response to supraliminal stimuli is accompanied, in addition, by a shortening of the latent period of the α-rhythm depression.

One can say, therefore, that the effects of light stimulation include increased sensitivity and reactivity of the local and generalized orientation reflexes. This is shown by intensification of the α-rhythm depression and reappearance of the galvanic skin reaction.

The increased sensitivity to light after illumination is related to the increased sensitivity of the visual analyser in response to sound stimulation. The light stimulus not only enhances the excitability of the centres during its period of operation, but also influences the sensitivity after it has ceased to operate. The enhancement of sensitivity in response to light is connected with the disinhibition and intensification of the orientation reactions. The stronger the orientation reaction produced by the light stimulation, the higher the sensitivity and the more intense the orientation reactions to test stimuli.

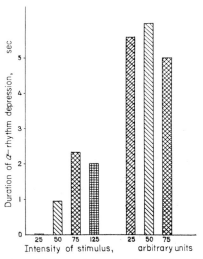

FIG. 32.   Increase of sensitivity and increased α-rhythm depression after light stimulation. Subject M., April 1955.

Another manifestation of the sensitization of the visual analyser is the enhancement of sensitivity resulting from the perception of weak, near-threshold stimuli. It shows as an increasing divergence between the threshold values for light stimuli when applied in the order of increasing, or diminishing, intensity.

By means of E.E.G. changes it can be shown that the threshold is higher when the stimuli are applied in the order of increasing intensity from subliminal to supraliminal, than in the case of the reverse order (from supra-liminal to subliminal).

The application of a variety of weak light stimuli in increasing and decreasing order of intensity, makes the counting of the number of α-rhythm depression reactions possible for any of the standard stimuli applied. It has been found that the number of reactions in response to a light stimulus of the same intensity is in each case different. The same weak agent gives rise to numerically more reactions when it is being applied after a stronger stimulus (Fig. 33). This diagram shows the difference between the thresholds measured in this way. For example, having taken as threshold value that intensity of stimulus which gives rise to a reaction in 50 per cent of cases, the threshold figures for light stimuli applied in the order of increasing or decreasing frequency can be calculated and are 125 and 75 respectively.

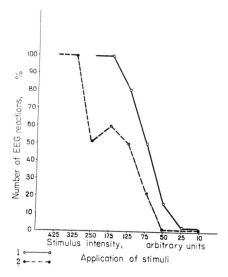

FIG. 33. Relationship between the number of α-rhythm depression reactions and the strength of photic stimuli presented in ascending and descending order. Subject P., September 1955. 1—After more powerful stimuli. 2—After weaker stimuli.

Simultaneously, with the change of threshold, one can observe intensification of the reaction. The reaction to a weak light stimulus following in the footsteps of a stronger one is more intense, its latent period is shorter and the duration of the period of depression is greater than if the order is reversed. It can be said, therefore, that the effects of a more clearly perceived weak stimulus include an increase of sensitivity to light. This is a relatively long lasting effect and can be evoked repeatedly without any noticeable weakening. The stimuli by which it is produced characteristically give rise to α-rhythm blocking. The sensitizing effect of such stimuli persists, however, for some time and still influences the response to the succeeding stimulus even though the α-rhythm has returned. One should not lose sight of the fact that the sensitizing effect of the light stimuli can be masked by the adaptation processes, if the intensity of the immediately preceding stimulus exceeds certain limits.

Similar phenomena are encountered in the course of audiometric studies. The threshold is lower with the transition from clearly audible sounds to the inaudible ones, than when the transition is in the opposite direction. The observation made by Maruseva and Chistovich (1951) was of the same nature; this indicated that, following the clear first perception of a new sound stimulus, the sensitivity increases, so that subsequent weaker stimuli began to give rise to reactions.

One can postulate, therefore, that adequate light stimulation results in an increase of sensitivity to both the generalized orientation reaction (brought into operation by the newness of the stimulus), and the local orientation reaction, and is manifested as increased excitability of the central end of the visual analyser. When the stimulus is sufficiently intense, increased central sensitivity is neutralized by diminished sensitivity at the periphery and it does not become evident unless the intensity of the stimulus is kept below a certain limit (i.e. weak light). This neutralizing effect of the periphery disappears some time after the strong illumination. Stimulation by darkness on the other hand, gives rise to increased peripheral and diminished central sensitivity, which has then a similar neutralizing effect. The results of any individual stimulus acting on the visual analyser depend, therefore, on the interaction of the orientation and adaptation reflexes and consequently on the novelty and intensity of the stimulus and on the degree of its departure from the background conditions.

In this way, the studies of the visual analyser brought into prominence the following:

1. *Generalized orientation reflexes* resulting in E.E.G. changes towards an accelerated basal rhythm, eye movements, dilatation of the pupil, suppression of respiration and increased sensitivity to light—developing simultaneously with the galvanic skin reaction.

2. *Local orientation reactions*, within the central segment of the visual analyser, consisting of increased excitability in response to light and diminished excitability in darkness.

3. *The photic driving effect*, consisting of reproduction of the rate of rhythmic photic stimulation by the visual cortex, depending on the intensity of the latter's excitatory state which, in turn, is determined by orientation reactions.

4. *Adaptation reflexes*, effecting changes at the periphery, which comprise pupillary contraction in response to light and pupillary dilatation in response to darkness; both being similar to the defensive reactions of the eye, which can be brought into operation by the action of a stream of air directed on to the cornea, or by intense illumination.

5. *Peripheral retinal adaptation reactions* in response to light or darkness.

G. Mechanisms of Interaction Between Orienting and Adaptation Reflexes

Comparison of the effects on the visual analyser of sound, light, darkness and a stream of air blown on to the cornea, shows that any of these stimuli gives rise to a combination of reflexes within it, which include the orientation and adaptation reactions.

Sound initiates non-specific orientation reactions only, within the visual analyser, involving an increase of its sensitivity. Corneal stimulation brings into operation the specific defence reaction as well as the orientation elements. Light, in addition to the orientation reaction (manifesting itself as α-rhythm depression coincident with a C.G.R. and cephalic vasodilatation), gives rise to a specific peripheral reaction consisting of reflex contraction of the pupil and diminished sensitivity to light. The development of the orientation reflex leads to increased central excitability, resulting from the local excitation response to light, and the simultaneous generalized orientation reaction.

The complex orientation reflex consists, therefore, of general and local reactions resulting from the activation of those analysers for which the stimulus in question proved adequate. In many of their properties the local reactions are similar to the specific reflexes. At the same time, the circumstances of development of the bio-electric reactions are typically those of the non-specific orientation reflex.

According to modern views, blockage of α-rhythm developing as an element of the orientation reflex, reflects generalized activation of the cortex and is functionally related to the diffuse reticular formation of the brain stem, the system of Moruzzi and Magoun (1949). The cortical element of the local orientation reaction is similarly related to the thalamic reticular formation of Jasper (1949), capable of selective activation of individual areas of the cortex.

Depending on the extent of the involvement of various parts of the reticular formation, different areas of the cortex become activated, and in this way a sufficiently powerful excitatory state is built up for the perception of the stimulus. In view of the fact that stimuli are associated to a different extent with the development of generalized and local orientation reactions and give rise to different specific reflexes, the effects of individual stimuli in the course of repetitive stimulation differ. Thus, repetitive sound stimulation results in the inhibition of the generalized orientation reflex, and consequently neutralizes the reactive increase of sensitivity of the visual analyser. This means that the reactive dilatation of the pupil ceases and that the eye movements and C.G.R. disappear.

The effects of darkness and light also change but in a more involved way. First, they cease to give rise to generalized excitation. The weakening of the generalized depression reaction coincides with extinction of the α-rhythm depression in response to sound. In addition, there are local reactions leading either to increased (light), or diminished (darkness), excitability of the centres. These reactions are relatively more persistent and obey the laws of non-specific excitation.

The pattern of interaction of the orientation and adaptation reflexes can be clearly seen in the records of the blink reflex, wherein air stimulation of the cornea continues to give rise to a specific reflex after the orientation reaction has been extinguished.

The sign of all the elements of the generalized orientation reaction to light, darkness, sound and corneal stimulation, is similar to that of the cortical reaction and the C.G.R. Repetitive stimulation by these means leads to the extinction of the orientation reflex, which becomes disinhibited again by any extraneous stimulus.

Figure 34 shows the relationship of the orientation and specific reactions within the visual analyser. The specific reactions of the visual analyser, such as blinking in response to a stream of air, diminution of light sensitivity in response to light and its enhancement in response to darkness, pupillary responses to light and darkness are obviously more persistent.

The cortical electrical responses to light and darkness are of the nature of local orientation reactions. At the same time they are more similar, as far as their parameters are concerned, to the specific than to the generalized orientation reactions. They are more persistent than the latter and vary depending on whether the stimulus is switched on or off.

The functional differences between the generalized depression of α-rhythm, dilatation of the pupil, enhancement of sensitivity to light and galvanic skin reaction on one hand, and specific adaptation reactions on the other, are confirmed by the effects of extraneous stimulation, which leads to enhancement of the generalized orientation reaction without showing any influence on the adaptation reactions. The final result of any type of stimulation is the outcome of the interaction of the various responses.

The visual analyser reacts to light by a combination of peripheral adaptation (contraction of the pupil and diminution of retinal sensitivity to light), which limits the effects of light on its central end, and by increased excitability at this centre. The peripheral changes, by limiting the number of impulses arising in the retina, weaken the effects of the central response. In this way a more or less constant level of central excitation is maintained which manifests itself in re-emergence of the α-rhythm during prolonged illumination of the eye.

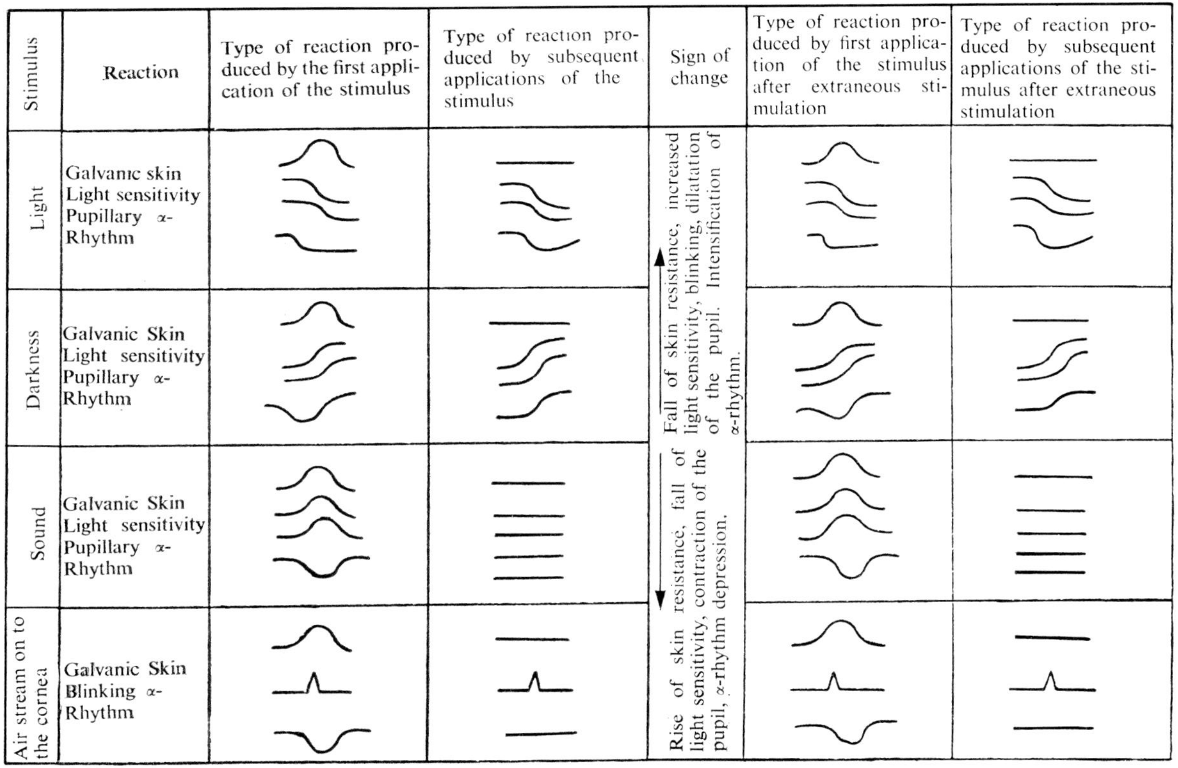

FIG. 34.   Schema of the relationships between orienting and adaptational reflexes in the visual analyser.

Similarly, the effect of darkness is a combination of peripheral adaptation leading to increased sensitivity to light (dilatation of the pupil, increased peripheral sensitivity) and a diminished sensory (visual) input. This combination of effects manifests itself in the form of accentuation of the α-rhythm or the appearance of slow rhythms. With continuing darkness, the central reaction weakens in time, due to increased peripheral sensitivity and the increased effects of, even weak illumination. Apart from this, darkness, as a novel stimulus, can give rise to a transient increase of central excitability of orientative nature.

Thus, the complex response of the visual analyser depends on the summation of orientation and adaptation reactions. The intensification of the generalized orientation reaction is superimposed on the local effects of light, increasing the latter's effect on the cortical bio-electric activity and in a similar way, detracting from the effects of darkness.

Figure 35 shows the effects of light and darkness as complex stimuli.

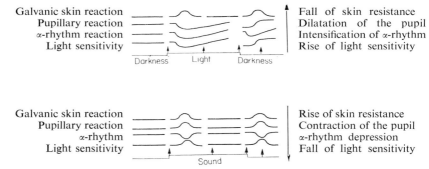

FIG. 35.   Schema of the effects of light and sound as compound stimuli.

It can be noted that the onset and end of stimulation of any type brings into operation an orientation reflex, which shows every time as a change in cerebral activity in the direction of increased excitation, coincident with the development of other elements of the orientation reflex.

The light, being an unconditioned stimulus, increases the excitability of the centres, which shows in the E.E.G. as an increase in frequency of the basic rhythms. Transition to darkness, a non-specific stimulus, gives rise to enhancement of excitation as a part of a generalized orientation reaction. The effects of darkness also depend on interaction of generalized and local orientation reflexes. With repetitive stimulation by means of light, the generalized orientation reflex, in response to the onset and end of stimulation ceases to operate, while the local reactions to both light and darkness continue to appear. Consequently, the darkness replacing light leads to a central change in the direction of greater inhibition. Depending on the initial conditions, the effects of darkness vary from case to case. When applied against a background of a high excitatory state with depressed α-rhythm, it gives rise to accentuation of the latter. When the initial state is one of stupor, with slow wave cortical activity, it results in accentuation of these slow rhythms.

So far as pupillary reaction and sensitivity to light are concerned, the manifestations of orientation reactions to darkness and light are obscured by the specific reactions of the same or opposite sign. The specific reactions, in the first instance, are dilatation of the pupil and enhancement of peripheral sensitivity in response to transition to darkness, and in the second, contraction of the pupil and diminution of sensitivity to light with the onset of illumination. Alongside these changes of sensitivity to light one has to consider the varying relationship of the different reflexes, if the possible final result of their interaction is to be foreseen. The light, by lowering retinal sensitivity and causing pupillary contraction, lowers also the general sensitivity of the analyser; and this occurs in spite of the fact that the cortical sensitivity in response to light increases. When the inhibitory effect on the peripheral sensitivity to light ceases to operate, the sensitizing effect becomes manifest. This sensitization, developed as an element of the orientation reflex, can be observed with the use of auditory stimulation which has no specific action on the retinal sensitivity. The augmentation of the retinal sensitivity under the influence of darkness greatly exceeds the fall of central sensitivity. Consequently, darkness gives rise, on the whole, to increased sensitivity to light.

The conception of a stimulus as a complex, giving rise to a combination of orientation and specific reactions, provides the explanation of the effects produced by intermittent light stimulation. To start with, the first application of a stimulus, at its onset, gives rise to the orientation reflex with its depression of α-rhythm and C.G.R. Further on, the local orientation reaction enters into the picture and leads to an increased excitatory state of the visual analyser. Finally, against this type of general background, one can observe the effect of the definite frequency of the flicker superimposed on the general changes of excitability. When stimulation ceases another orientation reaction develops and the associated depression of the α-rhythm soon gives place to its intensification in response to darkness.

In the phenomenon of photic driving, one can discern its dependence on the original rhythm and on the general level of excitability, which to a large extent is determined by the orientation reflex complex. The frequency of the flicker is reproduced by the cortex and at the same time one can observe the appearance of harmonics of similar range of frequencies. For example, flicker at a rate of 6 c/s, applied during sleep, gives rise to a subharmonic oscillation of 3 c/s. The same flicker at 6 c/s, superimposed on α-rhythm, gives rise to harmonic oscillations of 12 c/s. It seems, therefore, that reactive alteration of cortical rhythm depends on the initial state of cortical activity.

An important part in the maintenance of the cortical excitatory state is played by the thalamo-cortical connexions which participate in the reproduction of cortical rhythms and are linked with the non-specific path of stimulatory influences (Jasper, *et al.*, 1955). It can be assumed that the production of cortical rhythm under the influence of intermittent stimulation is connected with the operation of the non-specific paths. According to Gastaut's laboratory findings, the reticular formation is the site of the most intense reorganization of the excitatory stimuli.

The properties of the flicker-linked cortical rhythms are similar to those of the natural rhythm of the cortex, including those changes which result from the operation of the orientation reflex. For example, an extraneous stimulus intensifies the excitatory state through the activation of this reflex, and thereby facilitates following to high frequency flicker, simultaneously inhibiting linkage to flicker of lower frequencies. Thus, after auditory stimulation, one can observe an intensification of the 27 and 18 c/s rhythms, and inhibition of the 9 c/s rhythm, against a general background of α-rhythm depression. The effects are more intense when the rate of flicker is higher, in spite of the orientation reaction being extinguished, and seemingly, this intensification is due to the operation of the thalamic reticular formation. Similar results can be obtained when the level of the excitatory state of the cortex is sufficiently high as a result of background illumination. Conversely, darkness inhibits the reproduction of higher frequencies and this inhibitory effect may be observed during infrequent flicker stimulation of the dark-adapted eye.

In view of the close relationship between the rate-linkage phenomenon and the orientation reflex, it could be assumed that the linked rhythm is the result of incorporation of the non-specific mechanism into the reaction; the same non-specific mechanism which is associated with the production of the intrinsic cortical rhythms.

If this assumption is true then the photic driving effect itself can serve as an index of the functional state of the activating, non-specific mechanism and of the part it plays in the cortical activity.

Pavlov's observation on animals, that extinction of the orientation reflex results in the development of an inhibitory state which might lead to the onset of sleep, is well known. Similar phenomena can be observed in man during the absence of specific stimulation. The development of inhibition and sleep as a result of extinction of the orientation reflex shows in the E.E.G. as a transition from rapid to slower rhythms down to δ-activity of 1–3 c/s. Slowing down of the intrinsic rhythm is associated with a change of the driving effect. Zislina (1955, 1956) and Danilova (1957) have shown that, with the development of sleep, only low frequency flicker can be reproduced. We succeeded in demonstrating experimentally that the acceleration of basal rhythm at awakening (reappearance of α- and β-rhythms), is associated with a recovered ability to reproduce higher frequencies of flicker.

It seems, therefore, that the relationship established in our experiments between the extinction of the orientation reflex and the interference with driving at higher flicker frequencies, finds its explanation in partial, incomplete sleep and lowered excitability of the cortex resulting from inhibition of the activating influence of the reticular system.

CHAPTER 3

The Structure of the Orienting Reflex and the Functional State of the Analysers

A. Phasic and Tonic Orientation Reflexes

The orientation reflex plays an important part in the control of sensitivity. A novel stimulus, by giving rise to an orientation reaction, influences the effects of subsequently applied stimuli; and so, with a repeatedly applied stimulus, the original stimulus—orientation reaction, which had become extinguished on account of repetition, is activated once more if preceded by an agent which itself produces a strong orientation reaction.

As described above, light and sound, by giving rise to orientation reactions, lead to increased sensitivity of the respective analysers, which persists for a time after the usual orientation reaction to the stimulus in question has already become extinguished. This observation suggests the likelihood of existence of a slower, and externally non-manifest, orientation reaction, in addition to the rapidly developing orientation reflex, the various elements of which have already been described. By analogy with the well-known phasic and tonic muscular reflexes (Sherrington, 1949), similar forms of the orientation reflex can be distinguished. The phasic orientation reflex can operate in the form of rapid successive changes, at various levels of the state of tonic excitation. One deals, therefore, firstly with a rapid type of orientation reaction which shows a quick return to the original level and, secondly, with a slower reaction which persists for a longer time in the form of altered sensitivity.

The galvanic skin component of the orientation reaction exemplifies the phasic orientation reflex. The records of palmar skin electrical resistance show, in response to stimulation, a fall in resistance, with a short latent period, (1·5–3 sec) followed by a return to normal while the stimulus is still in operation. The curve of resistance shows also the presence of the tonic orientation reaction. Repetitive stimulation soon ceases to produce a reaction and at the same time one can observe a continuous rise of the skin resistance (Fig. 36).

This diagram shows the weakening of C.G.R. while the resistance of the skin increases. Towards the end of the experiment, one can observe "spontaneous escape" in the form of fall of the skin resistance associated with the development of phasic reactions (28–32). In this way, disinhibition of the orientation reflex leads to a fall in resistance illustrating the tonic form of the orientation reaction, and the phasic orientation reactions become intensified.

The rise of skin resistance reflects the fall of excitability and the spread of inhibition. A stable rise of skin resistance in man can be observed in sleep when the inhibition of the orientation reactions is particularly strong. On

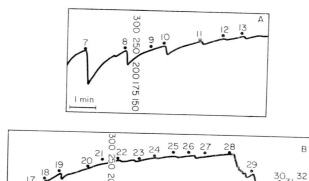

Fig. 36. Tonic and phasic orienting reflexes as reflected in the C.G.R. A. Subject G., March 1954. 7–13—Light, 32 lux on white, for 5 sec. B. 16–27—Persistence of extinction after an interval in the work. 28–32—"Spontaneous escape". Ordinate: resistance (kilohms).

the other hand, the moment of awakening is associated with the development of the tonic orientation reaction in the form of a persistent fall of skin resistance.

The phasic and tonic orientation reactions are intimately related. The relationship shows mainly in change of phasic reaction, depending on the level of the tonic reflex. Thus, the disinhibition of the C.G.R. by a strong, extraneous stimulus, which is the manifestation of the phasic orientation reaction, is associated with a fall in the baseline resistance, reflecting the development of the tonic reaction.

The tonic orientation reaction can also be traced in cerebral electrical activity. The moment of awakening is associated with an intensification of the tonic orientation reflex which coincides with the appearance of α-rhythm. On the other hand, any weakening of the reflex is associated with the replacement of the β- and α-waves by the slower δ-waves, more typical of sleep.

Depending on the level of the tonic orientation reaction, the phasic reaction is differently expressed. When the general background includes α-rhythm, the phasic reaction manifests itself in the latter's depression (change in the direction towards more rapid β-rhythm); when the basic rhythm is of slow type, in the accentuation of the α-rhythm. With transition to sleep, a single sound stimulus results in replacement of the slower waves by α-rhythm. In this case, a uniform auditory stimulus gives rise to an orientation reflex in the form of intensification of α-rhythm.

If one accepts the individual, temporary changes of the electrical activity as the phasic reactions, and, the basic rhythm dominating the picture before and after the effect of stimulation, as the tonic reaction, one can conclude that the change towards slower rhythms is the manifestation of the tonic orientation reaction arising alongside the spread of inhibition. At the same time, depending on the basic rhythm, the phasic reaction undergoes changes and appears either in the form of depression, or intensification, of the α-rhythm.

The complex of the orientation reflex, aiming at an increased state of preparedness of the whole body, and at better perception of the stimulus is, in fact, a combination of two types of reflexes, tonic and phasic, which remain intimately interwoven.

With continuous non-signal stimulation, the resulting orientation reflex becomes extinguished. The process of extinction manifests itself as the progressive reduction in the size of any recorded component reaction, lengthening of the latent periods of the reactions, at first temporary, and eventually permanent suppression of the individual responses, diminishing general excitatory state; intensification of inhibition up to drowsiness at times, and finally, reduction of sensitivity as measured by the reflex in question.

Investigations so far have shown that the galvanic skin reaction is a typical component of the orientation reflex and the laws which it obeys are applicable also to the other components of the latter. When the C.G.R. (Féré phenomenon) is being recorded, the extent of fall of the palmar skin resistance diminishes and, without changing its sign, it finally fails to develop altogether. Similarly, progressive reduction of the size of reaction can be observed by recording the occipital cortical component of the orientation reflex in response to auditory stimulation. Spread of inhibition results in relative weakening of the cortical responses to repetitive stimuli of unaltered intensity. With continued stimulation, the frequency change disappears, the change in amplitude of the predominant waves becomes progressively less, and the base line is regained in a shorter period of time.

During the process of extinction of the orientation reflex, the differences between the physiological intensity of the onset, middle part and end of stimulation become manifest. At first the stimulus evokes a reaction to most of its duration, and to its removal, and the maximum reaction is observed at the beginning and end of stimulation. In time, the effect of the middle segment becomes progressively weaker and only the beginning and end give rise to the reaction. Later on, only the onset of stimulation produces any effect and even that progressively weakens and disappears. Finally, the reaction is completely inhibited. The rate of stimulation has an important influence on the process of extinction. The greater the rate, the more rapid the process.

There is a definite connexion between the interaction of tonic and phasic orientation reflexes on the one hand, and the rate of extinction of the reaction on the other. Strong phasic reactions are often associated with a high level of the tonic reflex. For instance, a subject at rest ceases to respond to an auditory stimulus after a few repetitions; the galvanic skin component of the orientation reaction fails to develop. At the same time, the basic resistance increases, indicating diminished excitability and the onset of the inhibitory state. Extraneous stimulation at that particular moment results in a fall of the skin resistance, indicating a swing towards greater excitability, and auditory stimulation again becomes effective. Thus, the process of extinction depends on a certain balance of tonic and phasic reflexes.

B. "Over-Extinction" of the Orientation Reflex

The rate of extinction of the orientation reaction varies with the intensity and duration of action of the stimulus. The stronger the stimulus, the stronger the reaction and the more difficult the extinction.

The relationship between the course of extinction and duration of action of the stimulus is more complex. A sound of very short duration either gives rise to no reaction, or the reaction produced is quickly extinguished. The effects of a stimulus of longer duration are more difficult to suppress, but if the duration is very long, the difficulty is less and the rate of extinction is even greater.

There is also a degree of interdependence between the nature of the extinction process of the orientation reaction and the sensitivity of the analyser. The relative intensity of the stimulus depends on the degree of adaptation of the analyser. In darkness, even a light stimulus of what normally would be of moderate intensity becomes a strong one. Consequently, changes of the sensitivity of analysers influence the orientation reaction's process of extinction.

Usually, after 6–12 or more applications any stimulus ceases to evoke the orientation reaction, but the process of extinction is not uniform. From time to time some of the stimuli again give rise to the reaction which had been already extinguished.

In our research, the orientation reaction which fails to develop in response to 2–3 consecutive applications of the stimulus is considered to be extinguished. What would be the result, therefore, of stimulation continued beyond this point?

I

Experiments were carried out involving applications of the stimulus after it has ceased to evoke a reaction (Vinogradova and Sokolov, 1955). It has thus been demonstrated that in the course of "over-extinction", following chronic extinction, the orientation reaction becomes, paradoxically enough, disinhibited. This disinhibition was most prominent in the vasomotor component of the orientation reflex.

The whole process of extinction of the orientation reaction can be divided into two stages; first, that in which the reaction becomes progressively more inhibited up to complete suppression, and second, the paradoxical re-emergence of the orientation reaction in the course of the continuing extinction process of the already extinguished reaction.

The inhibition of the orientation reaction at a certain stage can result in widespread inhibition leading to sleep. This was observed in the course of experiments on dogs when inhibition of the orientation reaction was associated with the onset of sleep (Chechulin, 1923). Similar effects have been observed in man during non-specific stimulation. The development of drowsiness coincides with the extinction of the orientation reaction.

As described above, further chronic extinction of the orientation reflex by application of the stimulus which has already ceased to reproduce a reaction, leads to reappearance of the orientation reaction. The beat of a metronome at first gave rise to the usual orientation reaction, and this in time became extinguished. With the onset of "over-extinction", there resulted an even more forceful orientation reaction. The vasomotor component of the reaction, in this case, is rather similar to that usually associated with the defence reactions. At the same time, one can observe the re-emergence of intense reactions to extraneous stimuli which earlier were also incapable of producing the orientation reflex. The reactions so re-established do not undergo extinction in spite of further repetitive stimulation (in sets of ten applications). They become in fact "inextinguishable" and, as such, differ from the temporarily re-established reactions as seen after extraneous stimulation. It must be pointed out, however, that in these conditions the application of any extraneous stimulus of sufficient intensity results in temporary inhibition of the "inextinguishable" reactions. All agents leading to increased general tone of the orientation reflex have a similar effect.

In this way, therefore, a general inhibitory state of the cortex resulting from extinction of the orientation reaction gives rise to paradoxical intensification of the orientation reflexes produced by indifferent stimuli.

Over-extinction of the orientation reflex is associated with a substantial change in the curve representing its vasomotor component. The basic curve shows evidence of disinhibition, and spontaneous variations of the volume of vessels can be observed.

Tracings of cortical potentials show similar variation. In drowsiness, a sound which has ceased to give rise to depression of the α-rhythm starts again to produce a reaction but now in the form of accentuation of the α-rhythm. This accentuated α-rhythm sometimes persists in spite of a great number of repetitions of the stimulus.

The stability of the over-extinguished reaction has been described by other authors and its application to objective audiometry—by the use of intensification of α-rhythm reactions during drowsiness—has been suggested.

Disinhibition of the cortical orientation reaction and C.G.R. can be observed in the course of proprioceptive stimulation (passive raising of the arm), while records of occipital and rolandic area rhythms, C.G.R. and muscular contraction are taken. At first, proprioceptive stimulation, applied at a time when α-rhythm is being consistently reproduced, gives rise to a definite C.G.R. and general depression of the α-rhythm. After 15–20 applications the C.G.R. becomes extinguished; the depression reaction of the rolandic area rhythm undergoes extinction even more slowly. Repetitive proprioceptive stimulation leads to the appearance of slow waves which provide the background for the re-emergence of the C.G.R. and general intensification of the α-rhythm. It seems, therefore, that cortical activity must reach a certain intensity before the orientation reflex can undergo inhibition. This is confirmed by the fact that an extraneous stimulus, giving rise to re-emergence of α-rhythm, (i.e. by increasing the excitability of the cortex) can suppress both, the re-established cortical bio-electrical and, galvanic skin reactions.

What is the nature of the paradoxical re-appearance of the orientation reaction at a certain point in the development of inhibition resulting from the orientation reaction's extinction?

According to Orbeli (1949), the orientation reflex arises out of continuous inductive interaction of cortical and subcortical centres. Normally, the cortex controls the activity of subcortical formations and inhibits the unconditioned manifestations of the orientation reflex. Spread of inhibition in the cortex weakens this control and brings into prominence the subcortical reflexes and the defence-like orientation reaction subserved by the subcortical centres.

The fact that cortical inhibition plays an essential part in the re-establishment of the over-extinguished orientation reaction can be demonstrated by intensification of the cortical excitatory state in the subject. Then one can observe the inhibition of the "inextinguishable" orientation reaction. If, at the moment of recording an intense vasomotor orientation defence-like reaction, the subject is given a task leading to increased cortical tone (for instance, the subject is asked to discriminate between stimuli), a suppression of re-established reactions can be observed.

A strong stimulus which, during the period of spread of inhibition, disinhibits the orientation reaction, applied during the period of over-extinction, gives rise to temporary inhibition of the re-established reaction.

The subject's complaints of somnolence and drowsiness also indicate the close connexion between the "inextinguishable" orientation reaction and the inhibitory cortical processes.

The intensification of the orientation reaction, similar in nature to those caused experimentally, can also be observed in pathological conditions associated with abnormalities of the processes of cortical inhibition. Some types of neurosis are characterized by the marked intensification and inextinguishability of the orientation reflex (Shirokov, 1937; Gantt, 1944; Straumit, 1953), as are some forms of mental illness (Lichko, 1952) and of head injury (Gershuni, 1949). Similar observations were made in patients with brain tumours and cerebral vascular disease. Vinogradova (1957), has observed the ease with which the inextinguishable reactions could be produced, in the course of her studies of the vasomotor component of the orientation reflex in mentally deficient subjects who had diffuse cortical involvement.

The connexion between the process of extinction of the orientation reflex and the intensity of inhibitory processes has been studied by Vinogradov (1933). In the case of weak types of dog, no extinction of the orientation reaction to repetitive non-specific stimulation could be observed. Musiashchikova (1952), demonstrated the development of inextinguishable, autonomic orientation reflexes in dogs under the influence of bulbocarpin—a cortical inhibitor.

The difficulty in the extinction of the orientation reflex sometimes reaches pathological proportions in old people suffering from senile dementia, in mental deficiency (Kazmiin and Fedorov, 1951; Gamburg, 1953), and in certain cases of schizophrenia where the difficulties associated with production of conditioned reflexes indicate the weakness of the cortical processes (Spasskaya, 1955).

It was also observed in Pavlov's laboratory, that in dogs, removal of the cortex is associated with the development of "inextinguishable" orientation reactions.

The vasomotor orientation reactions observed in the course of our experiments were, in their intensity and other features, similar to defence reactions. This was made apparent by comparing the reactions recorded in the course of over-extinction with responses to painful stimuli. Their latent periods were similarly short, the decline equally acute, the magnitude of reaction similarly great, and they both included cephalic vasoconstriction.

In this way cortical inhibition can, within limits, result in intensification of the subcortical orientation reactions. This can also explain the marked intensification of cortical orientation reactions observed in drowsiness.

In conditions of normal cortical activity, all the elements of the orientation reflex arise out of cortical transformation of the impulse produced by stimulation. At the same time, the direct action of the stimulus on the subcortical centres can be inhibited by the cortical activity. In drowsiness, the cortical control weakens and subcortical orientation reactions predominate.

The increased tone of cortical activity is, in fact, an element of the orientation reflex. This effect is connected with the activity of the reticular formation and, depending on circumstances, manifests itself either as depression or accentuation of α-rhythm. This has been observed in the course of the above-described experiments where the development of slow waves was associated with re-establishment of the extinguished reactions, based on the participation of the reticular formation.

C. Afferent and Efferent Links of the Orientation Reaction

The extinction of the orientation reaction is associated not only with diminished reactivity, as measured by the orientation reflex (diminished magnitude of reaction), but also with diminished sensitivity, as measured by a number of objective elements of the orientation reflex. This lessening of sensitivity manifests itself in the failure of weaker stimuli, previously capable of producing the reaction, to give rise to any response and in the greater intensity required for its evocation. At the same time, the orientation reflex influences the specific sensitivity of the analyser.

The connexion between the fall in sensitivity and extinction of the orientation reflex, on the one hand, and the rise of sensitivity and intensification of the orientation reflex on the other, becomes manifest in the effect of sound on visual sensitivity and the development of the orientation reaction, as indicated by α-rhythm depression.

Experiments have been described above in the course of which the threshold of light sensitivity is determined. At first, the strength of depression of α-rhythm in response to test stimuli is studied, and then a subliminal light stimulus is applied before and after the application of sound. The auditory stimulation gives rise to the orientation reflex, associated with α-rhythm depression. At the same time, the sensitivity of the visual analyser is increased by the sound, and the weak, subliminal light stimulus is transformed into a liminal one. After a period, the sensitivity of the visual analyser, temporarily raised, diminishes again and the stimulus once more becomes subliminal. Another sound again produces the depression of α-rhythm, indicative of the orientation reaction, and raises the sensitivity of the visual analyser. The sensitization effect weakens and disappears *pari passu* with the extinction of the orientation reaction associated with diminishing α-rhythm depression (Steklova, 1957).

The reduction of the specific sensitivity of the analyser to stimulation is therefore a manifestation of the extinction of the orientation reflex, and inversely, the increased specific sensitivity of the analyser is associated with its development.

These changes of sensitivity, coinciding with different phases in the course of the orientation reaction, depend on the spread of inhibitory processes to both the efferent and afferent links of the orientation reflex arc.*

The inhibition within the afferent link, produced by the application of one or several stimuli, results typically in the inhibition of the orientation reaction to stimuli applied to adjacent areas. In some cases the inhibitory process spreads to other analysers. Irradiation of inhibition within the afferent link,

---

* By 'afferent link'—is meant the system of structures which participate in receiving the stimuli which produce the orientation reaction. By 'efferent link'—the structures controlling the responses to stimulation which make up the complex of the orientation reflex.

observed in the course of extinction of the orientation reflex, leads to reduction of reactivity to a whole range of stimuli.

The dependence of the generalization of inhibition of the orientation reflex
on the proximity of the cortical projection areas of the receptors, acted upon
by the stimuli in question, confirms that it is the receiving part of the apparatus
which becomes inhibited. The generalization of the inhibitory process,
associated with the extinction of the orientation reflex, is well exemplified as
follows: records of galvanic skin reactions, brought into operation by tactile
stimulation of various points on the skin, show that tactile stimulation of a
point on the skin of the wrist results in inhibition, which spreads to adjacent
points of the wrist, so that further stimulation fails to evoke the galvanic skin
reaction. The area in which inhibition spreads is, however, limited. In the
case of stimulation of the skin of the forearm and upper arm, the reaction is
greater, the greater the distance between the point stimulated and the area
where the orientation reflex has been extinguished in the first place. Thus,
the response to stimulation of the skin of the forearm is smaller than that of
the upper arm, back or neck (Fig. 37).

Figure 37A shows an experiment wherein a stage has been reached when
stimuli applied to the skin of the wrist and adjacent regions fails to give rise
to the reaction (15–19). A stimulus applied just above, (20), still fails to

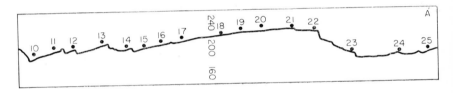

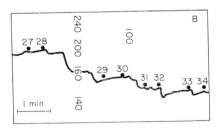

Fig. 37. Irradiation of the inhibition in the skin analyser on extinction of the
galvanic skin component of the orienting reflex. A. Subject D., August 1954.
10, 11—Stimulation of the central area on the back of the hand. 12—Stimulation
of the wrist. 13–15—Stimulation of the left border of the hand. 17–18—
Stimulation of the centre of the dorsum of the hand. Remaining notation in text.
B. Continuation of the experiment. Ordinate: resistance (kilohms).

evoke any response. A C.G.R. develops in response to stimulation of the skin of the forearm (21) and upper arm (22) and at the same time the response to stimulation of the centre of the wrist (23–25) becomes disinhibited. When the experiment is carried on further (Fig. 37B), it can be seen that a single application of the stimulus to the centre of the wrist produces no reaction (27), while intermittent stimulation of the same area, after the reactions arising there have been already extinguished, still gives rise to a C.G.R. (28). Gradually the reaction to both single (29–31) and intermittent stimulation undergoes extinction (32–34).

The spread of inhibition leads to a disappearance of the reaction arising at the wrist. The further away from the wrist the area of stimulation the more intense the reaction. A new area of stimulation re-establishes the reaction in the area of extinction. A change of the character of stimulation (staccato), without changing the area, also re-establishes the galvanic skin reaction.

The extinction of the orientation reflex is therefore associated with irradiation of inhibition, similar to that observed by Krasnogorskii (1911), Kogan (1914), Anrep (1917) and others, in the course of their studies on the spread of inhibition within the cutaneous and auditory analysers, during the process of extinction of a conditioned reflex in the dog. The inhibition of the orientation reflex, arising in certain afferent cells, spreads to the adjacent areas of the cortex and adversely influences the efficacy of the impulses arriving there. The most distant areas of the cortex, not reached by the inhibitory process, retain a higher degree of reactivity.

The auditory analyser shows similar properties. Application of sounds of diverse frequencies results in the generalized extinction of orientation reactions to sounds of similar but as yet unused frequencies. Application of light stimuli of several different intensities, results in the generalization of extinction of orientation reactions to light of similar intensities.

Spatial irradiation of inhibition, associated with the extinction of the orientation reactions, does not exclude systematic irradiation. This results in the reappearance of the extinguished orientation reaction to tactile stimulation when the stimulus, without altering the site of application, becomes intermittent. In this way, intermittent stimulation of an area of the skin gives rise to an intense galvanic skin reaction, after the reaction to touch at the same area has become extinguished. In spite of the fact that seemingly the same cells are being stimulated, their reactions to continuous and intermittent stimuli are different.

Similarly, an intermittent light stimulus gives rise to the orientation reaction, when the latter has been already extinguished (through generalized inhibition), in respect of light stimuli of various intensities. After the galvanic skin reaction to single light stimuli has been extinguished, for instance, the application of an intermittent light stimulus evokes it once more.

The experiments described above demonstrate a connexion between the inhibition in the afferent link of the orientation reflex arc, and the reduction of reactivity and sensitivity of the cortical cells. The inhibitory process, at the same time, is not limited to any single area but spreads to adjacent areas in accordance with the principle of both somatic projection and systemic connexions between the cortical cells.

Thus, afferent inhibition in the orientation reflex arc shows a definite tendency to generalization, associated with a certain degree of concentration. The laws governing the generalized extinction of the orientation reaction remain the same whether auditory, light or tactile stimulation is used. The mechanism of extinction depends on *irradiation of inhibition*, the extent of which is determined by the positioning of the cortical projection cells representing the periphery of the respective analysers (the principle of somatotopical projection) and, by the principle of systematic localization.

Taking into consideration the reticular formation, the mechanism of afferent inhibition can be explained as follows. The orientation reaction depends for its development on the cortico-reticular connexions transmitting impulses in the direction implied. Repetitive stimulation results in cortical inhibition; thus, stimuli of a certain range of intensity and of the class of inhibitory conditioned signals, undergo reduction in intensity as far as their capacity for producing the orientation reflex is concerned. The cortical areas not involved in the production of the inhibitory conditioned reflexes do not give rise to inhibitory influences, and the course of the orientation reaction is therefore not disrupted.

The extinction of the orientation reflex can be associated with various degrees of irradiation. It has been shown experimentally that the extent of irradiation of inhibition varies, depending on the conditions of stimulation. Moreover, in the course of extinction of the orientation reaction, one can observe inductive phenomena between various areas of the cortex. This manifests itself as the reinforcement of the orientation reflex by irrelevant stimuli during the process of its extinction by another group of stimuli.

Cases have been encountered in the course of our investigations where the extinction of the orientation reaction to one stimulus was associated with its intensification to another. For instance, when extinction of the orientation reaction to auditory and tactile stimulation has become generalized, application of the sound stimulation alone leads to the re-establishment of the reaction to tactile stimuli.

The positive induction—observed in the afferent link of the arc of the orientation reaction—in response to stimuli quite different from those which resulted in extinction, is the basis of intensification of the reaction by the *novelty* factor. This positive induction usually remains latent, and becomes manifest in response to all unusual stimulation. In natural conditions, the magnitude of the orientation reaction is the greater, the greater the degree of "novelty" and the more unexpected the stimulus.

If the general excitability of the cortex remains sufficiently high, the inhibition of the orientation reaction to one stimulus is associated with an increase of cortical excitability in other areas responding to different stimuli. Extinction of the orientation reaction is associated with a redistribution of the excitatory and inhibitory processes, in this way ensuring the maximum efficacy of reaction to novel stimuli.

The distribution of the excitatory and inhibitory processes varies with the conditions of stimulation. The greater the differences between the non-signal stimuli used, the greater the zone of irradiation of inhibition and, vice versa. The more similar the stimuli, the stronger their inductive influence on other, equally similar agents; the more different the stimuli, the weaker their inductive activity.

In addition to irradiation of inhibition, and positive induction, the extinction of the orientation reflex is accompanied by irradiation of excitation interacting with the cortical areas of excitation and inhibition already in operation.

Irradiation of excitation in the afferent limb of the orientation reflex arc results in disinhibition of the reflex. The excitatory wave, produced in one area by a strong extraneous stimulus, spreads in the cortex and results in intensification of the orientation reactions in other areas, depending on the degree of antecedent inhibition. By analogy to "extinguishing inhibition", so well studied in Pavlov's laboratory, the extraneous stimuli play the part of the "extinguishing stimuli" of the orientation reflex. The analogy is not apparent but real. The extraneous stimulus, as used in investigation of conditioned reflex activity, gives rise to the inhibition of conditioned reflex activity, inasmuch as it produces an orientation reaction which inhibits the latter. With repetition of the extraneous stimulation, the orientation reaction weakens, as does its inhibitory influence on the conditioned reflex activity. In this way the "extinguishing stimulus" of the orientation reaction is identical with the "extinguishing inhibitor" of the conditioned reflex.

The effects produced by the extraneous stimulation depend on the wave of excitation accompanied by changes of sensitivity in analysers. They result in intensification of orientation reactions arising in various areas of the cortex. The spread of the excitatory wave is spatially variable. For instance, strong light, used as the extraneous stimulus, disinhibits the orientation reflex for a longer period and its magnitude is greater in response to light, than to sound or muscular effort.

Re-establishment of the extinguished orientation reaction after a time interval is but a particular instance of the dynamic interaction of the excitatory and inhibitory processes in the course of extinction of the orientation reactions to non-signal stimuli. The recovery of the orientation reactions is quicker in the case of the stimuli involved in the spread of inhibition than in response to those which actually produced the inhibition in the first place.

It seems, therefore, that the wave of inhibition recedes in time, freeing the cortical segment of the analyser in accordance with the intensity of the inhibitory process in various areas.

Where exactly, within the afferent link of the orientation reflex, does the inhibitory process develop? As the extinction of the reaction does not block the perception of the stimulus and the specific reflexes do occur, it seems that the inhibition develops in the non-specific cells of the cortex concerned in the production of the orientation reaction. These cells seem to be distributed in between the specialized cells of the analyser which results in the excitability of the orientation reflex being selective, as found in the course of stimulation by different stimuli. This conception agrees with modern views on the function of non-specific nerve fibres reaching the cortex, which, in our opinion, participate in the production of the orientation reflex. These non-specific fibres reach various areas of the cortical projection of all analysers, ensuring the selective tuning of the latter and the participation of the reticular formation in the development of the reaction.

These findings are confirmed by the results obtained by Lagutina (1955), which have been already mentioned (direct stimulation of any area of the cortex can give rise initially to an orientation reaction which, with repetition, is replaced by the specific reaction).

The orientation reflex is, therefore, a non-specific, but at the same time a highly selective, functional system and includes a cortical apparatus capable of influencing the course of the associated reactions in the subcortical areas.

The orientation reflex, and its various elements, undergo changes in composition in the course of extinction. Individual elements gradually fall out, probably as a result of inhibition involving the efferent paths of the reflex.

Studies of inhibition of the efferent elements, in the course of extinction of the orientation reflex, have been carried out using the method of simultaneous recording of respiratory, galvanic skin, cerebral and oculomotor reactions to visual, auditory and tactile stimulation. It was found that different components of the reflex undergo extinction at different times. Initially all stimuli give rise to similar reactions, namely eye movement, arrest of respiration, a C.G.R. on the skin of the palm and sole and, depression of α-rhythm in the occipital area. This fact indicates wide irradiation of the excitatory wave which involves the effector apparatus of different organs, and, evoking an orientation reaction aimed at increased reactivity of the body. The simultaneous occurrence of α-rhythm depression, C.G.R., and eye movement is worth particular attention since it indicates the common nature of these reactions. During auditory stimulation, the first to be extinguished is the eye movement, followed by respiratory and galvanic skin reaction to sound and light and, α-rhythm depression in response to sound.

The depression of α-rhythm in response to light stimulation is much more persistent. It seems that in the course of stimulation, the first to undergo extinction are those components of the orientation reflex which have no direct connexion with the activity of the particular stimulus in operation. In the case of sound, neither the eye movement nor the galvanic skin reaction or depression of the occipital α-rhythm are connected directly with any specific aspect of the stimulus and are quickly extinguished. The light, a specific stimulus to the visual analyser, gives rise to a persistent depression of the occipital α-rhythm; the C.G.R. being a non-specific component of the reaction to light is rapidly inhibited.

In the case of stimulation by means of vibration, the C.G.R. and rolandic area rhythm depression, being more intimately connected with the proprio-receptors, persist for longer periods while the, in this case, irrelevant depression of the occipital α-rhythm undergoes rapid extinction.

It can be concluded, therefore, that the maintenance of the efferent elements of the reflex depends on the concentration of excitatory, activating influences in the analyser undergoing stimulation.

A comparison of the features of the inhibitory process in the afferent and efferent links of the orientation reflex shows the intimate connexion between them but, also some differences. Whereas the cortical area of the analyser gives origin to afferent inhibition, it also remains under the influence of the efferent mechanism of the orientation reflex for the longest periods of time.

The connexions between the inhibitory processes in the afferent and efferent links manifest themselves, for instance, in the fact that the reactions arising in inhibited (to various degrees) segments of the analyser, consist of varying numbers of efferent elements. Combined records of a number of components of the orientation reaction show that stimuli of various intensities applied in the course of extinction, bring into operation variable numbers of the components of the orientation reaction. A repeatedly-used sound for instance, produces no reaction, whereas a novel sound gives rise to C.G.R., α-rhythm depression and eye movement.

Another example of the connexion between the afferent and efferent inhibition can be observed during an interruption of the process of extinction. Some time after the last application of a non-signal stimulus, the number of the components of the orientation reaction to the stimulus in question increases. For instance, a sound, which at a certain stage in the extinction process gave rise to a C.G.R. only, after an interval, also produces α-rhythm depression. *Pari passu*, with the increase in the duration of the interruption, an increasing number of the components of the efferent reaction is brought back into operation.

Thus, depending on the reactions being recorded, the order of extinction of various efferent elements of the orientation reaction in the course of stimulation depends on the nature of the stimulus. The elements maintained for the longest periods of time, are those directly connected with the analyser participating in the reception of the stimulus in operation.

D. The Electrical Reactions in the Brain Associated with the Afferent and Efferent Elements of Orienting Reflexes

The relationship between the various afferent and efferent elements of the orientation reflex on the one hand, and the reactions of depression or intensification of the α-rhythm on the other, as well as the connexion of both with the changes in sensitivity of the analyser, are to be studied next.

It is well known that the primary reaction of the cortex to the arrival of an afferent impulse consists of an alteration in potential at the cortical projection area of the corresponding receptor. This primary reaction differs substantially from the reaction of depression or intensification of α-rhythm, the latter being in many respects similar to all the other efferent components of the orientation reaction. In this context, the depression of α-rhythm constitutes the cerebral reflex response to the stimulus, and, according to modern views, is based on the activating influence of the reticular system on the cortex.

The stimulus, however, having reached the cortex and having been transformed therein, can be redirected into subcortical centres. The strength of the orientation reaction varies as a result of the cortical activity and, being a complex activation reaction, includes, as one of its elements, the reciprocal subcortical influence on the tone of the cortex. This particular element of the orientation reflex manifests itself in the widespread irradiation of depression of α-rhythm, depending on the enhanced tone of the cortical cells. This depression, and also the corresponding type of intensification of the α-rhythm, can be considered as one of the efferent elements of the orientation reflex. The inhibition of this reaction, as well as of the other elements of the orientation reflex, seems to be connected with the blockage of impulses arriving at the reticular formation, which acts as the centre for the orientation reflex. This results in the weakening of the orientation reaction and a reduction in the number of its components. The reciprocal influence of the reticular formation on cortical tone is also affected.

The inhibition of the orientation reflex is associated with weakening of the effect of stimulation on the reticular formation and, consequently, with diminished cortical tone. At the same time, the reduction of cortical excitation weakens the direct specific effect of the stimulus on the cortex and the perception of the stimulus is altered.

One must remember, however, that the individual aspects of the orientation reflex undergo considerable changes as a result of inhibition of various efferent elements of the reflex. What is the significance, for instance, of the extinction of the vasomotor component of the orientation reaction? It does not means simply that the number of elements is reduced but, because the vasomotor component of the orientation reflex is an all important factor in increasing the blood supply of the brain and retina, its extinction signifies diminished activity of all other orientation reactions. Similarly, inhibition of the α-rhythm depression, signifies diminished excitability of the cortical cells.

Repetitive non-signal stimulation leads to the formation of inhibitory reactions with consequent weakening of the orientation reaction. Adjacent areas can become involved and the extinction of the orientation reaction may become generalized. The weakening of the orientation reflex appears as inhibition of some of its efferent components, which, in turn, by virtue of their reciprocal effect on the general excitability of the analysers, leads to the reduction of the latter.

Thus it can be stated that the inhibition of the orientation reflex partly lowers the specific sensitivity of analysers to stimuli. Disinhibition of the orientation reflex results in increased excitability of the cortex, the effect being subserved by a number of factors leading to an increase in the tone of the cortex.

If, at a certain point in the process of cortical inhibition when the inhibitory influences start to recede and the arrival of impulses into the reticular formation is being re-established, a stimulus is applied, it again gives rise to the orientation reaction which, at a subcortical level, assumes the features of the more coarse defence reaction. The concomitant increased excitability of the cortex intensifies its inhibitory effect on the subcortical centres, leading to the inhibition of the orientation reaction.

CHAPTER 4

Elaboration of Conditioned Adaptation Reflexes

A. Adaptation to Repeated Illumination

Repetitive stimulation, using the same stimulus, results in a failure of the orientation reaction to develop. In order to produce it again the stimulus must be changed. Usually the extinction of the orientation reflex is attributed to cortical inhibition alone. The spread of inhibition is considered a sufficient explanation of the phenomenon. This view of the part played by internal inhibition finds its confirmation in the association between the extinction of the orientation reflex and the onset of sleep (Chechulin, 1923; Rozental', 1929).

It was demonstrated experimentally that the orientation reaction develops not only as a result of a change in the properties of the stimulus, but also whenever a stimulus, being applied regularly at constant time intervals, at one point fails to appear. In this case, what is the nature of the factor responsible for the development of the orientation reaction? What is the actual significance of the "novelty" factor *per se*?

The significance of "novelty" is a relative one, depending on the number of times the stimulus in question has been applied in the past. The fact that to decorticate dogs, any stimulus is "novel" and produces an orientation reaction, must be taken into consideration. Obviously, any change of the stimulus can only mean something if it can be compared with stored information. What kind of stored information, then, is of primary importance in the case of the "novelty" value of the stimulus?

The analysis of the intimate mechanism of stimulus perception, associated with the development and extinction of the orientation reflex, is helped by the study of the interaction of orientation and adaptation reflexes. Whereas the former, with repetition, undergoes extinction, the latter is preserved. This preservation of the specific adaptation reflex can be observed only in the initial period of repetitive stimulation; with continued repetition, the specific reflex also usually weakens.

This can be exemplified in the results of repeated illumination of the dark

132

adapted eye. Records of light sensitivity show a special kind of adaptation to repetitive illumination (Golubyeva, 1957). It consists of a shortening of the duration of after-effects, and weakening of the anti-adaptation effect to light on the dark adapted eye from one application of the stimulus to the other (Fig. 38).

Figure 38(*a*) shows that light stimuli 1 to 4 result in a reduction of light sensitivity, 5 to 7 cease to produce any such reduction, while the last few applications (8–10), again give rise to reduction of sensitivity to light. Weak light stimuli lead to adaptation to illumination and the effects of light on the visual analyser are diminished.

Figure 38(*b*) shows that a number of applications of 4 lux, and 11 lux, light stimuli results in the development of adaptation. After a number of applications of the stronger light stimulus (7–10), transition to the weaker light stimulus (11), again produces a reduction of sensitivity reaction which, however, fails to develop in response to the subsequent application of the same strength stimulus. The intensification of the specific effect of the light coincides with the development of an orientation reaction, as indicated by the galvanic skin reaction. In this way, if the light stimuli used differ in intensity and duration, the development of adaptation to repetitive stimulation is difficult.

Adaptation to repetitive illumination can also be demonstrated by means of recording occipital E.E.G. changes. The more uniform the individual stimuli (their duration, order and intensity), the more readily the adaptation develops. The greater the differences between the conditions of stimulation, the more difficult the adaptation. After a while, a constant, repetitive light stimulus hardly gives rise to any depression at all, and it could be said that the stimulus becomes physiologically less active. Adaptation to repetitive illumination consists, therefore, of the weakening, or even complete suppression, of the α-rhythm blocking reaction in response to light. The depression reaction reappears if the conditions of stimulation are changed.

By means of infrared cinephotography of the pupillary reactions, one can also observe the weakening, or even complete suppression, of the specific reaction of the eye to light. It is found that contraction of the pupil in response to repetitive stimulation by a weak light stimulus grows weaker and, in time, is completely suppressed.

Adaptation of the pupillary reaction to weak light stimulation results not only in diminution of the after-effects, but also in the reduction of the magnitude of the immediate reaction to the stimulus still in operation, as indicated by the diminished maximal contraction of the pupil. The reaction begins to recede while the stimulus is still in operation. After five applications, the magnitude of the immediate reaction is sharply reduced (Fig. 39).

Figure 39(*a*) shows the condition of the pupil before application of the

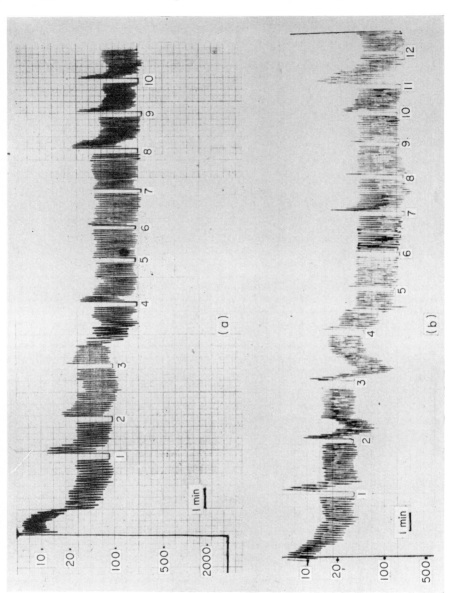

Fig. 38. Adaptation to light of various strengths in the dark-adapted eye (adaptographic examination). (*a*). Subject S. Ordinate: sensitivity (arbitrary units). 1–10—Light of 4 lux on white duration 10 sec. (*b*). Subject K. 3, 4, 5, 6, 11, 12—Light

stimulus and the subsequent maximum contraction of the pupil in response to light. It can be seen that with repetition, the difference between the two diminishes and disappears and does not become re-established until near the end of the experiment. The stimuli are applied to the other eye at the rate of one every minute. The "baseline" size of the pupil does not change significantly.

Figure 39(b) shows the diminished pupillary reaction to light. After five applications, the rate, magnitude and duration of the contraction are reduced, and the reaction begins to recede before the light is switched off.

In this way the connexion between the orientation reflex and the adaptation to repetitive illumination becomes apparent in the records of changes in both the sensitivity to light and, the E.E.G. Any alteration in the stimulus interferes with the process of adaptation, as does an extraneous stimulus, whereas the orientation reflex simultaneously becomes intensified. One cannot, however, identify the adaptation to repetitive illumination with the extinction of the orientation reflex, nor the failure of the former with the disinhibition of the latter. The absence of such direct relationship becomes apparent when a bright light is used as a stimulus. This gives rise to contraction of the pupil which does not wane in time and to a reduction of sensitivity to light, both persisting after the orientation reflex has been extinguished.

A distinction, however, must be made between the extinction of the generalized and the local orientation reactions, as demonstrated by the effects of light and darkness on the human E.E.G. Whereas, at first, the darkness results in depression of the α-rhythm as a part of the generalized reaction, later on the effect depends on the extent of the reduction in the level of cortical excitation in the area of the visual analyser participating in the production of the local orientation reaction, as already described.

The effects of light on the occipital E.E.G., being thus primarily dependent on the level of local cortical excitation, can continue to appear following each application of the stimulus and are, in that respect, similar to the pupillary adaptation reaction. However, complete re-establishment of the α-rhythm can be achieved, even though the light used for the purposes of stimulation is bright, and in this way it differs from the pupillary reaction.

Three forms of adaptation to repetitive illumination can, therefore, be distinguished, namely:

(a) weakening of the unconditioned pupillary reaction to weak light stimuli.

(b) a reduction in the extent of the diminuated light sensitivity response to weak light stimulation.

(c) weakening, or complete suppression, of the reactive depression of the α-rhythm in response to light stimuli of various intensities, developing first in the motor, and then in the visual, areas of the cortex.

K

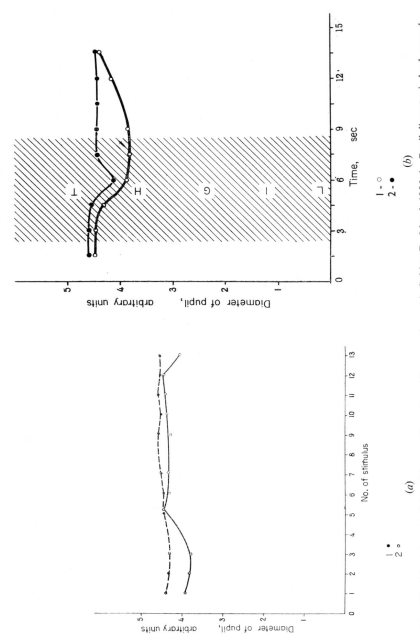

FIG. 39. Adaptation to light with recording of pupillary reactions. (*a*). Subject B., March 1956. 1—Pupil diameter in background illumination. 2—Diameter after light stimulation. (*b*). Subject V., March 1956. 1—2nd application of light. 2—5th application.

The assumed reduction in excitability of the mainly cortical segment of the visual analyser, under the influence of darkness, was confirmed by the local intensification of α-rhythm, which did not spread to the motor area (a low amplitude rolandic rhythm continued to be recorded), and which was observed as soon as the light was switched off.

The adaptation to repetitive stimulation, as indicated by the E.E.G., depends on the concentration of excitatory influences in the area of the cortex corresponding to the stimulus and on the removal of the influences of the reticular formation, as noted when the extinction of the orientation reaction was considered. This, however, still does not explain either the occurrence of an orientation reaction when a stimulus is missed during the application of a certain stereotypic succession of stimuli, or the development of adaptation, as shown by recordings of the specific pupillary reaction, or, the changes of sensitivity.

B. The Conditioned Adaptation Reflex and its Relationship to the Orienting Reflex

The nature of the weakening of the specific reflexes brought into operation by a repetitive light stimulus remains a problem; the following hypothesis represents an attempt at its solution. In addition to changes associated with the extinction of the orientation reflex, repetitive light stimulation results in alteration of the effects produced by the stimulus, through the influence of newly formed conditioned reflexes. The light–darkness sequence results in the light becoming the signal for darkness to arrive at a certain time, and therefore, one can assume the formation of conditioned adaptation reflexes within the visual analyser. The intensity of light, at the start of stimulation, becomes a signal of the duration of illumination and of the moment of onset of darkness. This is a special type of conditioned reaction to the duration of the unconditioned stimulus alone, the period of time following the application of the stimulus serving as its own reinforcement. It results in very fine adaptation of all specific reactions to the intensity and duration of the stimulus in operation. This is the reason for the weakening of effects which can be observed in the course of stimulation by means of a brief light stimulus applied against a background of darkness, and vice versa.

If brief light and darkness stimuli result in the formation of a reflex to their short duration, one can expect that the reaction to a stimulus of an unusually long duration will become, with repetition, similarly reduced in intensity in comparison to the reaction produced by the first application of this stimulus. That this is, in fact, true has been shown in the course of experiments involving infrared recording of the pupillary reflexes to stimulation by weak light and, darkness. Prolonged light stimulation (10 sec), initially gives rise to a stronger contraction of the pupil than that following a sequence of 8 brief stimuli, when the contraction of the pupil to light is quickly replaced by its dilatation to darkness.

Similar observations were made using darkness as the stimulus. The onset of stimulation was marked by switching off the point-source of light serving as a background illumination. After a number of short (4 sec) periods of darkness, extension of the period of darkness leads to slight contraction of the pupil at the moment when the light was due to appear. The next application of darkness produces the usual dilatation of the pupil corresponding to its dilatation when darkness was applied for the first time.

These effects are illustrated in Fig. 40.

Figure 40(a) shows the weakened reaction to a light stimulus of 10 sec duration given after 8 short (4 sec) light stimuli.

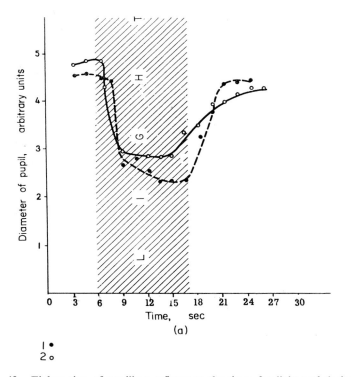

(a)

1 •
2 o

FIG. 40. Elaboration of pupillary reflexes to the times for light and darkness stimulation. (a). Subject Z., March 1956. 1—3rd application of long light (10 sec). 2—Application of the same light after 8 presentations of the short light (4 sec). (b). Subject Z., April 1956. 1—1st presentation. 2—8th presentation. 3—9th presentation of darkness. (c). Subject L., April 1956. 1—1st transition from light to darkness. 2—Transition from light to darkness after 8 periods of darkness lasting 2 sec.

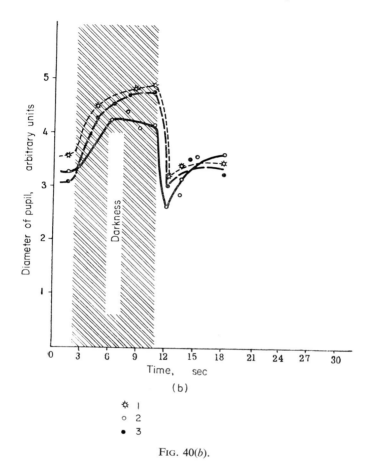

FIG. 40(*b*).

Figure 40(*b*) shows the weakening of the reaction (1) to a 10 sec of darkness after 6 applications of 4 sec periods of darkness. After the repetitive stimulation by brief periods of darkness, the contraction of the pupil (2) begins before the end of the longer period of stimulation. The subsequent application of darkness (3) gives rise to the usual reaction, corresponding to that which follows its first application.

Figure 40(*c*) shows that, after a number of short (2 sec) intervals of darkness produced by switching off the point-source of light, the transition from light to darkness for a longer period now gives rise to a biphasic reaction with temporary arrest of pupillary dilatation corresponding in time to the hitherto usual moment of reappearance of light.

The study of pupillary reactions thus indicates that the effects of light and

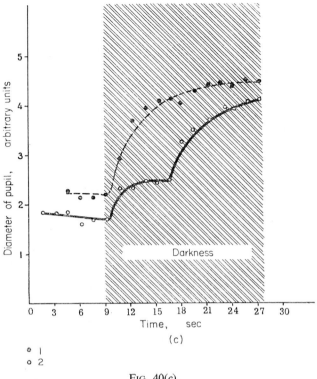

FIG. 40(*c*).

darkness can undergo alterations in the course of repetitive stimulation. These alterations are connected with the formation of the conditioned pupillary reflexes, the peculiarity of which is that it is a feature of the unconditioned stimulus itself which plays the part of the signal. Consequently, the properties of the unconditioned reaction become adapted to the varying conditions of stimulation. The production of pupillary reflexes, however, does not exhaust the problem of adaptation to illumination. As pointed out earlier, the course of the pupillary reaction itself depends in a number of ways on the adaptation reactions of the retina. Further search must be made for the possible mechanisms of adaptation to illumination in the conditioned reflex connexion influencing the level of sensitivity to light.

If the light stimulus is considered (e.g. combinations of such factors as intensity, duration, order of appearance in time and relationship to the background) it becomes clear that a light stimulus of a certain intensity can act as a signal for a certain duration of illumination, and for subsequent transition to darkness. Application of light, starts the process of adaptation in the form of reduction of sensitivity at the periphery. Removal of the stimulus and transition to darkness leads to an increase of retinal sensitivity. At the same time, darkness following a brief light stimulus, acts as a reinforcement of the latter's intensity and duration. It can be assumed, therefore, that the transition from light to background darkness is associated with the formation of a conditioned adaptation reflex "light–darkness". This consists of reflex regulation of retinal sensitivity.

The possibility that conditioned reflex elaboration may alter sensitivity has been demonstrated by Dolin (1936), Bogoslovsky (1936), Kravkova (1948), Snyakin (1948) and others. Their work was, however, concerned with the inter-analyser connexions.

According to our conception, the process of adaptation of sensory organs depends to a large extent on the conditioned adaptation reflexes formed within one (e.g. visual) analyser only. The possibility of the formation of this kind of connexion has been mentioned in the works of Gadzhiev (1955) and Ravich-Shcherbo (1956). We have made the conditioned reflexes in the visual analyser a subject of special study.

When considering the formation of conditioned reflexes in the visual analyser, the brief light stimulus, being a signal of darkness to follow, should with repetition, lead to the formation of the stereotype: "short light–long darkness". The effects of such a stereotype, say illumination–darkness, are but a particular example of the formation of the conditioned adaptation reflexes. It is the time, in these conditions, which acts as the signal for the conditioned changes of sensitivity.

In connexion with this concept, an attempt has been made to reproduce an artificial "light–darkness" connexion (Golubev, 1955). The experiment was carried out with the adaptograph in a poorly-lit room (0·5 lux). A source of light, brighter than the background illumination, served as the conditioned stimulus. Darkness, produced by switching off the illumination, served as unconditioned reinforcement. The light which, initially, had no effect on the level of the sensitivity to light, or else reduced it, started to increase sensitivity which is an effect typical of darkness. In the absence of reinforcement, the connexion disappeared. Obviously, formation of this kind of connexion is only possible using a conditioned stimulus having an intensity which remains within certain limits, but which at the same time will act as a distinct positive stimulus for the visual apparatus. The pattern of conditioned adaptation reflexes has also been demonstrated with a "light–strong light" sequence. The experiments were carried out in complete darkness. The weak light at first produced no change in the sensitivity but after 8–10 correlations with the strong light, started to give rise to reduction of the sensitivity to light. When the reinforcement (strong light) was omitted, the reaction became extinguished and the weak light again failed to produce any change of sensitivity.

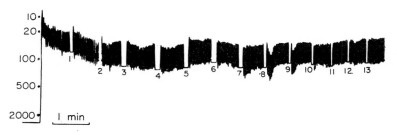

FIG. 41. Elaboration of a "light–darkness" connexion with recording of light sensitivity (adaptographic examination). Subject K., April 1954. Curve of light sensitivity as measured in a feebly illuminated room (0·5 lux on white). 1, 2, 8, 9, 10, 11, 12, 13—Light of 4 lux on white of duration 5 sec. 3–7—Combination of light of 4 lux for 5 sec and darkness for 5 sec (darkness was produced by switching off the background illumination).

Figures 41 and 42 illustrate the process of formation of the connexions "light–darkness" and "light–strong light". Figure 41 shows the gradual change taking place in the reaction, consisting of the increasing effects of darkness. After 5 correlations, weak light only gives rise to the immediately following increase of light sensitivity (8, 9, 10). After a further number of applications of the light stimulus only, this effect ceases to be reproduced (11–13).

Figure 42 shows that, until applied in association with the strong light, the weak light produces no noticeable reaction (3, 4). After such correlation (5–8), the lowering of light sensitivity becomes apparent (9). Omission of reinforcement leads to extinction of the reaction (10–12). Thus the effects of weak light become intensified by its association with strong light and the

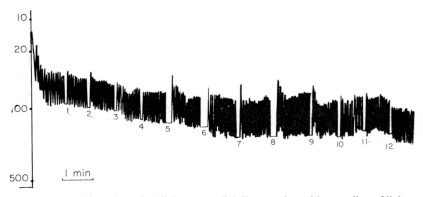

FIG. 42. Elaboration of a "light–strong light" connexion with recording of light sensitivity (adaptographic examination). Subject M., April 1954. Curve of light sensitivity from observations in darkness. 1–4 and 9–12—Light stimuli of 4 lux on white of duration 5 sec. 5–8—Combination of light of 4 lux for 5 sec and light of 32 lux for 10 sec.

resulting reduction of light sensitivity is greater. Conversely, the association of light with darkness results in a weakening, even to a complete reversal of its effects leading to an increase of sensitivity, typical of darkness.

The results of these experiments can help in providing an explanation for the weakening of the effect of repetitive illumination against a background of darkness. This gives rise to the phenomenon of "adaptation to repetitive illumination", which can also be demonstrated in recordings of pupillary reactions.

What actually happens in the cortical segment of the visual analyser during the closure of connexions "light–darkness" or "light–strong light"? The answer may be found in the E.E.G., changes at the time of closure of the "light–darkness" connexion. Beritov and Vorob'yev (1943), have studied such conditioned reflexes using darkness as unconditioned reinforcement and they succeeded in demonstrating the conditioned reflex intensification of α-rhythm. The problem of the relationship between the cerebral potential changes and the intra-analyser conditioned connexions found, however, neither theoretical nor experimental explanation.

The conditions of our experiments were basically the same as for the experimental study of conditioned reflex changes of sensitivity to light. Against weak light background illumination, a stronger light, followed by darkness was used as the conditioned stimulus.

The results of the application of the sequence "light–darkness", consist of an alteration in the reactions of its components and several phases of these alterations can be identified. Following the first application of the sequence, the effects of darkness are diminished as a result of the light preceding the darkness. Gradually, one can observe a weakening of the depression in response to light and an intensification of the α-rhythm increase in response to darkness. The latter, after some repetition of the sequence, also shows a tendency to weaken, but varies in extent from one application to another. The extra extension of the duration of the conditioned stimulus, intended to demonstrate the conditioned reflex nature of the connexion, shows an absence of any distinct conditioned reflex intensification of the α-rhythm. However, the depression becomes more prominent near the end of the illumination when darkness should have appeared. Darkness, applied after the light of extended duration, exerts a weaker than usual effect (less intensification of α-rhythm). This weakening can also be observed following the subsequent application of darkness.

The formation of the conditioned reflex connexion manifested itself in a different way. After repetition of the "light–darkness" sequence, the light applied on its own started to give rise to depression and only occasionally to the intensification of the α-rhythm. The intensification reaction was overshadowed by depression, associated with the generalized orientation reaction arising in response to the removal of the reinforcement by darkness. A great number of "light–darkness" correlations resulted in progressive reduction of responses to each component of the sequence, down to complete suppression. Similar results were obtained when the sequence "light–strong light" was used (Fig. 43).

The figure shows that the first application of the weak light or the prospective conditioned stimulus results in depression of α-rhythm and gives rise to a galvanic skin reaction. No depression can be seen after the 15th application of the weak light (Fig. 43(c)). The first application of the sequence (Fig. 43(d), gives rise to a depression of α-rhythm and a C.G.R. at the onset of stimulation by the strong light. Reinforcement leads to intensification of the reaction to the weak light which again produces α-rhythm depression and a C.G.R. (Fig. 43(e)). With further correlations, the effect of the weak light diminishes, but the strong light continues to produce the reaction at the beginning of its period of operation (Fig. 43(f), (g), (h).

An analysis of the bioelectrical manifestations of the connexions produced by the sequence "light–strong light" shows that the first application of the weak light stimulus gives rise to α-rhythm depression and a C.G.R. indicating the development of the orientation reaction. With repetition, it is not only the C.G.R. which becomes extinguished but the α-rhythm depression as well.

After correlation of the weak with the strong light, which produces α-rhythm depression and a C.G.R., the initial effects of the weak light become restored.

With repetition of the sequence, however, both its components cease to produce the reactions, but the effect of the strong light persists for much longer, or may even never become completely extinguished. After the sequence ceases to give rise to a reaction, application of a single weak stimulus gives rise to α-rhythm depression and a C.G.R. occurring at the moment when strong light would normally be applied; and then, separate applications of weak and strong light give rise to strong reactions.

What is the explanation of this phenomenon?

As a result of the formation of conditioned reflex links, the analyser anticipates the intensity of stimulus. The failure of its appearance at a certain moment, results in basically unaltered physical stimuli being analysed by the visual apparatus, the state of which has been reflexly changed. This results in a new set of circumstances corresponding to a situation when the visual analyser is acted upon by a novel, changed, stimulus. Similar effects are produced by a stimulus which, after setting up conditioned and adaptation links, becomes changed and inadequate in respect of the connexion produced and then gives rise to marked central excitation.

Thus, formation of the conditioned adaptation reflexes results in further weakening of the orientation reaction in response to repetitive stimulation;

moreover, reappearance of the orientation reaction occurs when the stimulus fails to appear.

This phenomenon throws new light on the development of the orientation reaction in response to changes affecting the stimulus, or to extraneous stimulation.

The levelling out of the bioelectrical activity of the brain under the influence of the "light–darkness" sequence can, therefore, be explained on the basis of conditioned reflex rearrangement of the peripheral apparatus of the analyser. The extinction of the orientation reaction should be considered as a complex result of cortical inhibition, associated with the formation of conditioned adaptation reflexes. This leads to a reduction of the efficacy of stimuli. The development of the orientation reaction, on the other hand, is associated with an alteration in the stereotype for the conditioned adaptation reflexes.

A comparison of the conditioned adaptation reflexes, (pupillary influence on visual sensitivity) with the conditioned reflex variations of occipital electrical activity, shows that a characteristic feature of the latter is its conformity with the rules governing conditioned reflex activity and, its extinction as a result of correlation with non-signal stimuli.

It seems, therefore, that elaboration of conditioned adaptation reflexes results in limitation of the specific effects of unconditioned stimuli on the cortical ends of the analysers. These, consequently, perform their function under more uniform conditions, and this facilitates progressive extinction of the orientation reactions.

From the view-point of the production of the conditioned adaptation reflexes, which control the action of the stimulus on the analyser, any change affecting the newly-formed conditioned connexion alters the effects of stimulation. This provides an explanation for the variation in the specific reflexes associated with the disinhibition of the orientation reflexes as a result of extraneous stimulation. The latter, by intensifying the orientation reaction, temporarily inhibits the conditioned adaptation reflexes. Consequently, the development of the orientation reaction is associated with an intensification (or a weakening, depending on the nature of the connexion which has been formed) of the specific unconditioned effect of the stimulus.

This view is confirmed by experiments leading to the formation of a conditioned blink reflex (Fig. 44). As pointed out earlier, sound stimulation does not usually result in blinking, and the blink reflex can be considered as a particular instance of an adaptation reaction (defence reflexes proper). Sound alone gives rise to an orientation reaction manifesting itself as depression of the α-rhythm and a C.G.R. A puff of air into the eyes, used as unconditioned reinforcement, also gives rise to a C.G.R. and α-rhythm depression, indicating the development of the orientation reflex, and, to the specific blink reflex (Fig. 44(a)).

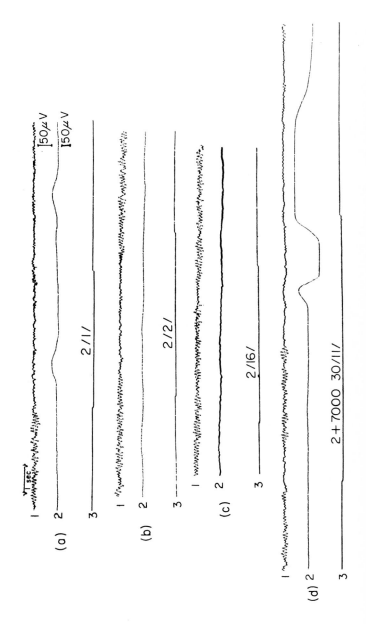

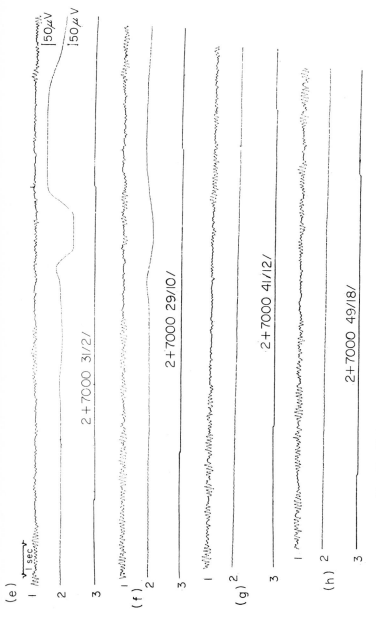

Fig. 43. Elaboration of a "light-strong light" connexion with recording of cerebral potentials and C.G.R. Subject K., February 1955. 1—E.E.G., of right occipital region. 2—C.G.R., of hand. 3—Stimuli with the intensity in arbitrary units and number of application (in brackets).

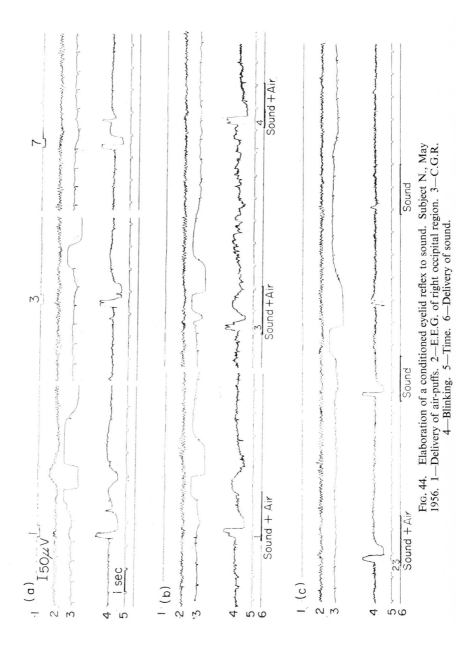

FIG. 44.   Elaboration of a conditioned eyelid reflex to sound. Subject N., May 1956. 1—Delivery of air-puffs. 2—E.E.G. of right occipital region. 3—C.G.R. 4—Blinking. 5—Time. 6—Delivery of sound.

Figure 44(b), (c), show that the first application of sound, together with air-puff reinforcement, give rise to blinking and an orientation reaction.

Repeated application of the two stimuli together results in the inhibition of the orientation reaction, whereas blinking persists, (4, 23). Application of the sound alone gives rise to the conditioned blink reflex, associated with the development of an orientation reaction the latter being due to the absence of the usual reinforcement. Failure of reinforcement leads to extinction of the conditioned reflex to the sound. Repetitive stimulation by means of sound alone, without the reinforcement, leads to its becoming an inhibitory agent. The subsequent correlation of the sound with the puff of air leads to a weaker blink reaction than usual, accompanied by an orientation reaction.

It can be seen, therefore, that the application, or the omission, of reinforcement gives rise to the orientation reaction. In the example described, the orientation reaction has been associated with the conditioned blink reflex. Any extraneous change of reinforcement results in the return of the specific (in this case, defence) reflex, associated with the development of the orientation reaction due to the failure of reinforcement. This kind of relationship between two types of reactions in all their aspects, resembles the interaction of the specific and the orientation reactions observed in the course of formation of the connexions, "light–strong light" and, "light–darkness".

The peculiarity of the blink reflex lies in the fact that this is a reaction of one sign only whereas light and darkness produce within the visual analyser, reactions of opposite sign. As a result, the sequence "light–darkness" leads to a reduction of the effects of light. And on the other hand, inhibition of the connexions, produced by an alteration in the sequence, brings about an orientation reaction and associated intensification of the unconditioned effects of light.

How can the intensification of the unconditioned effects of the puff of air on the cornea, resulting from inhibition of the conditioned adaptation connexion, be demonstrated in the instance of the conditioned blink reflex? A special form of experiment was designed to answer this question. When the subject is instructed not to blink, the sound, instead of becoming the conditioned stimulus giving rise to blinking, produces the opposite effect and becomes in fact, a conditioned inhibitor of the blink reflex, capable of weakening the effect of the unconditioned stimulus. With repetition of the sound–air-puff stimulus a weakening of the unconditioned blink reflex is observed. In these conditions an extraneous stimulus, which produces an orientation reaction and inhibits the newly formed link, gives rise to an intensification of the blink reflex. It has been shown experimentally that with repeated application of the sequence sound–puff of air, the blink reflex weakens and becomes suppressed. An interval leads to its reappearance. With further repetitions, the unconditioned blink reflex again undergoes inhibition.

This example of conditioned inhibition of the unconditioned blink reaction is very similar to the state of affairs met with as a result of repeated stimulation by means of light or darkness. For instance, the connexion produced in the course of adaptation to repetitive illumination, results in a weakening of the unconditioned response to light. It is obvious, that anything interfering with this connexion will at the same time give rise to the orientation reflex, and, by inhibiting the newly produced conditioned link, will intensify the unconditioned effects of light.

Extraneous stimulation is, therefore, associated with two processes, namely (1) inhibition of newly formed conditioned adaptation reflexes combined with intensification of the orientation reflex and (2) the resulting alteration in the unconditioned action of the stimulus.

C. A Conditioned Orienting Reflex in Response to a Sequence of Two Non-Signal Sound Stimuli

It has been demonstrated that the reinforcement of one non-signal stimulus by another, (for instance, light by darkness or weak light by strong light), results in the acquisition by the weak stimulus of the capacity to give rise to an orientation reaction, which becomes manifest in changes of cerebral electrical activity. This phenomenon calls for explanation.

One explanation could be that the reinforcement, in the same way as any other extraneous stimulus, results in the disinhibition of the orientation reflex and consequently, the weak light stimulus for a time gives rise to a stronger orientation reaction. There is one point, however, which makes this explanation inadequate.

It has been found that a weak stimulus reinforced by a strong one occasionally gives rise to a more persistent orientation reaction than the latter alone. In addition the strong stimulus, which on its own produces a sustained orientation reflex, ceases to act if it succeeds the weak stimulus. With a great number of repetitions, the whole complex, consisting of the weak and the strong stimulus, ceases to evoke the orientation reaction. What is the explanation for this intensification of reaction in response to a weak stimulus which can not be simply explained as in the paragraph above? And what is the mechanism of the more rapidly progressing weakening of the orientation reaction to the strong than to the weak component of the complex stimulation?

Let us assume that a combination of two, so-called, non-signal stimuli results in the parallel development of a conditioned orientation reflex in addition to the formation of conditioned adaptation reflexes. A strong stimulus, by its association with a weak one, not only disinhibits the orientation reaction to the latter (even if this only occurs on the first application) but also gives rise to formation of the conditioned orientation reflex. With the formation and stabilization of the conditioned specific link between the two components of the combination, the orientation reflex weakens, undergoes extinction and the combination as a unit ceases to produce it at all.

Kasatkin *et al.* (1953) and Mirzoyants (1954) experimentally investigated the conditioned orientation reflex to sound, reinforced by light, in children between 46 and 222 days old. These workers found that the first application of sound, even on its own, produces an orientation arrest of movement in general. This orientation reaction disappears on the 3–4th application. Light gives rise to a strong orientation reaction consisting of an eye movement associated with movement of the head. The conditioned orientation reaction to sound consists of the eye movement followed by head movement, both in the direction of the source of light following the sound. With repetition, the reflex becomes stabilized and its latent period is shortened. In view, however, of the orientative nature of the response to light used as reinforcement, this response undergoes extinction and the conditioned orientation reflex also weakens and is extinguished. In this case, interruption results in intensification of the conditioned orientation reflex.

In our experiments with sound (1000 c/s) a combination of two intensities 70dB, and 90dB above the threshold of hearing, was used. Féré's galvanic skin reaction served as an index of the orientation reflex. It has been found that, after the C.G.R. to a weak sound has been extinguished, reinforcement by means of a strong sound gives rise to an orientation reaction at the moment of reinforcement and to disinhibition of the orientation response to the subsequently applied, weak sound. In the course of further applications of the stimuli in combination, a weakening of the reaction to strong sound and an intensification of the reaction to weak sound can be observed.

With further repetition, both components of the combination lose their effect. This apparent indifference of the sound stimuli, however, masks newly formed links. It has been demonstrated that if the weak sound is applied on its own, a strong orientation reaction develops at the moment in which the strong sound should follow. This is followed by a temporary re-emergence of the reaction to both the weak or the strong sound stimuli, applied separately. It seems, therefore, that the formative stage of the conditioned orientation reaction has been replaced, not by a simple extinction of the orientation reflexes, but by organization of conditioned links between the stimuli, in such a way, that any interference results in the orientation reaction. If the reinforcement is omitted, the newly formed link manifests itself in the form of the orientation reflex. Omission of the reinforcement also inhibits the connexion, which shows in the fact that whereas each stimulus again gives rise to the orientation reaction (Fig. 45), the latter does not appear in response to their application in the usual combination.

Figure 45(*a*) (1–8) shows the progressive extinction of the reaction to a sound of 70dB. Reinforcement by means of a sound of 90dB (Fig. 45(*b*), 11–12) disinhibits the reaction to 70dB (*b*, 13–14) which becomes intensified with repetition of the sequence. Finally, one galvanic skin reaction to the combination develops (*b*, 17) after which it becomes extinguished (*b*, 18). The

L

sound of 70dB applied on its own gives rise to the reaction at the end of its
period of action at the point when reinforcement should follow (Fig. 45(*c*), 21).
The sound of 90dB regains its effectivity (*c.* 22) if applied outside the combination.

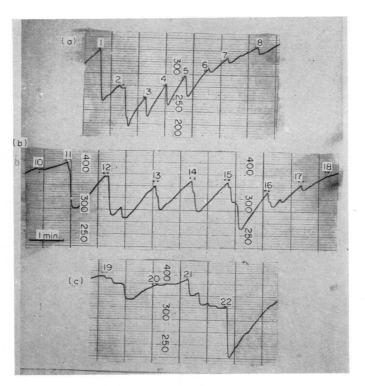

FIG. 45.   Elaboration of a conditioned orienting reflex between two acoustic
stimuli. Subject P., May 1956. 1–8—Sound of 1000 c/s, 70dB, 5 sec. 11–20—
Combination of sounds of 70dB and 90dB. 21—70dB. 22—90dB. Ordinate:
resistance (kilohms).

The experiments described indicate that the application of two non-signal
stimuli in combination, results in the formation of a conditioned orientation
reflex in addition to the conditioned adaptation reflexes.

Electrodermographic investigation of the cutaneous analyser yields similar
findings. A combination consisting of weak and strong electrocutaneous
stimuli leads to initial intensification of the response to the weak, and weakening of the response to the strong component. Later, neither of the components would evoke the reaction. Omission of either results in disinhibition.

Disinhibition of the orientation reaction to either stimulus also follows any extraneous stimulation.

More rapid progressive weakening of the orientation response to a stronger stimulus, when it is preceded by a weaker one, calls for further consideration. It has been shown experimentally that, in addition, to the conditioned intensification of the orientation reflex, there is a possibility of its continued inhibition; and so, a stimulus, the orientation reaction to which has been permanently extinguished, is capable of weakening an orientative response to a stimulus which on its own would normally produce a strong orientation reaction, applied subsequently. In the case of the "weak sound–strong sound" combination, the occurrence of conditioned inhibition of the orientation reflex to the strong component is the most likely explanation.

Confirmation of the role of the orientation reflex in the closure of the connexion between two non-signal stimuli, is found in the E.E.G. changes during the process of formation of the "darkness–light" connexion. As darkness gives rise to intensification of the α-rhythm, by using it as a conditioned stimulus, one may succeed in demonstrating the circumstances of development of the depression of α-rhythm, characteristic of the orientation reaction.

In the course of formation of the conditioned link "darkness–light", under conditions of poor illumination, the orientation reflex which becomes apparent as a C.G.R. and depression of α-rhythm, can be produced at first by either the conditioned or the unconditioned stimulus. At the same time, darkness gives rise to a twofold reaction; first, a generalized orientation depression and then an intensification of the α-rhythm as the reaction to darkness proper. In time, darkness gives rise to only the intensification of α-rhythm. Reinforcement of darkness by means of light results in a change in the effect of the former. Again it begins to produce the depression of the α-rhythm which indicates an intensification of the generalized orientation reflex to darkness, as a result of reinforcement by means of light.

With repetition of the sequence "darkness–light", extinction of the C.G.R. can be observed. The effects of darkness as an unconditioned stimulus also undergo alteration, intensification of the α-rhythm is further magnified, while its depression (being an index of the generalized orientation reaction at the onset of darkness) is again suppressed. Further repetition of the sequence results in further weakening of the effects of both light and darkness. The former gives rise to increasingly weak depression and the latter to increasingly weak intensification of the α-rhythm.

It can be assumed, therefore, that there is a general pattern of development of links, between two non-signal stimuli, which includes the conditioned orientation and the conditioned adaptation reflexes. However, the development of the conditioned orientation reaction is but a stage in the development of stable, conditioned adaptation responses. With repetitive application of the combination of stimuli, *pari passu* with the formation of the conditioned adaptation reflexes, the orientation reaction to all the components of the combination undergoes extinction.

D. A Conditioned Orientation Reflex Produced by Combination of Visual and Proprioceptive Stimuli

The analysis of the effects of proprioceptive stimulation revealed that the results of such stimulation have, in common with the effects produced by other stimuli, a twofold nature; they consist of a combination of orientation reactions and the reflex adaptation of the muscles to the load awaiting them (adaptation reaction). The orientation component appears either as generalized excitation, or as a C.G.R. and localized blockage of the rolandic rhythm which is closely associated with the cortical segment of the motor analyser.

What is the relationship of the orientation and the specific conditioned reflexes when the latter consists of peripheral muscle changes under the influence of combined visual and motor stimulation?

Investigation of this relationship involves the study of the pattern of interaction of the orientation and adaptation reflexes in the course of the combined activity of different analysers. This, of course, is the usual occurrence during the production of conditioned, for instance, motor reflexes. Such an investigation allows a deeper understanding of the role of the conditioned orientation reflex in the closure of specific conditioned connexions.

A combination of light, with a passive hand movement, can be taken as an example (Roger *et al.*, 1958). The hand is lifted by means of a system of pulleys.

After repetitive preliminary stimulation of the closed eyes of the subject, all the elements of the reaction, (i.e. C.G.R. generalized cortical depression and, local blockage of the occipital α-rhythm) cease to appear. Similarly, repetitive preliminary proprioceptive stimulation before the application of light, results in weakening of the appropriate responses.

What is the effect of the combined application of light (which in the meantime has become inactive), and proprioceptive stimuli? The first application of the proprioceptive stimulus, following closely and unexpectedly after illumination gives rise to generalized depression of the α-rhythm and a C.G.R. With repetition of the sequence, the generalized reaction undergoes extinction but the local depression of the rolandic area rhythm persists.

After a number of applications of light, combined with passive movement, the former starts to produce a conditioned depression of the rolandic rhythm. If the generalized orientation reaction is of sufficient intensity, the light can temporarily acquire the ability to evoke the generalized reaction. Soon the latter is, however, replaced by the conditioned localized rolandic rhythm reaction. In the course of the numerous subsequent repetitions of the combination, this local conditioned orientation reflex also becomes extinguished.

It seems, therefore, that in addition to the less stable generalized orientation reaction there are local conditioned orientation reflexes, more stable and aimed at a preliminary increase of the excitatory state in the area to which reinforcement is actually applied and where the motor reaction originates.

Generally speaking, this conditioned local orienting reflex obeys the same laws as the conditioned galvanic skin reaction in response to a combination of two light, or two sound, stimuli. Its peculiarity, however, consists in the fact that it involves different analysers. In this way, the conditioned light stimulus enhances the excitatory state of the motor area in anticipation of the proprioceptive impulses.

The conditioned orientation reflex should not be confused with the peripheral conditioned motor reflexes which develop, in the course of the experiments of the type described, as weak electromyographic reactions and which are appreciated by the subject as involuntary jerks of the hand. Excitation of the conditioned orientation reflex takes place as a result of both the excitation and the inhibition of the peripheral conditioned motor reflex.

Figures 46 and 47 show the pattern of the changes discussed and the relationship between the conditioned reflex excitation of the orientation reaction and the peripheral motor reaction.

Figures 46(a) shows that with the second application of the "light–proprioceptive" stimulus combination, the latter gives rise to generalized reaction. The light, after extinction of the reaction evoked by it, ceases to show any effect on the E.E.G. A conditioned blockage of rolandic rhythm is shown in Fig. 46(b). Figure 46(c) shows the development of the peripheral conditioned reflex in the form of activity preceding the passive movement upwards. Figure 47(d) shows that, against a background of slow waves, the combination of light with passive movement produces the reaction only in response to the latter. After a number of correlations, the light starts to produce the awakening reaction (Fig. 47(e)). Application of the light alone gives rise to an activation reaction at the moment at which the passive movement should follow (Fig. 47(f)).

One can therefore distinguish between, on the one hand, the conditioned generalized orientation reflex, appearing in the form of the conditioned galvanic skin reaction in response to stimulation by a combination of any agents and, on the other, the local conditioned orientation reflex; the latter specifically associated with enhancement of the excitatory state in an area of the cortex, and resulting from the local action of reinforcement, or from the inception of the motor reaction.

As demonstrated above, the expression of the orientation reaction in the

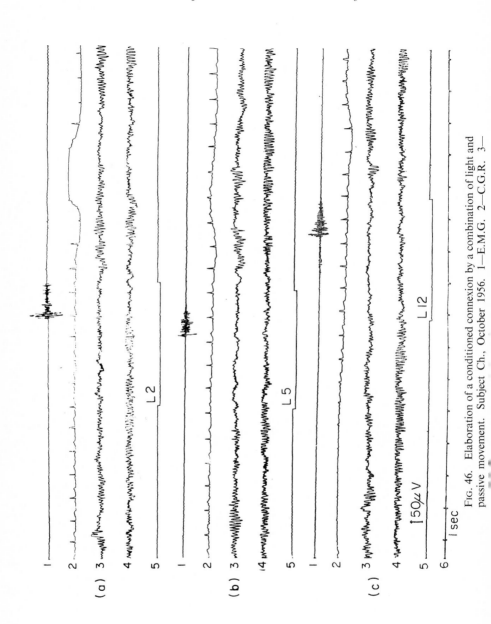

Fig. 46. Elaboration of a conditioned connexion by a combination of light and passive movement. Subject Ch., October 1956. 1—E.M.G. 2—C.G.R. 3—

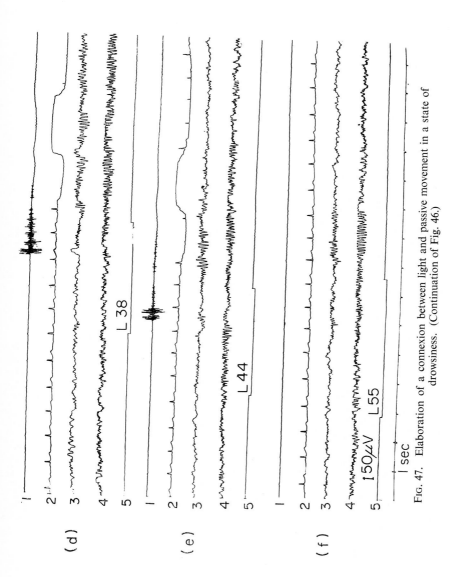

Fig. 47. Elaboration of a connexion between light and passive movement in a state of drowsiness. (Continuation of Fig. 46.)

cerebral electrical activity varies with the background of the latter against which the former develops. A stimulus, instead of blocking the α-rhythm, can bring about the replacement of prevalent slow rhythm by, α-rhythm. In the same way, the manifestations of the conditioned orientation reflex vary. Its closure can take place against a background of cortical inhibition and then, it consists of the conditioned awakening reaction. In this case, with the development of the conditioned orientation reflex the slow waves indicating cortical inhibition, are replaced by quicker waves in the α-waveband. Thus, as a result of its association with movement, the light activates the motor analyser.

In this way the conditioned orientation reflex produces a change towards increased frequency of cerebral rhythms. Depending on the prevalent background of the cerebral electrical activity, this results either in the transition from α- to β-waves frequencies with general desynchronization, or in the displacement of δ- by α-rhythm.

E. Conditioned Adaptation Reflexes and the Mechanism for Excitation of the Orienting Reaction

Combined recordings of the orientation and adaptation reflexes provide a good opportunity for the detailed study of the excitation processes of the orientation reflex, particularly in cases when the stimulus is provided, not by physical change of the agent in operation, but by an alteration of the cortical stereotype.

Conditioned adaptation reflexes play an important part in the extinction of the orientation reflex. In particular, an unexpected interference with the pattern of the established connexion can explain the reappearance of the effects of stimulation.

The existence of a connexion between the extinction of the orientation reflex and the formation of conditioned adaptation reflexes becomes obvious if the records of E.E.G., changes are compared with changes of sensitivity to light, pupillary reactions and the C.G.R.

Unexpected change of reinforcement in the "light–strong light" sequence interferes with the firmly established adaptation reflex and results in the simultaneous appearance of the conditioned adaptation and orientation reflexes, because of the discrepancy between the adaptive changes in the analyser on the one hand, and the intensity and nature of the stimulus on the other. It seems, therefore, that the development of the orientation reflex can be a result of interference with the pattern of the light stimuli which has produced a certain type of conditioned adaptation reflex.

Recordings of sensitivity to light, when compared with the data on galvanic skin reactions, show that the process of adaptation to illumination is associatated with the extinction of the C.G.R. An unexpected change in the pattern of the experiment produces a C.G.R., and interferes with adaptation to illumination. Thus the light becomes a relatively stronger stimulus. Similar observations have been made in the course of formation of the conditioned adaptation reflexes. Formation of the connexion, "light–strong light" is associated with a corresponding variation of the C.G.R., to both weak and strong, light. To start with, the reaction can be produced by each of the two components of the combination; later on, only the onset of the sequence is capable of evoking the response and finally, neither of the components is active. At the same time, the conditioned adaptation reflex to "light–strong light", makes its appearance, becoming manifest if the reinforcement is delayed or omitted. At the moment at which reinforcement (strong light), should take place, one can observe the development of a C.G.R. and, depression of α-rhythm. After that, both weak light and strong light give rise to galvanic skin reactions. Suppression of the orientation reflex to the combination of stimuli coincides with the formation of the conditioned adaptation reflex and, interference with the latter produces the orientation reaction.

The extinction of the orientation reflex is associated with the formation of the conditioned adaptation responses in the analyser, which, so to speak, soften the action of the external stimuli and are responsible for the adaptation in anticipation of the stimulus. Whenever the repetitive stimulus undergoes a change or is omitted, the specific link which has developed brings about the orientation reaction.

As the production of the conditioned adaptation reflex is closely associated with certain features of the stimulus, the complete omission of the latter itself becomes a strong stimulus in respect of the state within the analyser which has been produced. The discrepancy between the established pattern of the conditioned connexions, and the features of the stimulus in operation, excites the orientation reaction.

It should not be assumed, however, that the development of the orientation reaction has no effect on the conditioned adaptation reflex. The latter is actually inhibited by the former. Omission of reinforcement results in the appearance of the conditioned adaptation reflex, excitation of the orientation reaction, and subsequent inhibition of the conditioned adaptation reflex. Similar effects are produced by a strong extraneous stimulus. By virtue of the associated inhibition of the conditioned adaptation reflexes, the development of the orientation reaction prevents adaptation to illumination and magnifies the effects of any individual component of the combination of stimuli. This, in its turn, facilitates the temporary intensification of the orientation response to all the components of the combination.

The development of the orientation reflex, and the interference with the conditioned adaptation reflexes, are connected with each other. The new agent, appearing at the scene prepared for the reception of a different agent, acts as a novel stimulus and gives rise to the orientation reaction. It is novel, in so far as its action is not anticipated by any pattern of conditioned adaptation reflexes. The effects of light or darkness, as unconditioned stimuli, are weakened, as a result of the production of conditioned adaptation reflexes which limit their action on the cortex. The records of galvanic skin reactions clearly show that association of so-called non-signal stimuli is connected with the formation of conditioned orientation reflexes. These become extinguished as soon as the conditioned adaptation reflexes are firmly established.

Conditioned orientation reflexes can be produced by stimulation of one analyser or by a combination of stimuli acting on different analysers. In this respect, the conditioned local orientation reflexes, capable of the selective enhancement of the excitability of those areas of the cortex at which reinforcement is actually directed, are of major interest.

PART THREE

PERCEPTION OF SIGNAL STIMULI

Orienting, Thermoregulatory and Defensive Vascular Reflexes Produced by Signal Stimuli

A. Vascular Reactions during the Elaboration of Conditioned Motor Reflexes

In its broad meaning the term "signal stimulus" is applied to those stimuli which evoke a reaction in anticipation of external agents likely to appear in the future (Anokhin, 1957). Consequently, some of the unconditioned reactions, in addition to the conditioned ones, are of signal nature.

However, the signal nature of a reaction manifests itself most clearly as a result of the action of conditioned stimuli, which, while remaining under the control of the investigator, assume the capacity to produce reactions typical of the reinforcing stimuli. This narrower group of signal reactions, arising under the influence of conditioned stimuli, is the object of the present study. In discussing signal stimuli, we mean those acquired features of the stimuli which are the signals for certain reactions. In this respect signal stimuli are just the opposite of indifferent, non-signal stimuli.

In the case of man the term "signal stimulus" should also be applied to stimuli to which activity is directed by implication. It may be said that verbal instructions to react to certain stimuli confer signal significance on the other stimuli not specifically mentioned, even when the individual refrains from executing a motor reaction.

The signal stimulus gives rise not only to the reaction typical of the reinforcement which follows, but in its capacity of an unconditioned stimulus can bring about the orientation, adaptation or defence reactions, which are not without effect on the perception of the stimulus.

We must ask, what alterations take place in the interaction of these three reflexes, participating in the perception of a stimulus, when the latter becomes converted into the conditioned signal for a certain reaction? Let us first consider the changes affecting the relationship between the vasomotor components of the orientation, adaptation and defence reactions in the case of a stimulus converted, with the help of verbal instruction, into a signal for a conditioned motor reaction. With repetitive stimulation, the vasomotor component of the orientation reflex is suppressed. As soon as the stimulus becomes the signal for movement, however, the corresponding vasomotor component of the orientation reflex reappears and persists for a long time. A characteristic feature of this reappearance of the orientation reaction to signal stimuli, is its occurrence even if the subject has not yet performed the motor reaction required, for instance, has consciously suppressed the response.

The orientation reflex, reappearing as a result of the verbal instruction, can not be considered a result of muscular contraction itself, because the orientation reflex brought about by clenching the hand on request, rapidly disappears. This indicates that the sustained orientation reaction, associated with the closure of a new conditioned connexion, is of little significance in the stabilization of the reaction to the verbal order. The orientation reaction can also reappear when the subject is instructed to count mentally the stimuli applied. Increased excitability of the centre of the orientation reaction, resulting from the formation of the conditioned connexion and not the movement itself, seems, therefore, to be the cause of the reappearance of the orientation reflex which accompanies the conditioned motor reflex.

The reappearance of the vasomotor component of the orientation reflex as a result of verbal instruction, which connects the stimulus to the motor reaction, can be observed with diverse kinds of stimuli. In the case of those such as light, sound or touch, which, in the vasomotor system, gives rise only to orientation reactions, the vasomotor component of the latter weakens with the establishment of the conditioned reaction, and disappears completely when the motor response becomes automatic.

With signal stimuli, extinction of the orientation reflex is much slower than with non-signal stimuli. For instance, whereas the orientation reaction to a non-signal agent becomes extinguished after 3–12 applications, a signal stimulus can evoke it for dozens of times.

Extinction of the vasomotor component of the orientation reaction to signal stimuli is independent of the nature of the latter (Vinogradova and Sokolov, 1955). At the same time, certain general features of the process of extinction of the orientation reflex, discovered in the course of experiments with non-signal stimuli, are preserved even when the stimuli assume the significance of signals or motor reactions.

A common feature of the orientation reactions, evoked by signal or non-signal stimuli, is their disinhibition by any extraneous stimulation. For instance, after the orientation reflex to a signal stimulus has been extinguished, a strong stimulus brings about its reappearance. Disinhibition of the orientation reaction to signal stimuli is associated with a degree of inhibition of the corresponding conditioned reflex. After several successive applications, the disinhibitory effect disappears.

It must be pointed out, however, that the disinhibitory effect of the extraneous stimulus, in respect of the orientation reflex produced by a signal stimulus, is not uniform. The existence, for instance, of a stable conditioned reflex to a definite group of stimuli, can inhibit by itself the orientation reaction to extraneous stimulation. In this case the disinhibitory effect of the latter fails to manifest itself. In the course of audiometric investigation we have already seen that an external, extraneous, supra-threshold sound may produce no vasomotor reaction, while a weak, liminal sound, which has, however, the significance of a signal for a motor response, gives rise to such a reaction.

The vasomotor element of the orientation reflex which has become extinguished in the course of stabilization of the conditioned motor reaction, reappears and persists for a long time. This occurs as soon as the positive verbal signal is altered so that it acquires negative reinforcement by means of the following verbal instruction: "There is no need to clench your fist in response to this type of stimulus", calling for differentiation of stimuli.

Negative reinforcement results in a marked change in the features of the orientation reactions to all stimuli. After the motor reaction to one of the stimuli used has been negatively reinforced in this way, the orientation reflex reappears in response to both negative and positive stimuli. This intensification and increased stability of orientation reaction, as a result of negative reinforcement, is observed in the course of the application of all kinds of stimuli.

It must be pointed out that the enhancing effect of the negative reinforcement on the orientation reflex remains significant only if the basic instruction requiring the subject to react to a certain stimulus remains in operation. In the absence of instruction of any kind, all the stimuli become indifferent and the orientation reactions evoked are rapidly extinguished.

Intensification of the reaction, associated with differentiation of stimuli, differs from its temporary disinhibition under the influence of extraneous stimuli, or of an unexpected change in the conditioned stimulus itself. When a new conditioned stimulus is used, the orientation reflex becomes re-established for a short period of time, only to disappear again when the generalized condition reflex becomes stabilized. The subsequent applications of the stimulus at once give rise to the generalized conditioned motor reflexes, not associated with orientation reactions.

There are instances where alteration of the conditioned stimulus, by giving rise to the orientation reaction, results in the inhibition of the conditioned motor reflex. If the absence of the motor reaction to the novel stimulus is not commented upon by the investigator (which corresponds to positive reinforcement of a negative reaction) it is followed by the formation of differentiated conditioned reflexes associated with sustained orientation reactions to the agents employed.

The clash of excitatory and inhibitory processes, resulting from positive reinforcement of one and negative reinforcement of another, conditioned response, provides the conditions for sustained reappearance of the orientation reflexes. The more difficult the differentiation, the more stable and the more intense is the resulting orientation reaction. If the difficulty of differentiation reaches a sufficiently high degree, the vasomotor component of the orientation reaction still makes its appearence after hundreds of applications of the stimulus (Sokolov, 1954).

A particular instance of difficult differentiation, resulting in intensification of the orientation reaction, occurs in the case of stimuli nearing the absolute threshold. Here, a distinction must be made between the physiological background and the results of a weak stimulus. The orientation reaction in conditions of difficult differentiation and in response to liminal stimuli, is characterized by an unusually great intensity and duration (Vinogradova and Sokolov, 1955).

Intense stimulation is usually able to produce the orientation reaction for longer periods of time, but cortical intervention can result in substantial alteration of the dependence of the reaction on the intensity of the stimulus. The reactions to strong, but often-used stimuli, can undergo extinction at a time when weak but rarely-used stimuli may still be effective. During the course of a number of experiments it was found that agents of unusually low intensity can act as strong stimuli. In an unpublished work of Filaretov (Maiorov, 1954, p. 270) there is a description of a stable, persistent orientation reaction in a dog in response to a low intensity noise of long duration; "the exceptionally low intensity of the stimulus resulted in extraordinary strain on the motor orientation apparatus". Fleck (1953), also noted the intense orientation responses to weak stimulation in the course of his study of the cardiac component of orientation reactions in the dog. The fact that agents of such low intensity can act as strong stimuli for orientation reactions is a characteristic feature of the latter, which distinguishes them from the conditioned reflex, where the law of intensity usually holds good (Kupalov, Gent, 1952).

When a conditioned reflex is in the process of becoming established and when the numbers of applications of the negative and positive stimuli are equal, the orientation reflex to a negative stimulus undergoes extinction more quickly than that occurring in response to the positive stimulus. In fact, the pattern of extinction varies with the number of applications of each stimulus, and with the difficulties of discrimination.

The orientation reaction is re-established during the production of the conditioned motor reflexes even if the conditioned stimulus (cold, heat) gives rise to a specific vasomotor reaction. As noted earlier, the first few applications of non-signal thermal stimuli give rise to orientation reactions which inhibit the specific vasomotor response. As the extinction of the orientation reflex proceeds, the thermoregulation reaction becomes more prominent. Thus at first, heat causes orientation vasoconstriction in the hands and cephalic vasodilatation, and only later on is hand vasodilatation produced.

If, on the strength of the verbal instruction, heat becomes a signal for motor reaction, the orientation reflex reappears and inhibits the thermoregulation reaction. The result is again a reciprocal reaction with hand vasoconstriction and cephalic vasodilatation. The orientation reaction, re-established in response to heat, which in the meantime has acquired signal significance, is sustained and in this respect differs from the reaction disinhibited by the action of an extraneous stimulus. The effects of cold when having signal significance are similar. After a number of applications of a cold stimulus, it begins to give rise to adaptive vasoconstriction at the hand and head. When the verbal instruction "clench your fist in response to this stimulus", is given, the cold then gives rise to the orientation reciprocal hand vasoconstriction and cephalic vasodilatation reaction.

Reappearance of the orientation reaction is also observed during the formation of conditioned connexions by means of painful electrocutaneous stimuli, which, as long as they remain non-signal, give rise to the defence reflex in the form of vasoconstriction at both sites. As soon as the painful stimulus, by virtue of verbal instruction, acquires signal significance (conditioned motor reaction), it gives rise to the orientation, instead of the defence reaction, that is, vasoconstriction in the hand and cephalic vasodilatation, instead of concomitant vasoconstriction at both sites (Fig. 48).

At first the passage of current gives rise to the defence reaction (*a*). Following verbal instruction, it becomes a signal for movement (pressure on a key). As the conditioned connexion is closed, the electrocutaneous stimulus begins to give rise to the orientation reaction—reciprocal responses in the head and hand (*b*). With stabilization of the conditioned connexion (100–101), cephalic vasodilatation pointing to the orientative nature of the reaction, recedes (*c*), and ultimately (113–114), the electrodermal signal stimulus again gives rise to the defence reflex in the form of vasoconstriction in the head and hand (*d*).

Only after a great—sometimes over 100—number of applications of the conditioned stimulus, which results in very firm consolidation of the conditioned connexion, will a painful signal stimulus of this type give rise to the appropriate vasomotor reaction. The process of transformation from orientation into defence reaction is a gradual one.

The introduction of discrimination of conditioned stimuli, for example, in accordance with the site of application of the current, again results in reappearance of the orientation reaction. This occurs whether the area corresponding to the positive stimulus, or the area from which differentiation was

M

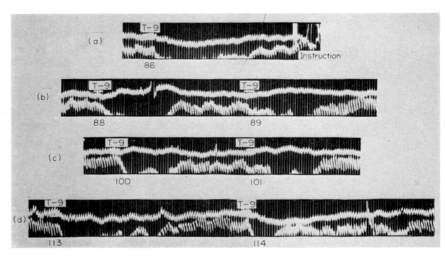

FIG. 48. Formation of a conditioned motor reflex to an electrodermal stimulus. Subject L.D., January 1956.

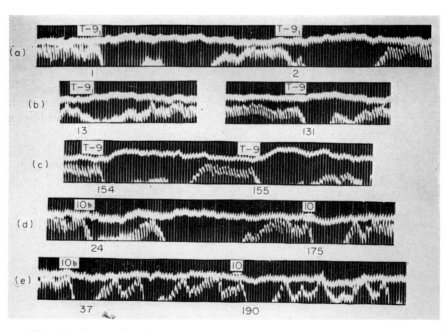

FIG. 49. Restoration of the orienting reflex to the electrodermal stimulus as a result of differentiation. (Continuation of Fig. 48.)

to be made, is stimulated. The development of the orientation reaction to either the negative or the positive, painful stimulus, when discrimination of the site of application of the stimulus is required, confirms the fact that this orientation reaction is not associated directly with the development of kinaesthetic impulses (Fig. 49).

The figure shows that electrocutaneous stimulation of the thumb instead of the index finger (1, 2) gives rise to the orientation reaction (a). At the same time, the orientation reaction reappears at the previous site (131) of stimulation (b). The orientation reflex (154, 155) is sustained (c). Only when the intensity of the electrocutaneous stimulus is increased to 10 units (24, 175) does the latter lead, in the course of further applications (37, 190), to the reappearance of the defence reflex ((d), (e)).

It is clear, therefore, that whenever the discrimination of painful stimuli is called for, the latter give rise to orientation reactions, and if appropriate defence reflexes are wanted, the intensity of the electrocutaneous stimuli must be increased. Then, and only then, will the positive and negative stimuli give rise to defence reactions. That increased intensity of stimuli is necessary in order to obtain defence reactions under conditions of stimulus discrimination, is of paramount importance. It indicates that the inhibition of the unconditioned defence reflex, as a result of the necessity to discriminate, is associated with a reduction of sensitivity to pain.

The extent of the reinforcement of the orientation reflex, as noted earlier, depends on the difficulties encountered in the course of discrimination, and this also applies to the differentiation of electrocutaneous stimuli.

After the defence reflex has become re-established during differentiation of positive and negative stimuli, introduction of a new instruction calling for discrimination by the subject in accordance with the duration of the stimulus (long-positive, short-negative), results in the displacement of the defence reflex by the orientation reaction, in spite of the fact that the intensity of the stimuli remains unaltered (Fig. 50).

This figure shows that, when the discrimination between the electrocutaneous stimuli (201, 202) is made still more difficult, it results in reappearance of the orientation reactions (a). With repetition, the reactions weaken (b), undergo extinction ((c), (d)) and are replaced by concomitant reactions typical of the defence reflex (e).

Thus the attempt at producing a positive conditioned motor reaction to the electrocutaneous stimulus of long duration, to be differentiated from the electrocutaneous stimulus of short duration, results in the reappearance of the orientation reaction to either stimulus. With the establishment of successful discrimination, the orientation reaction to both painful stimuli becomes replaced by the defence reflex.

A similar pattern of events can be observed with all types of stimuli whether auditory, visual, thermal or electrocutaneous. Every one of them, either as a result of instruction, or verbal reinforcement, becomes the signal for a motor reaction. They have in common the ability to intensify the orientation reflex which can then overcome the specific or defence effect of the stimuli on the vasomotor system. Furthermore, the reinforcement of the orientation reaction is particularly marked when discrimination of negatively and positively reinforced stimuli is required.

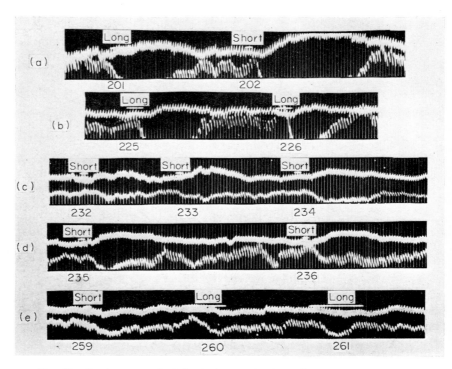

FIG. 50.   Replacement of a defensive by an orienting reflex on the introduction of stimulus differentiation based on a new characteristic (duration). (Continuation of Fig. 49.)

B.   Vascular Reactions during the Elaboration of Conditioned Reflexes with Electrodermal Reinforcement

Does the orientation reaction reappear only in case of closure of the motor conditioned reflexes with verbal reinforcement, or can the same effect be observed if other forms of reinforcement are used? Special experiments have been designed to answer this question. The sound of a metronome is used as the conditioned stimulus. As a non-signal stimulus, it only gives rise to the orientation vasomotor reaction, which, with repetition, undergoes extinction. Painful electrocutaneous stimuli (constant current of 100 impulses per sec, duration of impulse 0·2 m/sec), producing cephalic and hand vasoconstriction, are used as reinforcement.

Depending on the vascular reactions produced, the reinforcing stimuli can be classified into one of the following three groups. The first consists of agents such as sound or light, which can only produce orientation reactions in the vasomotor system. Consequently the orientating reinforcement when a sequence of two non-signal stimuli is used leads, first of all, to reappearance of the orienting reaction to the conditioned stimulus, the vasomotor reaction to which had already been extinguished, before reinforcement was started. With stabilization of the conditioned connexion, the orientation reaction undergoes extinction, only to reappear again when an attempt at discrimination is made. A characteristic feature of the process of formation of conditioned reflexes with reinforcement of orientative nature, is the fact that neither the conditioned signal nor the reinforcement give rise to the orientation reflex.

The second group of stimuli used for the purposes of reinforcement consists of those agents—heat and cold—which give rise to specific vasomotor reactions. As in the case of the stimuli of the first group, reinforcement by means of heat or cold leads, first of all, to the reappearance of the orientation reflex to the stimulus which acquired the signal nature. With repeated reinforcement, however, the orientation reaction undergoes extinction, and the specific conditioned reflex to cold or heat is produced. In this case the conditioned signal—light or sound—begins to give rise to the specific, instead of the orientation, reaction.

The third group consists of stimuli producing defence reactions. Even painful reinforcement, however, gives rise, first of all, to an orienting reflex to the conditioned stimulus.

The reinforcing agents, subsumed in the second and third groups, are typically productive of a specific vasomotor reaction, which permits the distinction to be made from the non-specific vasomotor component of the orientation reaction.

The pattern of reflexes produced by conditioned stimuli and their reinforcement has been studied during the formation of the conditioned defence reflex to sound, using electrocutaneous reinforcement (Fig. 51).

It may be seen that, applied separately, the electrocutaneous stimulation gives rise to a defence reaction (Fig. 51(*a*), 47), and that the metronome ((*a*), 17) does not evoke a reaction. The reinforcement of the latter by means of the former completely alters the picture. The detailed analysis of the first few applications of the combination is of paramount importance. The first application of the metronome followed by current shows no reaction to the metronome, while the effect of the painful stimulus is reduced (Fig. 51(*b*), 1). Vasoconstriction, which started at the head, as an index of the defence reaction, becomes a vasodilatation typical of the orientation reaction.

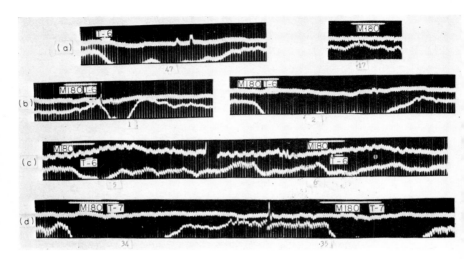

Fig. 51. Formation of a conditioned defensive reflex to sound with electrodermal reinforcement. Subject L.L., March 1956. M180—Metronome 180/min. T–6 etc.—Electrodermal reinforcement.

This weakening of the effects of the painful stimulus could be due to inhibition of the defence reflex, in connexion with the intensification of the orientation reaction to the electric current unexpectedly succeeding the metronome. It must be pointed out that the effects of the stimulus used for the purposes of reinforcement are much changed as a result of the action of the conditioned stimulus. It appears, therefore, that the combination of stimuli previously used separately, gives rise to disinhibition of the orientation reaction, and that the latter reaches a sufficiently high intensity to influence adversely the development of the defence reaction to unconditioned reinforcement. As a result of the association of the two stimuli, not only the effect of the reinforcing stimulus, but also that of the conditioned stimulus changes, the latter giving rise, however, not to the defence but to the orientation reflex. This consists of vasoconstriction in the hand, which actually begins before the electric current is applied (Fig. 51(*b*), 2).

It seems, therefore, that the single application of a painful stimulus for the purposes of reinforcement results, in the first place, in the reappearance of the orientation reaction to the conditioned stimulus, when the latter, applied repeatedly on its own. has ceased to produce it. The conditioned stimulus itself, however, also affects the activity of the reinforcing agent. The painful reaction to the latter weakens and is displaced by the orientation reaction. With further applications of the combination of stimuli in the course of production of the conditioned defence reflex, the intensified orientation reaction to both stimuli can be persistent (Fig. 51(c)). The defence reaction to the reinforcing stimulus does not reappear until the intensity of the latter is increased from 6 to 7 arbitrary units (Fig. 51(d), 34).

It should be noted that the closure of the conditioned link increases the threshold of the defence reaction—the intensity of the reinforcement must be increased before a defence reaction to it can be produced. With stabilization of the conditioned connexion, the defence-evoking effect of the reinforcement increases, and the conditioned stimulus ceases to give rise to the orientation reaction. Instead, a conditioned defence reflex develops before the actual application of the reinforcing stimulus. The action of the painful reinforcement further intensifies the conditioned reflex effect of the sound (Fig. 51(d), 35).

The experiments described above show that the first stage in the formation of a conditioned reflex, with painful reinforcement, consists of the reappearance of the orientation reaction to both the conditioned and the reinforcing, stimuli. The actual formation of the conditioned defence reflex coincides with the weakening of the orientation reaction to both stimuli.

When, by giving another sound stimulus (M-120), an element of discrimination is introduced, the orientation reflex is again enhanced and develops in response to the novel stimulus, which is not reinforced (Fig. 52(a), 4).

At the same time, the effect of the positive signal (M–180) undergoes a change and the orientation reflex is again produced (Fig. 52(a), 42). The enhancement of the orientation reaction shows in the effect of reinforcement, which now begins to give rise to the orientation instead of the defence reaction and conditions reminiscent of the first stage of the process of formation of the conditioned reflex develop once more. Both sound stimuli M–180 (reinforced) and M–120 (not reinforced) give rise to the orientation reaction, while the unconditioned defence-stimulating effect of the reinforcement is replaced by the orientation effect. In order to enhance the defence effect of the reinforcement in these conditions, the intensity of the electrocutaneous stimulus must be increased to 9 units (Fig. 52(b), 70).

With the discrimination proceeding satisfactorily, the orientation reflex disappears, the efficacy of reinforcement increases and the two sound stimuli acquire a different significance. The one which has been reinforced produces the conditioned defence reflex (Fig. 52(b), 71); the other—which has been differentiated gives rise to no reaction at all (Fig. 52(c), 24).

As with the development of the conditioned motor reflex, the more difficult the discrimination (the closer the frequency of the sound stimuli), the more

persistent is the orientation reaction and the more difficult is the formation
of the conditioned defence reflex. Introduction of still another sound stimulus
M–160 (Fig. 52(*d*), 1 and (*e*), 14) results in an intensification of the orientation
reaction to both the conditioned and the reinforcing stimulus. The metronome M–180 again gives rise to the orientation reaction (Fig. 52(*e*), 95).

This pattern of events is also found when a weak electrocutaneous stimulus
—producing the sensation of touch and an orientation vasomotor reaction,

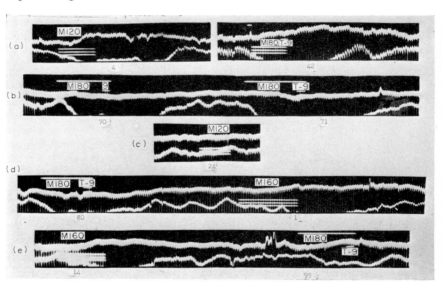

FIG. 52.   Intensification of the orienting reflex on elaboration of differentiation with
electrodermal reinforcement. (Continuation of Fig. 51.)

is used in the capacity of the conditioned stimulus, and a strong electrocutaneous stimulus—producing pain and a defence vasomotor reaction,
serves the purposes of reinforcement. After repeated applications separately,
the weak electric current ceases to produce any reaction, but the strong one
continues to give rise to the clear defence reaction. Application of the two in
association results in a weakening of the defence reaction to the strong
stimulus and reappearance of the orientation reaction to the weak one, which
becomes a signal of the former. Only after a number of applications does the
defence reaction to the conditioned stimulus replace the orientation reaction.
At that point the weak current starts to reproduce the effect of the strong one.
All changes affecting the conditioned stimulus, however, such as increased
intensity, duration, order of application etc. result, first of all, in the enhancement of the orientation reaction, and the weak current again reproduces the
orientation vasomotor reaction.

It seems, therefore, that the first result of defence reinforcement is the enhancement of the orientation reflex whatever the conditioned stimulus.

C. Measurement of Reactivity and Sensitivity by Means of Orienting and Defensive Reflexes

Any investigation of the mechanism of perception of non-signal stimuli has perforce been based on the study of involuntary reactions, and any request for verbal response to stimulation adds to it the quality of a signal. When the object of the studies changes to signal stimuli, this difficulty disappears and the relationship between the vasomotor components of the orientation and defence reflexes on the one hand, can be compared with the sensations produced by them, as reported verbally by the subject on the other. This relationship, as well as the nature of the association between the variations in vasomotor reaction—observed during the formation of conditioned reflexes—and the sensitivity and reactivity of the analyser, must be discussed next.

This problem has been studied by recording the subject's vasomotor reactions to stimuli, auditory or electrocutaneous, the subject classifying these stimuli into one of the following categories: 0—no sensation, 1—barely perceptible, 2—weak sensation (light touch), 3—moderately strong sensation, 4—strong sensation (slight pain), 5—very strong unpleasant sensation (severe pain).

It is found that the request for classification of stimuli acts in the same way as the process of formation of a condition reflex, namely it restores the orientation reaction. Comparison of vasomotor reactions with classification of the stimuli by the subject, shows that Category 1 corresponds to a very strong orientation reflex indicating the near liminal intensity of the stimulus. An orientation reaction is also associated with the Categories 2 and 3. Category 4 coincides with an orientation reaction which gradually, during the stimulation, becomes replaced by the defence reaction. Category 5 corresponds to a strength of stimulation which produces an immediate defence reflex.

In this way a relationship has been established between the nature of sensation as classified subjectively, the nature of the vasomotor reactions, and the intensity of the stimuli. This correlation once established, we could, on the basis of the vasomotor reactions recorded, begin to analyse those changes in the relationship of reactivity and sensitivity—as measured by the orientation and defence reflexes, which are the result of acquisition of signal significance by the stimuli employed.

As stated above, with repetitive stimulation the threshold of the orientation reflex rises and that of the defence reflex diminishes. A definite relationship between the two thresholds becomes eventually established (Fig. 53), stimuli of different intensities giving rise to different reactions. In Fig. 53(*b*), (*c*), the orientation reflex is produced by a stimulus of 5, a weak defence reflex by 8, and a strong defence reflex by 11–15, arbitrary units. The threshold of the orientation reaction equals 5, and that of the defence reaction, 8 units (*b*), whereas stimuli of 1; 2; 3; 4 arbitrary units (*a*), remain subliminal.

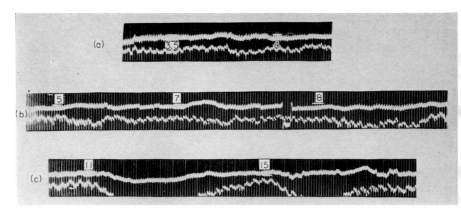

FIG. 53. Non-signal electrodermal stimulation thresholds for orienting and defensive reflexes. Subject A.S., March 1956.

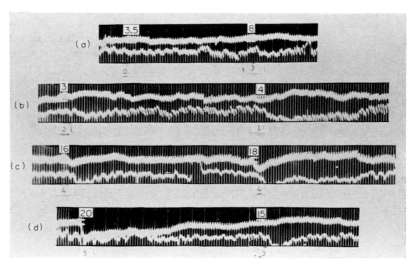

FIG. 54. Thresholds of orienting and defensive reflexes with the strengths of the electrodermal stimuli subjectively classified. (Continuation of Fig. 53.) The numbers below are the strength "numbers" of the stimuli.

Under the influence of the investigator's instruction calling for classification of the stimuli (Fig. 54) the threshold of the orientation reaction is lowered to 4 units (Category 1) (*b*) and that of the defence reaction is increased to 16 units (Category 4) (*c*). The appearance of the threshold reaction (Category 1) deserves attention.

By comparing Figs. 53 and 54 one can see that, under the influence of mental exercise (classification), the threshold of excitation of the orientation reflex falls from 5 to 4 and that of the defence reflex increases from 8 to 16 arbitrary units.

A similar pattern of changes can be observed in the case of stimulation by sound (Fig. 55).

This tracing represents a case where the threshold of the orientation reflex to non-signal sound stimuli of 512 C.P.S. equals 50dB, and that for the defence reflex, is 60dB (Fig. 55(*a*), (*b*)). The request to classify the stimuli raises the latter threshold to 80dB (*c*), (*d*), whereas the former falls to 5dB (*e*).

The acquisition by the stimulus of signal significance results in a fall of the threshold for the orientation, and an increase of the threshold for the pain reaction. The range of stimuli giving rise to the orientation reaction widens whereas that of painful stimuli narrows. This change of relationship between the orientation and defence reactions, resulting from the request to differentiate various sound and electrocutaneous stimuli, coincides with formation of a conditioned reflex in respect of the stimulus in question.

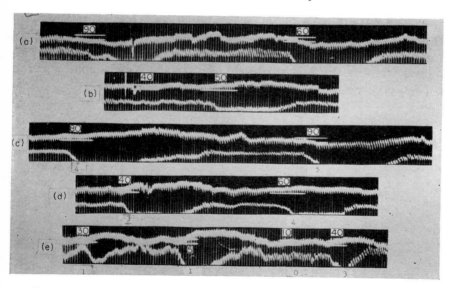

FIG. 55. Changes in the vascular reactions produced by assessment of the strengths of acoustic stimuli. Subject A.S., March 1956.

This statement is of great importance, since it allows us to associate all instances of completion of a conditioned connexion with a certain pattern of sensitivity change as revealed by this method of classification of stimuli. The production of a conditioned reflex brings about considerable changes in the reactivity and sensitivity of the body, both with respect to the stimuli which are in the course of becoming conditioned, and also to those which are employed for the purposes of reinforcement. The closure of the conditioned connexion is associated with an increase in the "orientation sensitivity". At the same time, the reactivity as measured by the defence reaction is diminished at the site of application of both the conditioned and the reinforcing stimuli. The occurrence of a substantial change in the objective effects of the stimulus, as a result of acquisition by it of signal significance, has thus been demonstrated, using the above method of simultaneous classification of stimuli and vasomotor reaction recording.

This technique reveals a definite pattern of relationship between its two elements. The nature of the vasomotor reactions can therefore throw light on the perception of non-signal stimuli in respect of which, no direct evidence can be provided by the subject. The changes in the mechanism of perception of non-signal stimuli are connected with alterations of various kinds of sensitivity such as sensitivity to pain, and, of the orientation reflexes (Fig. 56).

Figure 56 shows the variation in vasomotor reaction in response to electrocutaneous (*a*) and sound (*b*) stimulation when the subject is asked to differentiate the stimuli. It can be seen that the range of orientation reactions stretching from Categories 1 to 4 inclusive, extends as a result of both an increase in the threshold of pain and a reduction in the threshold of the orientation reaction. With auditory stimulation, the latter alteration plays a more prominent part than the former, with electrocutaneous stimulation, the reverse applies.

A comparison of tracings of cephalic and hand vasomotor reactions, with the subject's classification of the stimuli, fails to provide an adequate explanation for a number of peculiarities. These concern the reactions occurring in response to liminal stimuli or, at the moment of transition into the zone of defence reflexes. Quantitative assessment of the vasomotor reactions is necessary, and to make it possible, a coefficient has been suggested, equal to the product of the size of the reaction by its duration, expressed in mm.[2]

The dependence of the vasomotor (cephalic and hand) reaction coefficient on the varying intensity of signal stimuli has been studied in the course of experiments involving the use of signal sound stimuli. The reaction coefficients obtained for sounds of various intensities are compared with the classification of stimuli by the subject (Fig. 57).

Five ranges of the intensity of reaction, as measured by means of the suggested coefficient, can be singled out. The first range, corresponding to

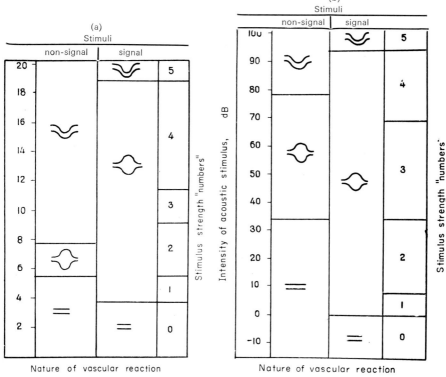

Fig. 56. Relationships between vascular reactions, assessed strengths and level of sensitivity for non-signal and signal electrodermal and acoustic stimuli. (*a*). Subject A.S., March 1956. Electrodermal stimuli. (*b*). Subject L.A., March 1956. Acoustic stimuli.

Category 0 (absence of sensation) is produced by stimuli slightly weaker than 0 dB. This includes a certain number of subsensory reactions occurring in response to stimuli but not expressed verbally. These reactions are associated with slight vasoconstriction in the hand while there are no visible cephalic vasomotor changes. The second range, corresponding to Category 1, shows a typically more intense vasoconstriction in the hand. These reactions, associated with the weakest sensation, are produced by stimuli of 0–15dB, above the threshold of hearing. The associated vasomotor reactions are several times stronger than the reaction produced by more intense stimuli.

    Certain features of the reactions of these two ranges require further consideration. The subsensory reactions, characterized by insignificant vasomotor changes, are not a result of simple inhibition of movement during difficulty in the differentiation of the threshold signal. As a rule, when a

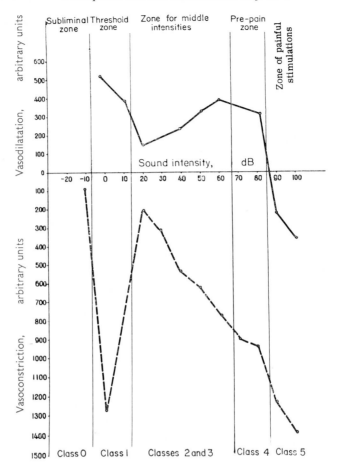

Fig. 57.   Relationship between vascular reactions and the assessed strengths of a strong acoustic stimulus. Subject L.S., March 1956. 1—Vascular reactions in the head region. 2—Vascular reactions in the hand.

subject is uncertain as to whether or not he has perceived the sound and he in fact has, one can observe strong vasomotor reactions—frequently much stronger than the reactions produced by distinctly perceived stimuli—in spite of the absence of any motor reaction.

In the ranges in question, therefore, two groups of reactions can be distinguished. Those in the second range develop as a result of secondary inhibition of movement under conditions of difficult identification of the threshold stimulus, and are comparable with the reactions occurring as a result of attempts at differentiation of stimuli. Those in the first range are the subsensory reactions proper, not associated with the conscious perception of sound; they are not related to the intensification of the orientation reaction produced by weak but, nevertheless, perceived stimuli.

The stimuli of the third range, corresponding to the 2nd and 3rd category are from 15 to 65dB above threshold and the corresponding reactions, whether in the hand or head, conform strictly with the law of intensity. The fourth range includes stimuli from 65 to 85dB, which are just below the threshold of pain, and which give rise to a cephalic reaction of diminishing intensity down to complete suppression or even reversal of sign (transition to vasoconstriction). The intensity of the hand reaction at the same time increases. The fifth range (Category 5) corresponds to painful stimuli of 85–100dB above threshold and typically shows cephalic vasoconstriction and a still more pronounced hand vasoconstriction.

The diminished intensity of the cephalic vasodilatation to painful stimuli, as observed in the course of transition to vasoconstriction, depends on the reciprocal inhibition of two reactions, the orientation and defence. Co-existing at this moment, they undergo summation so far as the vasomotor reaction in the hand is concerned, but partially neutralize each other in the cephalic reaction.

Elucidation of certain quantitative relationships between the intensity of cephalic and hand vasomotor reactions, on the one hand, and the subject's classification of stimuli and the actual intensity of the auditory stimulation on the other, is of great practical importance. If a certain magnitude of cephalic or hand reaction corresponds to a definite category of stimuli as subjectively assessed, and if the descent to the threshold of audibility manifests itself as a special kind of intensification of vasomotor reactions, then the determination of the levels of sensitivity and reactivity of the human auditory analyser from the recording of vasomotor reactions only, becomes a possibility. The nature of the response to a certain known stimulus provides the basis for assessment of the function of perception and of the level of sensitivity with some degree of accuracy. It could also be used as a method of determination of the absolute threshold of audibility using the "threshold reaction", and of the threshold of pain (or discomfort), as indicated by the development of cephalic vasoconstriction associated with further increase of vasoconstriction in the hand.

Measurements of the vasomotor reaction coefficients in the hand and head in the course of electrocutaneous stimulation, with stimuli classified by the subject in a similar way, are productive of similar findings. As in the case of auditory stimulation, absence of conscious perception is associated with a weak vasomotor hand reaction only (Category 0). Threshold stimuli (Category 1), produce a somewhat more intense hand and cephalic reaction. Stimuli of moderate intensity (Categories 2 and 3), give rise to reactions which obey the law of intensities. When the strength of the stimulus approaches higher levels (Category 4), the cephalic reaction weakens, to become reversed (vasoconstriction), in response to painful stimuli (Category 5).

The above method of determination of the absolute threshold of sensitivity and threshold of pain, and the curves which are so obtained, help in the objective assessment of the disorders of hearing associated with the phenomenon of loudness recruitment. In this condition, reduction of the absolute auditory sensitivity is associated with preserved, or even enhanced, sensitivity to sounds of higher intensity, the subject complaining of painful discomfort caused by the apparent excessive loudness of such sounds. This abnormality of perception gives rise to a deformity of the curve plotted by means of measuring vasomotor reactions. The range of sounds perceived normally is greatly reduced and that of the sounds giving rise to defence reactions increases.

It can be seen from these experiments that the two types of sensitivity, as determined by means of the orientation and defence reactions to electro-cutaneous stimuli, are in inverse relationship, each having an inhibitory effect on the other. They correspond to epicritic and protopathic sensitivity, respectively, as described by Head in 1920. The factors which in our experiments enhance one kind of sensitivity, have an opposite effect on the other, which is also in agreement with Head's findings.

A similar kind of inverse relationship between "orientation" and "defence" sensitivity, is observed in the course of auditory stimulation. The effects of sounds of high intensity—which give rise to the defence cephalic and hand vasoconstriction reflex—change as a result of the formation of a conditioned motor reaction instead.

Repeated application of a painful signal stimulus leads to extinction of the orientation reflex, in the same way as when pain is not the signal of a motor reaction. The process of extinction is, however, slower. This phenomenon was studied in the course of specially designed experiments in which the effects on vasomotor activity of signal and non-signal stimuli of varying intensity were repeatedly compared (Fig. 58). It was found that the thresholds of the orientation reflex to both signal and non-signal stimuli, increase during such repetitive stimulation. At the same time, the threshold of the defence reaction to both kinds of stimuli is reduced from one experiment to the next. When the conditioned reflex activity becomes more complicated (as when a simple motor reaction is replaced by an attempt at classification of stimuli), the threshold of the defence reflex increases and that of the orientation reflex diminishes but, the threshold of both reflexes to non-signal stimuli remains unchanged.

These experiments are of fundamental importance. They show that the relationship between the different kinds of sensitivity at various stages of

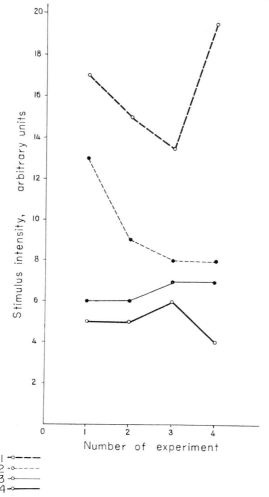

Fig. 58. Relative changes in the thresholds of orienting and defensive reactions. Subject A.S., March 1956. 1—Thresholds of defensive reactions to signal stimuli. 2—The same to non-signal stimuli. 3—Thresholds of orienting reactions to non-signal stimuli. 4—The same to signal stimuli. 1, 2, 3—Experiments for consolidation of the conditioned reflex. 4—Experiment for assessment of the stimulus strength.

reinforcement is not the same. Consequently, when evaluating changes in the mode of perception of a stimulus under the influence of the formation of a conditioned reflex, the type of the conditioned reflex in operation must be taken into consideration. The relationship between "orientation", and "painful" sensitivity, undergoes considerable changes in the beginning of the

N

process of formation of the conditioned connection, but a gradual return to the initial state of affairs can be observed. The more difficult the classification of stimuli, and consequently the stronger the orientation reflex participating in the operation of the link in question, the higher the sensitivity and reactivity measured with the help of the orientation reaction and, the lower the sensitivity to pain.

There is still another process underlying the changes of sensitivity and reactivity found in the course of measurement of the thresholds of the orientation and defence reactions; this is the development of a dominant focus. It comes into particular prominence in the course of repetitive painful stimulation. Any signal or non-signal painful stimulus sets up a dominant focus as a result of which, even a weaker stimulus gives rise to the pain reaction. The associated change in the vasomotor reactions is also reflected in the subjective classification of the stimulus. Thus, after several applications of a very strong sound (100dB), a weaker sound (90dB), which before has been producing an orientation reaction and was classified in Category 4, begins to give rise to a reaction typical of pain and is classified in Category 5. Similar findings are obtained using electrocutaneous stimulation. When a single application of a very strong electrocutaneous stimulus—producing a pain reaction associated with cephalic vasoconstriction, is followed by a weaker stimulus—which before did not give rise to sensation of pain, the latter now gives rise to pain and is subjectively reclassified in a higher category. At the same time, cephalic vasoconstriction becomes intensified, or, if absent, develops and serves as an objective proof of the defence nature of the reaction. In a number of cases the intensification of the defence reflex, even if not reflected in reclassification of the stimulus, was shown by augmentation of the vasoconstriction. There is a tendency, however, for both the reclassification and the vasomotor reactions, to coincide.

A reliable indication of the increase in the level of sensitivity to pain under intense stimulation is obtained in the course of the studies on recruitment within the auditory analyser, when after several applications, even a 70 dB sound gives rise to pain. In this way, it seems, repeated application of very strong stimuli results in an increase of "pain" sensitivity and a decrease of "orientation sensitivity". This is accompanied by reclassification of the stimuli and simultaneous alteration of vasomotor responses.

Extraneous stimulation inhibits the defence and enhances the orientation, reflexes. This effect manifests itself as a temporary reduction of "pain sensitivity", and an increase of "orientation sensitivity". It shows certain similarities to the process of disinhibition of the orientation reflex in response to a non-signal stimulus.

As shown above, the stabilization of a conditioned reflex to an electrocutaneous stimulus is associated with the progressive extinction of the orientation reaction and its replacement by the defence reflex. An attempt at discrimination disinhibits the orientation reaction; this is associated with a reversal of the relationship of the two thresholds, the threshold of the orientation reflex falls and that of the defence reflex rises. Accordingly, increasing anew the range of painful stimuli results in the evocation of the orientation, and not defence, reflex.

The formation of a motor conditioned reflex is therefore associated with a re-establishment of the orientation reaction, the threshold of excitation of which is also lowered. In contrast, the defence reflex is inhibited and its threshold of excitation rises.

The study of the relationship of the two sensitivities provides the data for determination of not only the absolute sensitivity of the hearing apparatus but also the limits of intensity of sounds where the latter begin to approach the threshold of pain.

The usual type of audiogram shows the loss of hearing in respect of its normal absolute threshold, as measured with the help of verbal (or motor) reactions. On the audiograms obtained by means of the technique used by us the following are indicated:

1. The absolute threshold of auditory sensitivity in respect of signal sound stimuli as measured for various frequencies with the help of vasomotor reactions.

2. The absolute threshold of auditory sensitivity in respect of non-signal sound stimuli, measured as in (1).

3. The threshold of the defence reaction in respect of signal sound stimuli, as measured with the help of the cephalic vasoconstrictor response.

4. The threshold of the defence reaction in respect of non-signal sound stimuli, measured as in (3).

The audiogram is obtained by measuring first the thresholds to non-signal and then to signal stimuli. During the latter stage of the procedure, the motor conditioned reflexes are recorded as well as the vasomotor reactions (Fig. 59).

It has been demonstrated experimentally, using the vasomotor component of the orientation reaction, that the threshold in respect of non-signal stimuli only initially coincides with that for signal stimuli. With repeated measurements the threshold rises and reaches the level corresponding to near-painful stimulation. The threshold measured by the vasomotor response to signal stimuli corresponds, roughly, to the threshold as indicated by the conditioned motor reaction. Only in certain cases can the development of a small subsensory range (5dB), be observed.

The threshold, as measured by means of the defence response to signal stimuli, is found to be higher than if non-signal stimulation is used.

This method of investigation of the function of the auditory analyser via

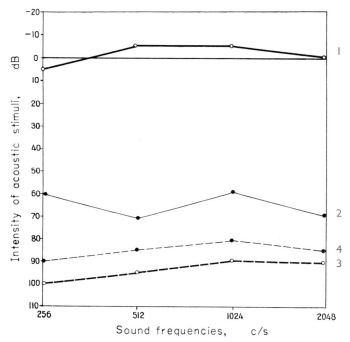

Fig. 59. Absolute auditory and pain thresholds as measured from vascular reactions to signal and non-signal stimuli. Subject Ye.S., March 1956. 1— Thresholds as revealed by orienting reflexes to signal stimuli. 2—Thresholds as revealed by orienting reflexes to non-signal stimuli. 3—Thresholds as indicated by defensive reflexes to signal stimuli. 4—The same to non-signal stimuli.

the vasomotor reactions, provides the means for objective study of the whole frequency range of sound stimuli giving rise to the orientation reaction, and indicates the changes resulting from the use of signal or non-signal stimulation. Similarly, study of the effects of sound stimuli, reaching the limits of discomfort, enables objective criteria concerning the effects of intense noise on the human nervous system to be determined.

The experiments described above were concerned with changes of sensitivity accompanying the formation of the conditioned motor, (or speech) reflexes. The effect of reinforcement, in this case, consists of stimulation of the orientation reaction.

What are the variations of sensitivity, however, when reinforcement is effected by means of painful stimuli? This problem has been studied with the help of electrocutaneous stimuli, serving as both the conditioned stimulus and the reinforcement. The sensitivity was measured using a stimulus of 25 V—giving rise to no vasomotor reaction, in association with an unconditioned stimulus of 75V—giving rise to the defence reflex. As a result of the formation of the conditioned defence reflex, the sensitivity, as measured by means of the orientation reaction to the conditioned stimulus, increases; stimuli of liminal intensity (12·5 V) now give rise to the orientation reaction. The threshold of the defence reaction to the signal stimulus increases to 80 V. This picture, however, can only be observed during the first stage of the experiment. With repeated application of the combination of stimuli, the liminal (down to 12·5 V) conditioned electrocutaneous stimuli begin to give rise to the defence reaction.

It seems, therefore, that, as a result of defence reinforcement, the "orientation sensitivity" in respect of the conditioned stimulus at first increases, while the "defence sensitivity" falls. The closure of the conditioned link, on the other hand, is associated with a rise of the latter. Finally, even the weakest of the conditioned stimuli set up defence reactions.

Thus, the variations of sensitivity under the influence of conditioned stimulation are associated with, firstly, general intensification of the orientation reflex and, secondly, with the formation of specialized conditioned reflexes, depending on the nature and intensity of the reinforcement.

D. The Galvanic Skin Reaction in Relation to Stimuli Acquiring Signal Significance

As shown earlier, the galvanic skin reaction recorded from the palmar skin or sole of the foot, denotes the orientation reaction—the response of the body to the novelty factor of the stimulus. The records of vasomotor reactions show that reinforcement (whether verbal or defence) increases the effects of the stimulus mainly as far as the orientation reaction is concerned. It would be expected, therefore, that the cutaneogalvanic reaction, so closely associated with the orientation reaction, would also be intensified by reinforcing stimulation. Verbal reinforcement, as used in the production of conditioned motor reflexes, can serve as an example.

In our experiments we employed simultaneous recording of the galvanic skin and motor reactions. The latent period of motor response was measured with the help of a recording chronograph. The time record was derived from three discs of the chronograph, rotating at uniform speeds. One disc, divided into 1/100th of a second, rotated at the rate of 1 rev/sec., another disc (seconds), at the rate of 1 rev/min. and a third disc (minutes), was making 1 rev/hr. Closure of the circuit brought into operation a special small hammer which came into contact with the recording tape and with the scales of the relating disc, providing in this way the time marking on the former. The difference in time between the closure of the circuit by the investigator and its opening by the subject, automatically indicated the length of the latent period of the motor reaction with a margin of error of 5 msec.

The high accuracy of the apparatus was due to the fact that the discs were powered by a synchronous motor, fed by a special quartz generator. The latter was kept in a special chamber provided with a thermostat, so that the maximum accuracy was assured. The crystal oscillations were transformed by divisors into waves of 100 c/s which were then fed to the motor of the recording chronograph. At the same time, the tape of the ink-recording potentiometer provided the record of the galvanic skin reaction, and of the motor reaction (pressure on a key connected by means of air transmission and rubber balloon to the potentiometer).

The origin of the electrical and sound stimuli was a sound frequency generator, 3G–10. A specially adjusted Belostotski's adaptometer provided accurately measured light stimuli, and a ceramic heater served as the source of thermal (infra-red) stimuli. Sinusoidal alternating current at 1000 c/s provided by the device 3G–10, served as the electrocutaneous stimulus. Closure of the circuit by means of a tripolar key controlled by the investigator, switched the sound stimulus to the subject's earphones, closed the circuit of the chronograph used for the measurement of the latent period, and at the same time produced a record of the moment of stimulation on the tape of the electronic potentiometer. The subject's response consisted of pressure on a key, resulting in breaking of the circuit of the chronograph, which therefore measured the length of the latent period of the motor reaction. The record of the motor reaction, obtained by means of air transmission starting at the subject's key, was obtained together with that of the galvanic skin reaction and with the record of the moment of application of the stimulus, on the tape of the apparatus E.P.P.–09. The magnitude of the galvanic skin reaction was compared with the force exerted in pressure on the key, and with the latent period of the conditioned motor reflex. This elaborate mechanism provided the means for recording the galvanic skin responses and conditioned motor reflexes with a high degree of accuracy.

In order to be able to assess the effects of reinforcement, the dynamics of the background galvanic skin activity in the course of experiment must first be studied.

Before the actual start of the experiment, two stages of background activity can be distinguished. The skin resistance is at first low and usually shows spontaneous variations, indicating an increased level of excitability. With the subject becoming habituated to the situation, the resistance increases and the spontaneous fluctuations disappear. With the start of the experiment (Fig. 60), application of the stimuli, which are later to acquire signal significance, gives rise to galvanic skin reactions which are gradually extinguished (1–8). The extinction process is associated with an increase of the general skin resistance. The request to react to sound produces a galvanic skin reaction followed by stabilization of the resistance at a lower level (9). The stimulus which had been given signal significance in respect of the motor reaction produces a sustained and very slowly extinguished galvanic skin response (10).

The figure shows the increased intensity of the reaction as a result of verbal instruction. After three applications of the non-signal sound stimulus, the reaction disappears against the general background of increased resistance. Verbal instruction lowers the level of resistance of the skin and the non-signal sound stimuli, which follow, produce galvanic skin reactions which, with repetition of the signal stimulus, gradually become extinguished.

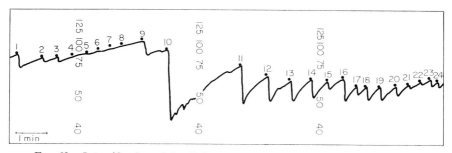

FIG. 60.   Intensification of the C.G.R. on the acquisition of signal significance by a stimulus. Subject K., March 1954. 1–8—Non-signal acoustic stimuli. 9—Instructions—"Close the hand in response to the sound". 10–24—Sounds producing movements. Ordinate: resistance (kilohms).

The increased magnitude of the galvanic skin reaction could be attributed to proprioceptive stimulation resulting from movement and superimposed on the effects of auditory stimulation. By studying the reactions to the word "press", not followed by the execution of the instruction; to the positive order "press", and to the negative order "do not press", it is found that the C.G.R., already extinguished after response to the word "press", which became a non-signal stimulus, reappears with increased intensity to both the positive request associated with movement and the negative request not associated with the motor reaction. It seems, therefore, that in the conditions of discrimination between the requests "do not press" and "press", the galvanic skin reaction has not been necessarily associated with the execution of the movement.

A method of "conditioned reinforcement" (Voronin and Sokolov, 1955) has also been used. It consists of the approval of the reaction expressed, not in the words of the investigator, but by another application 5 sec later of the same agent, which served initially as the conditioned stimulus. The subject is told that the repetition of the stimulus corresponds to the statement "you are to press the key in response to this stimulus" or "your reaction to this stimulus was right". The failure of the repetition corresponded to negative reinforcement: "you are not to press in response to this stimulus" or "you should not have pressed in response to this stimulus".

The use of a signal stimulus in the place of verbal reinforcement possesses the advantage that the changes in the tone of the experimenter's voice, which are difficult to control, are avoided. The importance of their exclusion lies in the possibility of these changes of intonation playing an important part in the production of conditioned reflexes with verbal reinforcement, in man. This method of conditioned reinforcement, which, in a somewhat different form, was first described by Rokotova (1954), has still another advantage. It allows comparison of the effects of the conditioned stimulus and the reinforcing stimulus in identical experimental conditions.

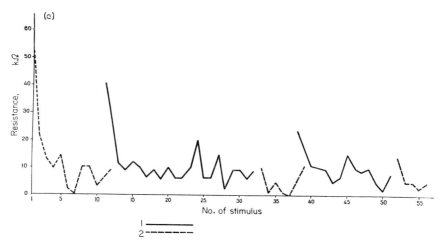

Fig. 61. (*a*) C.G.R. changes in response to positive and negative acoustic stimuli during the elaboration, consolidation and switching of a conditioned motor reflex with "conditioned reinforcement". Subject B., October and December 1954. Stimuli: 1—Sound of 400 c/s and 70dB; 2—sound of 1000 c/s and 70dB.

Figure 61 shows the variations of the C.G.R. in the course of the elaboration, stabilization and switching of the conditioned motor reflex to an acoustic stimulus reinforced by the very same sound used as signal stimulus.*

It must be added that the formation of the conditioned motor reflex is not a cause of any difficulty for the subject whose motor reactions strictly conform to the significance of the signal stimuli.

The negative stimuli were used in the first stage of reflex elaboration for the purpose of studying the effect on the C.G.R. of the acquisition by the

---

* Before switching transformation: 400 c/s—positive stimulus, 1000 c/s—negative stimulus. After switching, vice versa.

stimulus of signal significance not associated with movement. It can be seen that the reactions to this stimulus grew weaker with repetition. Application of the positive stimuli produced stronger reactions, and the reactions to the negative stimuli were then also increased. Each transition from negative to positive stimulation or vice versa resulted in increased intensity of the reaction (*a*).

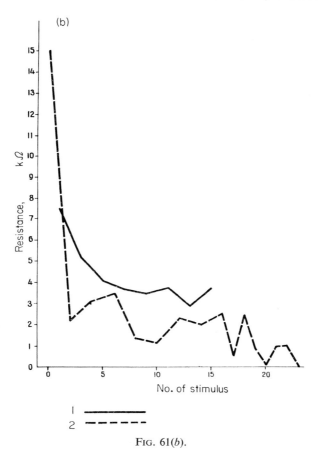

Fig. 61(*b*).

In the next experiment, the positive and negative stimuli alternated. Extinction of the galvanic skin reaction was then particularly slow. Omission of the positive stimuli made extinction of the response to the negative stimulus easier (*b*).

The reactions to both negative and positive stimuli were restored in the next experiment but their extinction proceeded more rapidly in spite of the fact that the stimuli were applied alternately. The reactions to negative stimuli were extinguished more rapidly (*c*). In subsequent experiments, extinction of the re-established reactions was even more rapid.

Switching of the signal significances of the stimuli, led to temporary dis-inhibition of the reactions to positive and negative stimuli. As the new relationship are established, the pattern of extinction repeats itself (*d*).

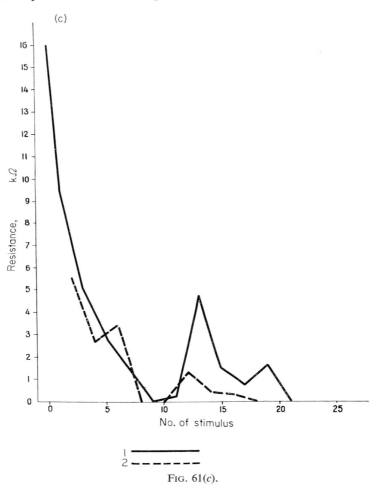

Fig. 61(*c*).

Any change affecting the conditioned motor reaction thus stimulates the galvanic skin response. This indicates the part played by the orientation reaction in the production of conditioned motor reflexes. Similar results were obtained with other forms of reinforcement such as speech (preliminary instructions), orientation or defence reinforcement. The experiments involving defence reinforcement have already been described. It was found that a combination of a weak with a strong sound stimulus at first produced an intensification of the C.G.R. to the conditioned stimulus, but soon the response to both the conditioned stimulus and the reinforcement (strong sound), was extinguished.

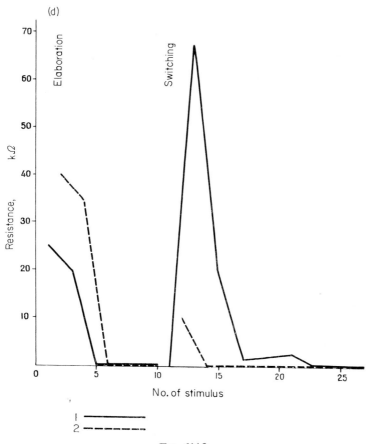

FIG. 61(*d*).

A similar pattern (production of a conditioned galvanic skin reflex followed by its extinction in spite of the repetition of the sequence) was observed when a weak current–strong painful current, stimulus sequence was used.

It can be stated, therefore, that the most diverse types of reinforcement give rise to an intensification of the galvanic skin reaction occurring in respect to signal stimuli. Furthermore, the fact that the C.G.R. is intensified when there is any change in the conditioned reflex activity also deserves attention.

The galvanic skin reaction occurring in the complex of the conditioned reflex still remains a component of the independent orientation reflex. The proof of this is its reappearance as a result of any change affecting the signal stimulus, in which it closely follows the behaviour of the orientation reflex developing in response to non-signal stimuli. With the link established, the reaction becomes extinguished but can reappear if the signal responsible for the conditioned reaction changes. This orientation reflex develops in response to any change of the stimulus, i.e. closure, removal, weakening or strengthening, in the same way as in the case of non-signal stimulation. The process of extinction of the reaction is much slower in the case of signal stimuli than if non-signal stimulation is applied; the transition from signal to non-signal stimuli and vice versa, is associated with intensification of the C.G.R. The speed of extinction differs widely from one subject to another and depends to a large extent on the subject's general condition.

The start of switching of the signal significances of the stimuli, achieved by repetition of the previously negative stimulus (positive reinforcement) and no repetition of the positive stimulus (negative reinforcement), results in reappearance of the reaction to both stimuli. At the same time, the general level of the skin resistance is lowered. The C.G.R. reappears in response to both positive and negative agents even before the subject begins to react correctly to them.

Switching of the reflexes, as with the start of elaboration, is associated with spontaneous background fluctuations. With stabilization of the new links, the C.G.R. becomes extinguished once more. Switching again, results in another increase of the intensity of the C.G.R. The degree of intensification of C.G.R., associated with such switching varies greatly from one subject to another, but the general pattern remains the same. In some cases spontaneous reappearance of the C.G.R. to both positive and negative stimuli can be observed.

A comparison of the effects of the non-signal and signal sound stimuli, led to the conclusion that the processes of C.G.R. extinction were similar in the two cases. The C.G.R. developing in response to signal stimuli is, generally speaking, an independent phenomenon in that it is in some measure independent of the motor reactions. In the reaction to negative stimuli the reaction develops before the motor responses appear and disappears when the motor reflex becomes firmly established.

There is a certain reciprocal relationship between conditioned motor reactions and galvanic skin reflexes. The less firmly established the motor reaction, the stronger the C.G.R., and vice versa. This inverse relationship between the two types of reaction to signal stimulation refutes the view that galvanic skin reactions develop only as conditioned reactions to motor reinforcement (Samsonova, 1953; Merlin, 1954).

Experimental work points to the relative independence of the orientation reflex. At the same time, orientation reactions are stronger to signal stimuli than to non-signal stimuli. The independent occurrence of the orientation reflex during the production of a conditioned response is seen clearly when there is interference with the functioning of the latter. Whatever the course of the nervous processes—from inhibition to excitation in the elaboration of a conditioned connexion, or, from excitation to inhibition in case of an established conditioned connexion left unreinforced, the galvanic skin reflex remains the same and always appears as a fall of skin resistance whether the stimulus is negative or positive. The same intensification of the C.G.R. is observed whether positive reinforcement of a negative reaction or negative reinforcement of a positive reaction is used. In either case, the discrepancy between the conditioned connexion and the reinforcement used, results in intensification of the orientation reflex.

Extinction of the C.G.R. to a signal stimulus is indicated by changes of sensitivity and reactivity, as measured with the help of the orientation reflex. With repetition of the signal stimulus, the threshold of excitation of the orientation reflex increases, while the amplitude of reaction to supraliminal stimuli diminishes. This indicates diminished sensitivity and reactivity. Any factor capable of initiating the orientation reaction increases the sensitivity and enhances the reactivity, as measured with the help of the reaction.

The galvanic skin reaction, which first of all is a reflection of the orientation response, is very similar to the reciprocal vasomotor reaction of the head and hand in one respect. In both, the principle of intensity does not hold good in the range of stimuli of low intensity; the reaction to near-liminal stimuli is often stronger than to stimuli of moderate intensity. Nevertheless, in the range of strong stimuli, the law of intensities operates in the usual way.

The reactivity of the galvanic skin component of the orientation reflex, arising in response to stimuli of various intensities, was studied by means of simultaneous recording of C.G.R. and subjective assessment of the intensity of the auditory stimuli applied. The intensities of the sound, as perceived by the subject, were subjectively divided by him into 10 grades in the course of familiarization with the auditory stimuli used. Sounds of 1000 c/s and differing by 5dB in intensity were applied and each sound was classed by the subject. If the intensity of several sounds was deemed closely similar, they were grouped together and the mean intensity of the group was calculated, as well as the mean of the subject's assessment and the mean magnitude of the corresponding galvanic skin reaction.

Repetitive application of sound of various intensities resulted in progressive inhibition of the C.G.R. By determining the total sum of galvanic skin reactions to any of the intensities chosen, we were able to estimate the reactivity in respect of the orientation reflex. The mean grade scores given by the subject to the stimuli used, pointed to the special effect of sound on the auditory analyser (Fig. 62).

It has been shown that the special effects of sound, as shown by the subjective assessment of intensity, increase as the logarithm of its intensity. At the same time, the reactivity of the C.G.R. is increased in the range of the weak, near liminal stimuli; somewhat lowered in the range of mean intensities, and then increased—in accordance with the law of intensity—in the range of strong stimuli, as the logarithm of the stimulus intensity.

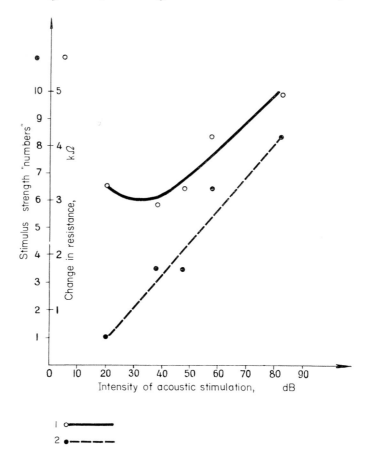

FIG. 62. Relationship of the assessed strength of acoustic stimuli and the average value of the C.G.R. to the actual stimulus strengths. Subject K., May 1955. 1—C.G.R. 2—Assessed strengths of stimuli,

The galvanic skin reaction, similarly to the vasomotor component of the orientation reflex, is relatively stronger in response to near liminal stimuli. A characteristic feature of the C.G.R. to liminal stimuli is the increased duration of the latent period, in which, the C.G.R. is also similar to the vasomotor component of the orientation reaction. In a number of cases, a C.G.R. develops even in response to stimuli which are so weak that no motor reaction appears; this indicates a higher degree of sensitivity of the orientation reaction. The increase in the threshold of the C.G.R., observed as a result of repetitive stimulation, leads to a situation in which the threshold of the motor reaction is lower than that of the C.G.R.

It can therefore be said, that the relationship of sensitivities, as measured by the conditioned motor reflex and by the C.G.R. component of the orientation reflex, changes; this relationship depending upon the degree of stabilization of the conditioned connection in respect of the stimulus in question. The "orientation" sensitivity can be higher, the same as, or lower than, the sensitivity measured with the help of the conditioned motor reflex. Stimula-

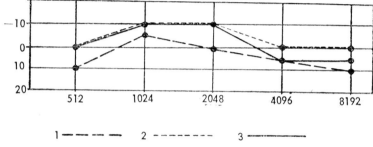

FIG. 63. Audiogram constructed from a conditioned motor reaction and the galvanic skin component of the orienting reflex. Subject T., May 1955. 1— Audiogram from the C.G.R. to a non-signal acoustic stimulus. 2—Audiogram from the C.G.R. to a signal acoustic stimulus. 3—Audiogram from the E.M.G. response to a signal acoustic stimulus. Ordinate: loss of hearing (dB). Abscissa: sound frequency (c/s).

tion of the orientation reflex leads to an increase of sensitivity. In a number of cases the increase of "orientation" sensitivity is accompanied by an increase of sensitivity as measured by the motor response. With stabilization of the conditioned reflex, the relationship of the two types of sensitivity is reversed.

The pattern of the relationship described enables the use of the C.G.R. for the determination of auditory sensitivity to non-signal and signal stimuli. If the orientation reflex is sufficiently strong, the audiogram obtained using non-signal stimuli is similar to the normal record. With repetition the threshold rises. By recording the C.G.R. to signal sound stimuli, one can obtain an audiogram basically similar to the audiogram obtained using the motor reactions. In some cases it may be possible to demonstrate a small range of subsensory stimuli (about 5 dB) which give rise to reactions not shown by the motor system (Fig. 63).

The threshold, as measured by the C.G.R., to non-signal stimuli is higher than that to the signal ones and, in the latter case, it more or less coincides with the threshold measured with the help of the motor reaction. Reactions to a number of subsensory intensities can be observed. With repeated measurements, however, the sensitivity, measured by the C.G.R., falls below that measured by motor reactions.

The thresholds of vasomotor and galvanic skin reactions reflect the excitability of the orientation reflex system but not directly that of the analyser. The latter is mirrored only in the initial stages of the development of conditioned reflexes. The thresholds of the conditioned reactions (motor or defence as shown by vasomotor changes) characterize the specific sensitivity of the analyser, which may differ from that measured by the orientation reflex. Subjective assessment is also closely and directly connected with the specific reactivity of the analyser—which does not always coincide with the reactivity as measured by the orientation reflex.

E. The Orientation Reflex in the Structure of the Conditioned Reflex

An analysis of the relationship of the vasomotor and galvanic skin components of the orientation reflex leads to the conclusion that a non-signal stimulus, having acquired the capacity of giving rise to a signal reaction, enhances the orientation reflex. This effect is observed whether the conditioned stimulus or the reinforcing one is used, and becomes particularly evident when the latter is of painful nature. The specific effect of the painful stimulus is inhibited by the preceding conditioned stimulus, and whereas it acquires the capacity of producing the orientation reaction, the relative intensity of pain is much diminished. At the same time the reactivity of the respective analyser is increased by the reinforcement whatever its nature (electrocutaneous, verbal instruction or conditioned reinforcement). Its fine sensitivity as measured by the orientation reflex, increases, whereas the coarse one (sensitivity to pain), diminishes.

In the course of repetitive application of non-signal stimuli, the regular appearance of specific reflexes is associated with an inhibition of the orientation reaction. The apparent intensification of the specific reflexes is due to the fact that the orientation reaction can mask or inhibit some of the manifestations of these specific reflexes which, in time, can become freed from this inhibitory influence. Heat, for instance, having become a signal for a motor reaction, produces orientation vasoconstriction of the hand; and cold, in the same circumstances, gives rise to orientation cephalic vasodilatation.

With repetitive signal stimulation, the condition, characteristic of the extinction of the orientation reflex to non-signal stimuli, is established.

A similar pattern of effects can be observed in the case of weak, painful stimuli. At first they give rise to the orientation reflex, which, with repetition, is replaced by the defence reaction. As a result of the formation of the conditioned link, the orientation reflex reappears. Introduction of the element of discrimination enhances the orientation reaction and temporarily inhibits the defence reflex.

The patterns described above help in understanding certain aspects of the development of conditioned vasomotor reflexes which, hitherto, have been puzzling in the light of the orthodox point of view. The difficulty of producing conditioned thermal vasodilatation in the hand, using heat as the reinforcement, is well recognized. In many cases when the supposedly established conditioned link is tested, vasoconstriction appears instead of vasodilatation. The appearance of this vasoconstriction reaction, to a conditioned stimulus reinforced by heat, is a result of the operation of the orientation reflex reappearing under the influence of thermal reinforcement. The easily obtained conditioned vasoconstriction reflexes are frequently components of the orientation reflex and not pure thermoregulation reactions. In fact, reinforcement of sound by means of cold produces at first vasoconstriction in the hand associated with cephalic vasodilatation. With repeated application of the combination, the response becomes a true conditioned reaction to cold, consisting of concomitant vasoconstriction.

Similar reactions are produced by weak, though painful, stimuli. When, after a number of non-signal applications, the response consists of cephalic vasoconstriction, acquisition of signal significance results in the reappearance of orientation cephalic vasodilatation.

In this way, the first stage of the formation of a conditioned reflex is associated with the reappearance of the orientation reaction. This is confirmed by the recordings of galvanic skin reactions or, the vasomotor responses. The intensification of the orientation reaction to a signal stimulus, can result in the temporary inhibition of the specific reactions (to cold, heat, etc.) which become displaced by the orientation response.

With repetitive signal stimulation, the specific responses reappear because the orientation reaction undergoes extinction. In contrast to the orientation reaction to non-signal stimuli, the extinction of the orientation reaction to signal stimuli is more gradual. This could possibly be due to the fact that the focus of excitation created in the motor analyser, in the course of execution of the motor response, increases the excitatory state of the analyser responsible for the perception of the signal stimulus.

The intensification of the orientation reflex is effected by a wave of excitation travelling along the conditioned reflex arc in the opposite direction;

o

i.e. from the motor area and regions responsible for the perception of reinforcement, to the analyser at the receiving end of the signal stimulus, through the intermediation of the orientation reflex. The possibility of such an antidromic wave traversing the conditioned reflex arc was demonstrated in Pavlov's laboratory, in the course of association of paw movement with a digestive reflex in the dog. When the dog was hungry it lifted a paw, and when the paw, for the purposes of experiment, was passively lifted, there was a reflex secretion of saliva. The motor analyser was here responsible for the excitation of the taste analyser and thus for salivary secretion; while the digestive excitation was transmitted to the motor area with the production of the corresponding motor reaction (Pavlov, 1949).

In our experiments, reinforcement and execution of the motor response resulted in an increase in sensitivity and reactivity of the analyser responsible for the perception of the signal stimulus. The orientation reflex recorded is characteristically stronger in response to the range of stimuli of liminal intensity than to the more intense, clearly perceived ones. Closer similarity between the stimuli to be differentiated results in the intensification of the orientation reflex. The increased reactivity of the analyser in the case of signals difficult to differentiate is associated with increased sensitivity, as measured by the orientation reflex.

It can be said, therefore, that the intensification of the orientation reaction to a signal stimulus is due to its disinhibition through the effect of reinforcement, and to the formation of a conditioned orientation reflex between the signal, the subsequent reaction and the reinforcing stimulus. This conditioned orientation reflex is similar to a temporal link if the reinforcement is provided by a strong sound stimulus. Furthermore, having been produced in the course of the first few applications of the stimulus it becomes extinguished with repetition. The orientation reflex, which is persistently recurring in response to signal stimuli, increases the sensitivity of the analysers and facilitates the formation of the new conditioned connexion.

Furthermore, it should be pointed out that it is the conditioned reflex of high order which calls for the participation of the orientation reaction. For instance, the conditioned defence reaction occurs though the subject remains in a state of drowsiness. In this case, no activation of the orientation reflex can be observed, the specific defence reflex is rapidly developed but simultaneously there is no obvious sign that linkage within the verbal system occurs. Similar effects can be observed in association with the automatic motor reflexes. The more automatic the conditioned motor reaction, the less the participation of the orientation component.

A comparison of the results of the subjective classification of stimuli—reflecting their specific efficacy on the analyser concerned, with the character of the orientation and defence reactions evoked, indicates the existence of differences between the *specific, orientation* and *defence* types of sensitivity. A comparison of sensitivities, as measured by the orientation and conditioned motor reactions, shows that the difference resulting from the extinction of the orientation reaction can be considerable. Any factor which tends to raise the intensity of the orientation reflex may diminish the difference between these two types of sensitivity.

When a stimulus is transformed into the signal for a specific response, its effects, especially in conditions of difficult discrimination, are substantially altered. The sensitivity and reactivity of the subject, as measured by the orientation reflex, increase, whereas the sensitivity measured with the help of the defence reflex, is reduced.

As sensitivity and reactivity are the indices of the quality of perception, it can be said that the perception of a stimulus which has acquired a signal significance, is substantially changed and continues to undergo further changes, at various stages during the production of the conditioned reflex.

Visual Orienting and Adaptation Reactions During Elaboration of Conditioned Reflexes

A. Enhancement of Visual Sensitivity and Reactivity for Non-specific Signal Stimuli

The considerable part played by the orientation reaction in the formation and operation of conditioned reflexes having been thus experimentally demonstrated, the next area for investigation is the relationship between the various components of the orientation reflex and, the enhancement of the sensitivity of the analysers concerned with the production of the conditioned reflex.

As already shown, a great variety of non-signal stimuli are capable of producing orientation changes in the visual analyser. With repetitive stimulation, the orientation reflex undergoes gradual extinction. What remain are the adaptation reactions to specific (adequate) stimuli, such as light or darkness, and the defence blink reflex evoked by an air stream directed on the cornea. The balance of the orientation and specific reactions achieved, undergoes change if certain conditioned, and particularly motor conditioned, reactions to the stimuli in question develop.

In order to exclude complications arising from the specific reactions of the visual analyser to light, let us study, initially, the effects of stimuli which produce an orientation reflex in the visual analyser, but which are incapable of evoking any of the specific reactions. A good example of such agents is sound. The first applications of a sound stimulus produce a generalized depression of α-rhythm (including the depression of the occipital E.E.G.), a galvanic skin reaction, eye movement, respiratory arrest, dilatation of the pupil and an increase in visual sensitivity. With further applications these reactions become extinguished.

However, if the stimulus is given a signal significance (for instance by means of the verbal instruction to clench the hand), the orientation reaction to the sound stimulus reappears, and manifests itself, not only as α-rhythm depression, but also as a C.G.R. (and often as eye movement and rotation of the head) on closure of the stimulus. All these components of the orientation reaction are gradually extinguished as the conditioned connexion becomes consolidated. First to be extinguished is the eye movement, followed by the C.G.R., respiratory arrest and α-rhythm depression. All these reactions, including the depression of the occipital α-rhythm, reappear again as soon as a request is made to differentiate the sound stimuli, either by frequency or intensity (Fig. 64).

Figure 64(*a*) shows how the second application of a sound of 70dB, 500 c/s, gives rise to α-rhythm depression, eye movement and a C.G.R. The electrical activity of the finger flexor muscles shows no noticeable change. All these reactions disappear after about the 6th application of the stimulus (Fig. 64(*b*)).

Following verbal instruction giving the stimulus signal significance (Fig. 64(*c*)), the depression of the occipital α-rhythm reappears and actually begins before the onset of movement. Eye movement and a C.G.R. reappear as well.

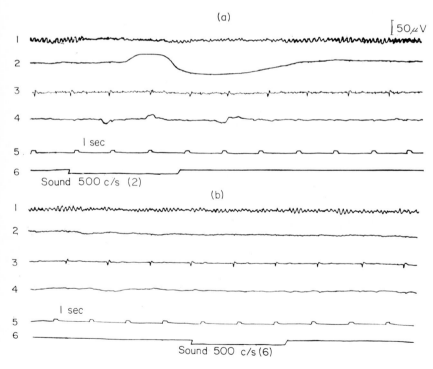

FIG. 64 (continuation on page 204)

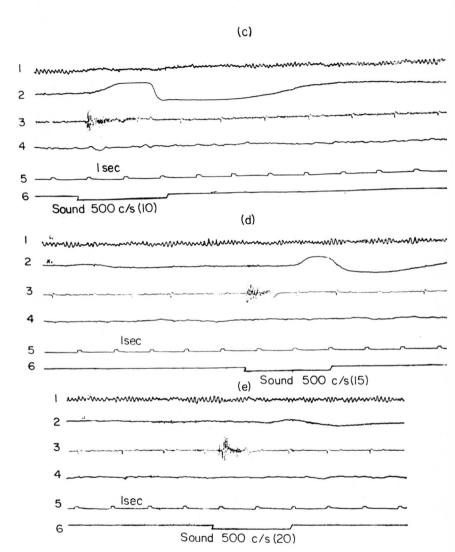

FIG. 64.   Extinction of the orienting reflex to a non-signal acoustic stimulus and its restoration when the sound acquires signal significance. Subject N., March 1954. 1—E.E.G. of right occipital area. 2—C.G.R. 3—E.M.G. of the digital flexors. 4—Eye movements. 5—Time. 6—Acoustic stimuli.

Gradually, all three reactions become extinguished, but the muscle electrical activity associated with the conditioned motor reaction persists (Fig. 64(*d*), (*e*)).

The more difficult the differentiation of stimuli, the greater the number of the components of the orientation reflex which reappear, and the more persistent the reactions. It should be noted that the intensification of the reactions observed cannot be explained by the introduction of additional impulses associated with execution of movement. The blockage of the α-rhythm occurs before the electrical activity of the muscles becomes manifest, and is a direct effect of the sound. The same conclusion can be drawn from the appearance of strong orientation reactions to differentiated stimuli, not accompanied by movement.

The intensification of the orientation reactions, resulting from the attempt at differentiation of stimuli, is associated with inhibition of the conditioned motor reflex. Its latent period increases, and the electromyogram shows a diminished amplitude and altered form. (Lengthening, with the appearance of a phase of low amplitude preceding the main phase of change of muscle action potentials.)

In the same way, therefore, as in the case of the simultaneous recording of the vasomotor and galvanic skin components of the orientation reflex, one can talk of a divergence in the intensity of the processes of excitation and inhibition within the systems of the specific conditioned and orientation reflexes.

The activation of the orientation reflex by the addition of signal significance to a sound stimulus extends also to the visual analyser. This is shown in the appearance of those components of the orientation reaction which are directly connected with it—eye movement, dilatation of the pupil, blockage of the occipital α-rhythm.

One of the results of the production of a conditioned motor reflex to a sound stimulus is the increase of reactivity. The ability of the visual analyser to respond to the stimuli applied (non-specific auditory stimuli in this case) is enhanced, and the extent and duration of the depression of the occipital α-rhythm are increased. If the level of sensitivity to the non-signal sound stimuli (indicated by the occipital α-rhythm component) appears to be relatively low during the course of extinction of the orientation reaction, the request for a motor response to weak sounds produces a marked rise in sensitivity. Consequently, weak sound stimuli, which before the formation of the conditioned link were unable to give rise to the depression reaction, begin to produce it after such links have become established. This increase in sensitivity, as measured by the α-rhythm blockage, coincides with the rise in sensitivity as indicated by the galvanic skin component of the orientation reflex (Fig. 65).

This diagram shows that before such a request has been made, sounds of

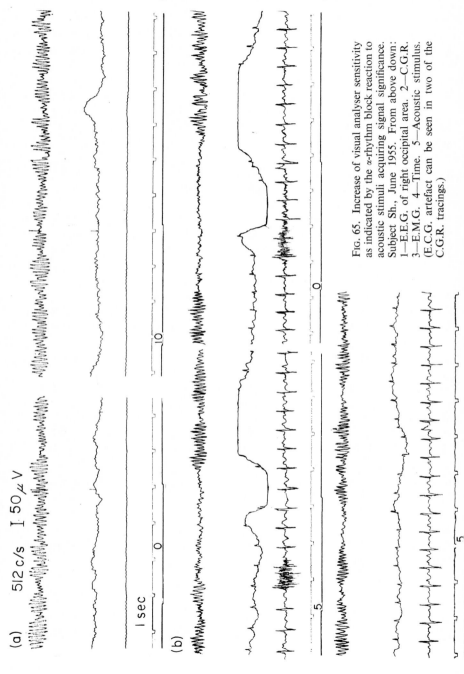

FIG. 65. Increase of visual analyser sensitivity as indicated by the α-rhythm block reaction to acoustic stimuli acquiring signal significance. Subject Sh., June 1955. From above down: 1—E.E.G. of right occipital area. 2—C.G.R. 3—E.M.G. 4—Time. 5—Acoustic stimulus. (E.C.G. artefact can be seen in two of the C.G.R. tracings.)

0 and 10dB produce no reaction (*a*); as soon as the instruction has been given (*b*), sounds of 5 and 0 dB give rise to motor reactions accompanied by a C.G.R. and α-rhythm depression. A sound of −5dB (below the normal auditory threshold), gives rise to a subsensory reaction not associated with hand movement but accompanied by slight α-rhythm depression at the onset and end of the stimulus, and, by a C.G.R. The experiment also demonstrates the parallel variations of sensitivity as measured by the C.G.R. and, α-rhythm depression, both being components of the intensified orientation reaction.

The increase in reactivity of the visual analyser under the influence of non-specific auditory stimuli, combined with an attempt at differentiation, can also be observed in the course of experiments involving the use of the adaptograph. Continuous recording of sensitivity to light show its rise as an effect of sound endowed with signal significance. As soon as the subject is asked to discriminate between the stimuli in accordance with their frequency or intensity, an increase in sensitivity to light, which disappears in the course of repetitive non-signal stimulation, becomes apparent. Similarly, a non-signal sound stimulus which has ceased to give rise to dilatation of the pupil, begins to cause dilatation again as soon as it becomes a signal of a motor reaction. These findings were confirmed by K. S. Smirnov (1952), who observed a temporary intensification of the dilatation reaction of the pupil even if the reinforcement was provided by light, which on its own produced pupillary contraction.

Once the conditioned reflex to sound is established, the orientation reflex is extinguished; both the α-rhythm depression and the galvanic skin response to signal stimuli disappear. At the same time, the associated direct effect of α-rhythm depression on the visual analyser, namely increased sensitivity, also disappears.

Any novel complexity in discrimination again produces an intensification of all the components of the orientation reflex, including those concerning the visual analyser. The more difficult the differentiation, the stronger the orientation reactions and the more marked the rise in sensitivity and re-activity of the visual analyser to the non-specific auditory stimuli. Thus, the orientation reflex, by its participation in the closure of the conditioned con-nexion, increases the level of excitability of the cortex. This increases the sensitivity of the other analysers, as well as the one to which the stimulus is directed.

The combination of eye movement, α-rhythm blockage and pupillary reaction, occurring as a result of stimulation by sound, seems therefore to be related to the sensitization of the visual analyser. It follows that the development of a conditioned reflex could be expected to be associated with intensification of the orientation reflex, and thus, increased sensitivity of the visual analyser to specific light stimuli.

B. Electrographic Manifestations of a Conditioned Motor Reflex to Photic Stimuli

Before passing to the analysis of changes in sensitivity to specific stimuli under the influence of the development of conditioned reflexes, we have to consider the relationship between the orientation and the specific adaptation reflexes, occurring in the visual analyser as a result of the operation of specific stimuli when they acquire signal significance. As already shown, the effects of light and darkness on the visual analyser are the result of the summation of the orientation and specific adaptation reflexes. The signs of the reaction to light or darkness in the central and peripheral parts of the analyser are different. Light, by causing decomposition of visual purple and contraction of the pupil, lowers sensitivity peripherally but, by exciting the cortex, it increases central sensitivity.

Darkness, on the other hand, by facilitating the restoration of rhodopsin and dilating the pupil, increases peripheral sensitivity. The initial generalized depression of the α-rhythm, indicates an increased level of excitation centrally, but the diminished sensory input during darkness lowers the excitability of the cortical segment of the visual analyser. Thus, against a background of α-rhythm depression indicating a state of increased excitation, darkness gives rise to the appearance of α-rhythm—a change towards a slower frequency, evidence of the development of the process of inhibition.

Repetitive applications of darkness show how its effects pass through two main stages. The first is the phase of the generalized orientation reflex consisting of α-rhythm depression. This is followed by the phase of inhibition of the depression and the reappearance of α-rhythm. It appears, therefore, that during the first few applications of darkness there is a conflict between excitation—developing as part of the generalized orientation reflex to changing conditions of illumination—and inhibition, associated with the consequent reduction of sensory input.

The characteristic E.E.G. changes of the generalized and local orientation reactions to darkness are of opposite sign. When darkness becomes a signal, the generalized orientation reaction caused thereby is intensified while the resulting inhibition is weakened; the net result is intensification of the α-rhythm depression and a weakening of the subsequent enhancement response. With the formation of a conditioned reflex darkness begins to give rise to α-rhythm block instead of enhancement, and this effect is associated with the development of a galvanic skin reaction. A request for the differentiation of periods of darkness in accordance with their duration, further intensifies the α-rhythm depression and other components of the orientation reaction. With the establishment of the conditioned connexion, the depression reaction weakens again and the α-rhythm reappears as an expression of the local inhibitory effect of darkness on the visual analyser.

The intensification of α-rhythm depression, produced by darkness endowed with signal value, is of a similar nature to the intensification of the depression in response to signal sound stimuli and is associated with the activation of the orientation reflex (Fig. 66).

It can be seen that after the sixth application, darkness, replacing a background illumination of 50 lux on a white screen, ceases to give rise to depression of the α-rhythm. In view of the high amplitude of the background α-rhythm in the presence of illumination, the enhancement reaction is not prominent. When the subject is asked to clench his hand towards the end of the period of darkness, the α-rhythm enhancement is replaced by block at the onset and end of darkness (*8*). It should be noted that the α-rhythm blocking observed during elaboration of a delayed conditioned reflex connexion to darkness, is not a result of the movement itself as this is not performed until near the end of the period of stimulation. With the conditioned link established, as shown by increased amplitude in the electromyogram, the depression weakens and eventually disappears (Fig. 66, *15*).

It can be said, therefore, that darkness, after many applications during the development of a conditioned reflex, produces weak alpha rhythm depression towards the end of its period of operation; that the α-rhythm activity during the period is usually of high amplitude, and that there is no reaction to the onset of illumination. When darkness acquires signal significance it ceases to produce α-rhythm depression (*19* and *20* in Fig. 67) but introduction of differentiation gives rise to the reappearance of the α-rhythm depression reaction again (*21* and *22* in Fig. 67).

After a request for the differentiation of stimuli, the first application of an unexpectedly long period of darkness results in inhibition of the conditioned motor reflex as indicated by an increase in its latent period (*20*). At the same time the orientation reaction is intensified as shown by the pronounced α-rhythm blocking at the end of darkness. After negative verbal reinforcement of this reaction by the investigator, a short period of darkness gives rise to an α-rhythm depression reaction, particularly at the beginning and end of the period (*21*). A differentiated stimulus—a long period of darkness not accompanied by movement—gives rise to still stronger depression of the α-rhythm (*22*).

The effects of darkness on the central segment of the visual analyser seem, therefore, to undergo a considerable transformation as a result of the development of a conditioned motor reflex. The intensification of the orientation reaction to a specific signal stimulus is associated with an increased level of central excitation. Stabilization of the conditioned link is associated with the extinction of the orientation reflex and reappearance of the characteristic effect of darkness—enhancement of the α-rhythm. When differentiation is attempted, the orientation reaction is intensified. This intensification is

FIG. 66. Changes in the effect of darkness on the occipital E.E.G. produced by elaboration of a conditioned motor reflex to darkness. Subject P., May 1956.
1—E.M.G. 2—Right occipital E.E.G. 3—Stimulus. 4—Time.

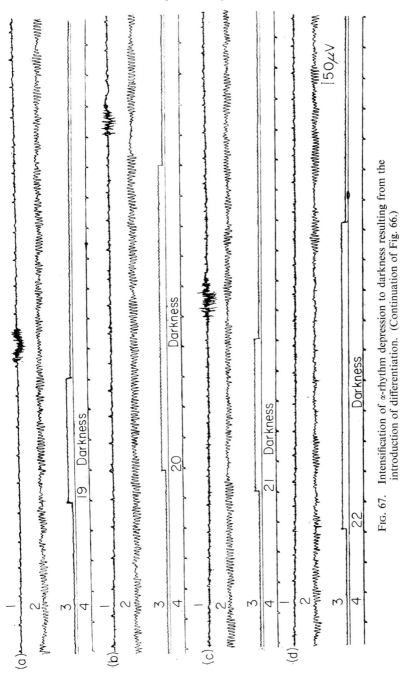

FIG. 67. Intensification of α-rhythm depression to darkness resulting from the introduction of differentiation. (Continuation of Fig. 66.)

particularly marked if the reaction to the differentiated stimulus has been negatively reinforced verbally by the experimenter. The most intense α-rhythm depression can then be observed in accordance with the general features of the orientation reaction, at the moments of onset and ending of the stimulation, i.e. the beginning and end of the period of darkness. Figure 68 shows the general features of the variations in the α-rhythm depression, occurring at the beginning and the end of the period of darkness during the development of a conditioned reflex. Non-signal darkness replacing general

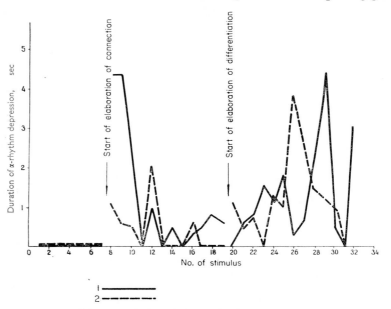

FIG. 68. Graphic representation of changes in the duration of α-rhythm depression in response to darkness at various stages in the elaboration of the conditioned reflex. Subject P., May 1956. 1—α-rhythm during action of darkness stimuli. 2—α-rhythm depression in response to ending of the darkness stimuli.

illumination of the room (32 lux on a white screen) produces no α-rhythm depression. The beginning of the formation of the conditioned link is associated with an increased reaction to the onset and end of stimulation. The increased reaction in the course of differentiation is most characteristic; the subject finds the differentiation difficult in spite of the considerable difference between the stimuli. Incorrect reactions are negatively reinforced by the experimenter. With repetitive reinforcement, the duration of the α-rhythm depression reaction to darkness increases.

The relationship of the electrographic effects, attributable to the orientation and specific responses to light, is difficult to analyse. The E.E.G.

shows a depression of the α-rhythm (or its development against a background of slow potentials) which is similar in the case of the specific, or the general and local orientation reactions. However, the experiments described above, involving the use of darkness as the stimulus, also help in understanding the effects of light. The general pattern of changes in the effects of light, during the formation of conditioned reflexes, is similar to that observed in the case of darkness. The α-rhythm blocking response to light is intensified and becomes even more prominent if the subject is asked to differentiate between the stimuli. This change during signal stimulation is especially noticeable in the course of experiments involving "conditioned reinforcement" of conditioned motor reflexes to light stimuli of 0·15 and 0·4 lux (Fig. 69). Instead of the

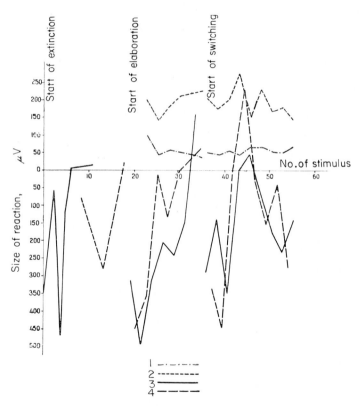

Fig. 69.   Graphic representation of changes in α-rhythm produced by the action of a non-signal photic stimulus, by consolidation of the conditioned connexion and by switching. Subject M., October 1954. 1—E.M.G. amplitude. 2—Latent period of the movement. 3—E.E.G. reaction to a light of 0·4 lux. 4—E.E.G. reaction to a light of 0·15 lux.

words "correctly done" or "clench your hand", reinforcement was provided by a repetition of the stimulus serving as the signal, 5 sec later. Conditioned reinforcement was not used after the stimuli to which no response was required.

The magnitude of the α-rhythm depression reaction was measured in the following way. The amplitudes of individual α-waves occurring during the 5-sec preceding the application of the light stimulus were added and this total (the background α-activity), was deducted from the figure similarly obtained during 5 sec of stimulation. The sign of the calculated difference indicated the nature of the reaction. When negative, the reaction was one of α-rhythm depression, when positive it indicated α-rhythm enhancement. The curve thus plotted shows the changes of electroencephalographic reaction during repeated stimulation by light; during the formation of conditioned connexions and, during the latter's transformation. In addition, we determined the latent period of the motor reaction (L_m) and its amplitude (A_m).

It was found that intensification of the α-rhythm depression reaction coincided in time with the production, or the transformation of the conditioned connexion.

It should be noted that this result can be observed during the transformation of the link, whether by means of positive or negative stimuli. The latent period and the duration of the first motor reaction are often greater, but stabilization takes place later on. The duration of the latent period of the motor reaction may increase in the case of difficult differentiation.

The intensification of the α-rhythm depression, occurring in response to signal light stimuli, is a result of the activation of the orientation and inhibition of the conditioned adaptation reflex (which weakens the unconditioned effect of the light). The effect of a light stimulus acquiring signal significance may be illustrated in experiments using the adaptograph. As shown before, repetitive stimulation of the dark adapted eye by means of a weak light results in adaptation to such stimulation. The sensitivity to light diminishes less and less at every period of illumination and, the duration of its reduction also diminishes. When the stimulus (weak illumination) is given signal significance, as for instance by a request to differentiate the stimuli according to their duration or intensity, the previous effect reappears and the sensitivity to light again diminishes in response to illumination (Fig. 70).

In this figure, the sensitivity in arbitrary units is shown on the axis of ordinates. It can be seen that non-signal light stimuli do not affect the level of sensitivity to light. When the subject is asked to differentiate the stimuli according to their duration the effect of lowered sensitivity reappears.

The E.E.G., taken in the course of formation of a conditioned reflex to light, shows evidence of disinhibition of the orientation reflex which results in an enhancement of central excitation. This increases the reactivity of the

P

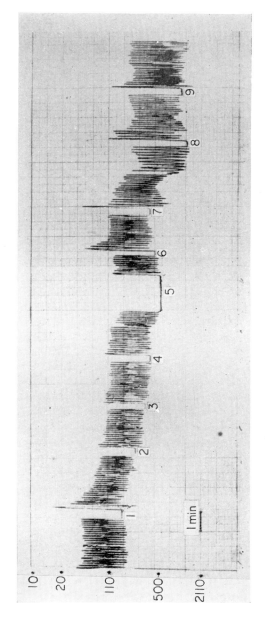

Fig. 70. Disturbance of adaptation to photic stimuli produced by instructions to differentiate the durations of the photic stimuli presented in the experiment. Subject B., January 1954. *1, 3, 6, 8*—Light of 4 lux on white of duration 7 sec. *5*—Instructions to distinguish between the stimuli. *2, 4, 7, 9*—Light stimuli of the same intensity but lasting 11 sec.

visual analyser to the stimuli in operation, and in experiments using the adaptograph, the signal light appears as a stronger stimulus.

What is the explanation for this discrepancy? It seems that the increased central excitability produced by the signal light stimulation, is associated with a greater fall in light sensitivity. It has been already shown that adaptation to illumination is but a particular instance of a conditioned adaptation reflex and it limits the effects of light on the visual analyser in accordance with the basic conditions of stimulation. The addition of signal significance brings about the intensification of the orientation reflex and the inhibition of the newly formed, conditioned adaptation reflex—which had been weakening the after-effects of the repeated light stimulation in darkness. Its inhibition results in the intensification of the unconditioned effect of light as an agent, resulting in a fall in light sensitivity.

The intensification of the orientation reflex, as shown by an increased depression of α-rhythm during the formation of a conditioned connexion to light, is associated with increased lability of the cortical segment of the visual analyser. This is shown in the effects produced by photic stimulation. After a while the effects of such stimulation at a constant high frequency, diminish and the driving phenomenon becomes increasingly less evident. A request to differentiate in accordance with the frequency of the flicker (which in fact may may remain unaltered), intensifies the photic "linkage" or "driving" effect. At the same time, an increased galvanic skin response to light indicates the activation of the generalized orientation reaction. The fact that lability of the centres increases, is confirmed by experiments involving photic stimulation at alternate high, and low frequencies. Stimulation by this means at frequencies of 9 and 18 c/s in turn, allowed one to observe an intensification of the reaction to the lower, and a weakening of the reaction to the higher, frequency in the course of extinction of the orientation reflex. When the stimuli were given signal significance, the linkage effect at 9 c/s was lowered and that at 18 c/s was increased. At the same time the secondary harmonic effect to the 9 c/s stimulation was also increased (Fig. 71).

Figure 71(*a*) shows that, after a number of applications, photic stimulation at 9 c/s produces a reaction not only to the basic frequency, but also to the secondary harmonic of 18 c/s. Stimulation at 18 c/s produces the reaction to the basic frequency (Fig. 71(*b*)). After the subject has been asked to clench his hand when the stimulation stops, flicker at 9 c/s produces a stronger reaction to the secondary harmonic (*c*); and flicker of 18 c/s produces a stronger reaction to the basic frequency (Fig. 71(*d*)).

It seems, therefore, that one result of verbal instruction is an increase in the lability of the cortical nerve cells. This leads to activation of the higher harmonics of low frequencies, and to the strengthening of the linkage reaction to higher frequencies. The diminished lability and reactivity of the cortical

α-rhythm depression and C.G.R. elements of the orientation reflex). Secondly, it reflects the delay arising from the need for impulse transmission from the visual analyser to the motor apparatus, which is associated with an intensification of the orientation reflex and a transient inhibition of the conditioned reaction to the liminal stimulus. This delay in reaction to liminal light stimuli is similar to that observed in the case of motor reaction during exacting differentiation of supraliminal light stimuli. Here, the accentuation of the α-rhythm depression is associated with a parallel extension of the latent period of the altered motor reaction. However, in this case, the α-rhythm depression indicating intensification of the orientation reflex, occurs at the beginning of the stimulus without any extension of the latent period, which is characteristic of weak, (so far as their absolute intensity is concerned) light stimuli.

Under conditions of liminal stimulation, the number of intersignal reactions is frequently increased. These reactions are identical with the responses evoked by light stimuli of liminal intensity. The onset of movement is preceded by α-rhythm depression and a C.G.R.; and the motor component also shows features of a response to a liminal stimulus. In some cases the α-rhythm depression and C.G.R. components of an intersignal reaction are not accompanied by movement. This type of reaction is quite distinct from those having the form of a motor response conforming to instruction, where the α-rhythm depression is almost synchronous with the onset of movement or, is absent altogether. It may be inferred from all these observations that intersignal reactions are a result of sensory processes caused by enhanced sensitivity of the central parts of the visual analyser, during a state of vigilance produced by the request to react to liminal stimuli (Fig. 77).

Figure 77(*a*) shows the reaction to a weak but clearly perceived stimulus of 875 arbitrary units. The duration of the α-rhythm depression is relatively short and its onset is quickly followed by muscular contractions and a C.G.R. —with the usual latent periods.

Figure 77(*b*) represents the reaction to a liminal stimulus of 25 units. The marked increase in the latent period of the α-rhythm depression reaction is very characteristic. The movement itself is preceded in the E.M.G. by preliminary low amplitude discharges. The interval between the onset of depression and the beginning of the motor reaction is not very pronounced. The galvanic skin reaction to the light stimulus shows an increase in its latent period corresponding to that of the α-rhythm depression.

Figure 77(*c*) represents the reaction to a liminal stimulus of 50 units (change of threshold). The α-rhythm depression which occurs at the beginning of the light stimulus does not develop any further. It reappears after an interval, while the stimulus is still in operation. The C.G.R. also shows two phases. The first is weak, and corresponds to the first phase of α-rhythm depression,

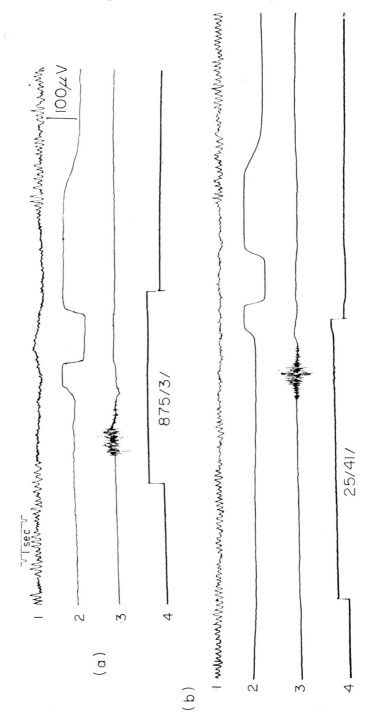

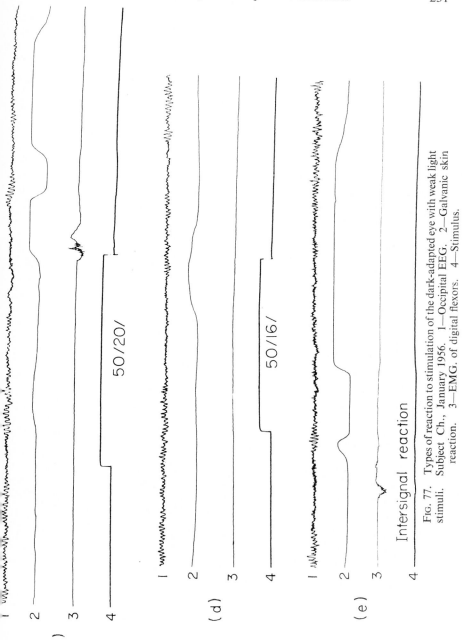

FIG. 77. Types of reaction to stimulation of the dark-adapted eye with weak light stimuli. Subject Ch., January 1956. 1—Occipital EEG. 2—Galvanic skin reaction. 3—EMG. of digital flexors. 4—Stimulus.

and the second, associated with the onset of perception, corresponds to the second phase of the depression. The motor reaction is quite distinct in time from both phases of the α-rhythm depression reaction and only develops towards the end of the peiod of stimulation.

Figure 77(*d*) shows the reaction to a subsensory stimulus. The latent period of the α-rhythm depression reaction is very long and that of the C.G.R. is similarly increased. There is no motor reaction.

Figure 77(*e*) shows the tracing of an intersignal reaction. α-rhythm depression begins before the onset of movement, and a C.G.R. follows after an interval. All features of this reaction are reminiscent of a reaction to light of liminal intensity. Special experiments have been designed to establish the relationship between the α-rhythm depression reaction and the conditioned motor responses (Mikhalevskaya, 1957). After a period allowed for dark adaptation, the subject was asked to discriminate between light stimuli of various intensities, from sub-threshold up to 100 (in terms of threshold), presented in random order.

It can be observed (Fig. 78 (*a*)), that as the intensity of the stimulus increases, the latent period of the α-rhythm depression reaction diminishes. Typically, the latent period to known supraliminal stimuli does not exceed 1 sec. A latent period of this order always indicates the near-liminal intensity of the stimulus.

An abrupt lengthening of the latent period may be used as a reliable sign that the threshold is being approached. Similarly, Fig. 78 (*b*) shows that as the

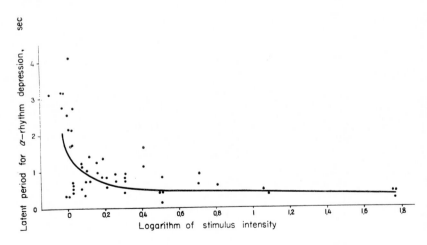

FIG. 78 (*a*). Relationship between the latent period of α-rhythm depression and the strength of photic stimulation in the region of near-threshold intensities. Subject Ch., January 1956.

remain constant, whether the change is due to an alteration of the conditioned, or of the reinforcing, stimulus. The intensified orientation reflex has then an inhibitory effect on the conditioned motor reaction.

These findings are very similar to the observations made in Pavlov's laboratory in connexion with the transition of external into internal inhibition. Fursikov (1921), demonstrated that the first phase in the evolution of conditioned inhibition, and differentiation, consists of external inhibition associated with the development of the orientation reflex. This is followed by the phase of internal inhibition. In later years the process of transition from external into internal inhibition, has been studied by Maiorov (1940), Zimkin (1934), Serebrennikov (1940), Anokhin (1952), and Skipin (1928, 1941, 1956). The results lead Pavlov to conclude that the effects of a conditioned stimulus are complex in character and may consist of the orientation, followed immediately by the conditioned, reaction. The process could be observed particularly clearly in excitable dogs in whom, the onset of stimulation was almost constantly associated with the investigatory reflex (orientation reaction). In the case of delayed reflexes, it manifested itself in the form of the initial, more or less intense, disinhibition of the inhibitory phase (Pavlov, 1947, p. 247). Anokhin *et al.*, (1941, 1949, 1956) using the method of combined recording of the secretory–motor and secretory–respiratory responses during differentiation, extinction and summation, have demonstrated that "any change of the stereotypical conditions of the experiment inevitably results in the development of the investigatory reaction" (Anokhin, 1949, p. 53). The reappearance of autonomic reactions in the course of conditioned reflex activity has also been recently mentioned by Dedobrishvili (1953).

Some elements of the orientation reaction also appear in the E.E.G., recorded at various stages of conditioned reflex activity. This is confirmed by the changes in the electrical activity of the brain resulting from alterations affecting the conditioned stimuli used (Laptev, 1949; and others).

As differentiation proceeds, the participation of the orientation reflex diminishes. It should be noted here that during differentiation the α-rhythm depression is much more accentuated in response to the positive than to the negative stimuli (Voronin and Sokolov, 1955). This helps considerably in understanding the mechanism of tuning the visual analyser by the influence of the signal significance of the stimulus.

It is recognized that the widespread irradiation of the α-rhythm depression is associated with the tonic influence of the reticular formation, which raises the level of cortical excitability. Experimental study of the dependence of α-rhythm depression on the signal nature of the stimulus is of fundamental importance. Fine differentiation of stimuli is impossible without the participation of the higher cortical centres. This is why the intensification of electrical activity by positive stimuli, when compared with negative ones, demonstrates that the excitation of the reticular formation itself depends on certain complicated cortical processes, probably mediated by cortico-reticular connexions. This conclusion becomes even more evident if various types of α-rhythm depression reaction produced by verbal stimuli of different significance, are compared. The dependence of the depression reaction on the meaning of the words has been studied in our laboratory by Marushevskii (1957), and this work confirms the importance of cortical control of the cortex stimulating activity of the reticular formation.

In this way external stimuli, having undergone transformation in the cortex, influence the subcortical centres through the system of feedback connexions. The mechanism of the reticular formation's influence on the cortex is not brought into operation until afterwards. Consequently, it can be stated that the main part in the activation of the cortex is played by the cortical nerve cells themselves, which are responsible for the preliminary selection and transformation of the information coming from outside. In addition, the stimulus, reaching the reticular formation by direct paths, is also able to give rise to processes therein which are reflected by the cortical nerve cells in the form of α-rhythm depression.

Conditioned orientation reactions developing in the initial phase of closure of the conditioned motor reflex, could possibly serve as the underlying mechanism for the cortical control of the activity of the reticular formation.

The conditioned orientation reflex, manifesting itself as sustained depression, appears particularly clearly when reinforcement is being provided by the orientation reaction to a light stimulus of liminal intensity. By applying weak liminal stimuli at the rate of one per minute, Mikhalevskaya (1957), succeeded in demonstrating the sustained conditioned reflex depression of α-rhythm at the moment in which the sensitivity to light usually diminishes.

Stabilization of the conditioned reflex is associated with the extinction of various elements of the orientation reaction and, with the weakening of the specific effect resulting from the establishment of the conditioned adaptation reactions. However, any further difficulty associated with differentiation again intensifies the orientation reflex and consequently, increases the sensitivity and reactivity of the visual analyser.

Reinforcement, by giving rise to intensification of the orientation reaction, plays an important part in increasing the sensitivity of the visual analyser to signal stimulation. The latent period of the conditioned motor reflex itself is, however, long in view of the inhibitory effect of the intensified orientation reflex.

The varying relationship of conditioned motor, orientation and specific reflexes, at various stages of stabilization of the conditioned motor reflexes, provides the explanation for the peculiarities of the reactions to light stimuli of liminal intensity. In this range of intensities there takes place, in fact, a continuous process of difficult differentiation of the signal against the general physiological background activity of the visual analyser. This implies intensification of the orientation reaction and inhibition of the conditioned motor reflex, and shows as α-rhythm depression to liminal stimuli, combined with the separation in time between the onset of the effects of light and the beginning of the motor reaction. The objective criteria for the approximation to the absolute threshold provides the basis for the technique of testing stimuli and makes possible its use for the investigation of light sensitivity.

The Functional State of the Analyser During the Elaboration of a Conditioned Reflex

A. The Afferent and Efferent Links of the Orientation Reaction and Analyser Reactivity to Signal Stimuli

To instruct the subject to react to a stimulus is the simplest way of endowing that stimulus with the significance of a signal, i.e., of linking it with a particular response. This process is associated with disinhibition of the orientation reflex which had been extinguished as a result of preliminary repetitive application of the stimulus in question.

The disinhibited orientation reaction is of a general nature, and the process of its reappearance is best studied with the help of one of its components, such as the C.G.R. This reaction now develops, not only in response to the agent which has acquired the significance of a positive conditioned stimulus, but also to other similar stimuli, even those which do not bring about the motor reaction.

The greater the difference between the stimulus actually applied and the signal, the smaller the magnitude of the C.G.R. One can talk therefore of a selective reactivity, which reaches its maximum in the range of stimuli closely similar to the signal. With the application of the signal stimulus one can observe the concentration of the excitatory processes in those nerve elements of the cortex to which the stimulus is directed. Consequently, when the conditioned reaction becomes established, only the signal and very closely allied stimuli give rise to a C.G.R.; any agent differing further from the conditioned stimulus ceases to be effective, even though it has been previously capable of evoking a C.G.R.

The selective increase of reactivity in the range of stimuli near the signal, also manifests itself in the fact that the nearer the stimulus used to the signal, the greater the number of repetitions required in order to extinguish the reaction. The same picture of events can be observed using cutaneous, visual, or auditory stimuli (Sokolov, 1955).

The formation of the conditioned reflex is therefore associated with the general disinhibition of the orientation reaction, but as the conditioned reflex becomes established, only the agents similar to the signal remain still capable of evoking the orientation reflex. The concentration of the excitatory processes, in the cells representing the positive signal stimulus, is associated with the inhibition of the orientation reaction to the negative stimuli. This concentration can develop, either in different analysers or within a single analyser. In the records of the vasomotor orientation responses to various light or sound stimuli, one can see that the request, "react to the sound" results in an intensification of the orientation reflex to the sound, while the orientation response to the light diminishes and soon disappears altogether. On the other hand, if the subject is instructed to lift his arm in response to a light, the orientation reflex to light is enhanced and that to the auditory stimuli is inhibited (Sokolov, 1954).

The occurrence of the orientation reflex predominately in response to signal and closely related stimuli is annulled by the novelty factor in any stimulus. A strong, sufficiently novel extraneous stimulus, applied against the background of an established conditioned reflex, is capable of giving rise to a C.G.R. on one or two occasions. A particular instance of this phenomenon is the enhancement of the orientation reaction during transition from one type of stimulus to another. Thus, a negative stimulus applied after a number of positive ones, also evokes the reaction, which then gradually becomes extinguished (Novikova, Sokolov, 1957).

The concentration of the excitatory process at the point of impact of the signal stimulus is confirmed by the following observation. When the auditory threshold is being determined with the help of an audiometer, a weak liminal sound stimulus gives rise to a strong orientation reaction, whereas a strong extraneous sound does not.

By recording the C.G.R., during the formation and establishment of differentiation, the effect of at first the distant, and then the more and more closely related negative stimuli, may be seen to weaken. Selective excitation of the orientation reaction can be reached not only in different analysers, but may also be achieved with a high degree of efficiency within a single analyser. The areas of generalization and concentration depend on the properties of the cortical projection of the receptor in question, and on the selective enhancement of excitability in the afferent cells of the analyser concerned with the production of the orientation reflex.

As the conditioned reflex becomes more firmly established, the magnitude of the C.G.R. diminishes and finally, neither the negative nor the positive stimuli are capable of evoking it. With any complication in differentiation, the zone of generalization becomes re-established and the orientation reaction then occurs, not only to the signal stimulus, but also to closely related stimuli which previously had ceased to be effective.

In the course of formation of the conditioned connexion, the concentration of excitation also occurs in the efferent link of the orientation reflex. At the beginning of the process, the signal stimulus gives rise to a group of the efferent components of the orientation reaction. For instance, the first application of a signal auditory stimulus gives rise to eye movement, α-rhythm depression and a galvanic skin reaction. Repetitive signal stimulation is associated with the progressive elimination of these efferent components of the orientation reaction. Simultaneous recording of the various reactions shows a progressive narrowing of the range of the orientation reaction evoked, so that in time only the local reactions restricted to the analyser directly acted upon by the stimulus continue to appear.

The various elements of the orientation reaction have differing significances; this is also true of the reactions of the visual analyser. It has been shown that eye movement is not an absolutely essential element of the reaction to light. The repetitive appearance of a pin-point source of light in darkness resulted in the movement of the subject's eyes only in response to the first few applications, and the reaction was soon extinguished. On the other hand, the α-rhythm depression reaction continued to develop for a long time, pointing to the stability of the local reactions of the visual analyser.

The processes of generalization of excitation in the afferent and efferent links of the orientation reflex—when it enters into the structure of the conditioned reflex—are interconnected, and depend on the functional characteristics of the conditioned connexion. For instance, repetitive application of a series of stimuli, similar to the signal, eventually results in the progressive extinction of various elements of the orientation reflex, which thus becomes restricted to specific reactions based on the analyser actually stimulated. This leads to efferent concentration. At the same time, however, a number of related stimuli which have not been applied also lose their effects. This is the result of afferent concentration of excitation in the area of representation of the conditioned stimulus. The interdependence of the processes of afferent and efferent concentration results in the specialization of the orientation reaction, associated with the restriction of the conditioned response to only definite, signal stimuli.

The selectivity observed in the case of orientation response to signal stimuli is associated with certain properties of the conditioned reflex. The more difficult the differentiation, the wider the generalization in the afferent and efferent systems of the orientation reflex. This selectivity provides for the selective sensitization of the analyser responsible for the perception of the signal stimuli during the formation of the conditioned link.

Selective sensitization of an analyser, occurring during the course of action of a stimulus, can be demonstrated experimentally by measuring the sensitivity of the retina to light at various points. It is found that repeated determination of sensitivity at any part of the retina results in an increase of sensitivity, under the influence of the measurements themselves. Eventually the sensitivity becomes stabilized at a definite level. Unexpected shifting to measurement at another point on the retina results in an overestimate of the threshold, increasing with the distance between the two points. Further repeated measurements at the new point bring the value of the threshold down to that of the point at which the original measurements were made.

Similar phenomena can be observed in the course of measurements of the auditory threshold. Following repeated measurements using one frequency only, an overestimation is obtained when a different frequency is used. After one or two measurements using the new frequency the values obtained are similar to the original.

B. Tonic and Phasic Orienting Reactions Associated with the Acquisition of Signal Significance by a Stimulus

When a stimulus is given a signal significance by means of reinforcement, the reactivity of the analyser responsible for its perception is increased This increase is in contrast to the fall of reactivity associated with the inhibition of the orientation responses to non-signal stimuli.

The increased excitability manifests itself in connexion with both tonic and phasic orientation reflexes; the tonic form can be demonstrated as a general fall of skin resistance, which reflects the increased level of excitation of the cortical cells. A continuous recording of palmar skin resistance shows that non-signal stimulation is accompanied by a rise in resistance. A request to react to a sound, by compressing a rubber bulb, results in a fall in resistance which usually persists for some time. This sustained rise of conductivity of the skin is a manifestation of the tonic orientation reaction.

Auditory stimuli give rise to strong phasic reactions in the form of a transitory fall in resistance. The first stage of link formation is accompanied by a further general fall of resistance (Fig. 80).

In this experiment, the reactions to various non-signal sound stimuli are initially extinguished. Then, the subject is asked to compress a rubber bulb when a sound repeats itself (the method of conditioned reinforcement). This instruction is followed by a sustained rise in the excitatory state, and the curve is established at a new level (the onset of the experiment).

The positive stimulus (1000 c/s 70dB), and the negative one (400 c/s 70dB), applied after instructions have been given, give rise to a C.G.R. not associated with movement, the C.G.R. occurring after both positive and negative stimuli. Phasic changes apart, under the influence of the application of the signal stimulus, there is also a general fall in skin resistance which is due to the tonic reflex. At first, both the positive and the negative stimuli (4–7), give rise to the motor reactions. With the establishment of discrimination, the C.G.R.

to either are weakened. As from the 15th application the sign of the stimuli is reversed (400 c/s becomes positive and 1,000 c/s negative). This alteration results in the restoration of the reaction to both stimuli and a tonic fall in the general level of resistance.

Another example of the tonic orientation reaction may be seen in the level and nature of the electrical activity of the brain. Verbal reinforcement, or any instruction, result in the appearance of quicker rhythms. Where there is a background of large-amplitude α-rhythm for example, the request for a motor reaction to a signal stimulus is associated with α-rhythm depression,

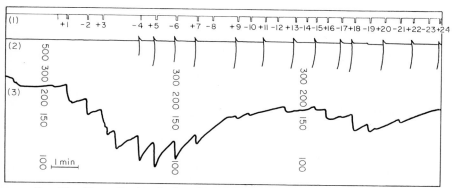

FIG. 80. Generalized excitation of the G.S.R. in response to two sound stimuli of 70 dB (1000 c/s Positive; 400 c/s Negative; reversed as from the 15th stimulus) showing relationship of phasic and tonic reactions. Subject K., October 1954. 1—Stimulus. 2—Motor reaction (compression of a bulb). 3—Galvanic skin reaction. Ordinate: resistance (kilohms).

which persists for a considerable time. In the case of drowsiness, characterized by low frequency rhythms (up to δ-frequency), the result of verbal reinforcement or instruction, is the development of α-rhythm while the slow rhythms disappear. In a number of cases where there is a background of a high state of neuronal excitation associated with α-rhythm depression, one can clearly observe the intensification of the faster rhythms as a result of verbal instruction, which indicates a further increase in the level of excitation.

As the link becomes established, tonic excitation diminishes and the general level of the tonic orientation reflex is lowered. The latter is intensified again by any difficulty in the differentiation of stimuli. The relationship between the phasic and tonic orientation reflexes is seen as an intensification of the phasic orientation reflexes against a general background state of increased excitation.

Fluctuations of the tonic orientation reflex follow those of the reactivity and sensitivity of the analyser. Any intense sound gives rise to a simultaneous fall of skin resistance, α-rhythm depression and increased light sensitivity of the visual analyser, as measured with the help of conditioned motor reactions to weak light stimuli (Sokolov 1955; Steklova 1957).

The effect of the tonic orientation reflex may also be seen in the level of cortical lability at the central end of the analysers as shown by the rise in the optimum frequency for photic driving of cortical rhythms.

C. Change in Reactivity during Elaboration of a Conditioned Motor Reflex

As has been repeatedly indicated already, every stimulus giving rise to an orientation reflex results in the adjustment of the analyser for the better perception of the agent in operation. Repetitive stimulation is associated with the production of the conditioned adaptation, and inhibition of the orientation, reflexes. The onset, main body and end of the stimulation, and the subsequent background, constitute together a complex stimulus, the different elements of which are connected by a system of conditioned connexions in such a way that the effects of the stimulus are self-limited.

In the course of investigation of the relationship between the inhibition of the orientation reactions and the production of the conditioned adaptation reflexes, it has been found that any intensification of the orientation reaction as a result of interference with the stereotyped use of the non-signal stimulus, is associated with the inhibition of the conditioned adaptation reflexes. The sequence of "light–strong light", initially gives rise to a C.G.R. at the onset of both components, each producing an independent orientation reaction. With repetition, an adaptation reflex to "light–strong light" is formed, and at the same time, the galvanic skin component of the orientation reaction is inhibited. Any interruption in the stereotyped presentation of the components of the complex, such as application of the weaker element alone, evokes an orientation reaction at the moment when the omitted element, in this case strong light, should follow.

The reappearance of the orientation response to signal stimuli is associated with the inhibition of the conditioned adaptation reflex and the consequent alteration of the specific effect of the signal stimulus. The existence of a relationship between the orientation reaction and the conditioned adaptation reflex, as described above, is also confirmed by the interruption of the process of adaptation to light as a result of a request to discriminate between the light stimuli according to their intensity and duration. In this case, light stimulation again begins to result in a sharp fall of sensitivity to light, and to a more intense galvanic skin reaction.

Interference with the adaptation to signal light stimuli coincides with an alteration in the effects of the light on the E.E.G. Analysis of the E.E.G., recorded during the application of the sequence "light–strong light"—endowed with the significance of a signal for a conditioned motor reaction—

confirms the existence of a connexion between the inhibition of the orientation reaction and the production of the adaptation reflexes; and also, between the disinhibition of the orientation reaction and the inhibition of the conditioned reflexes. With repetition of the sequence "light–strong light", the E.E.G. reactions become less and less obvious. The request for a motor response to the stimulus complex results in reappearance of the orientation α-rhythm depression reaction; initially, to each of the constitutents of the sequence. Subsequently the reactions become partially extinguished, being more consistently evoked by the signal component.

A similar series of events may be observed when recording the C.G.R. during the formation of a conditioned motor response to a signal sequence.

Initially, each element of the sequence gives rise to the orientation reaction, the C.G.R. appearing at the onset of the first and, the end of the second element of the sequence, coinciding with the motor reaction. When the conditioned link is established the orientation responses to the different elements of the sequence are extinguished but not in the same way. Whereas, in the case of non-signal complex stimulation the effects produced depend on the physical intensity of the stimuli, once the conditioned link underlying the motor reflex is established, the galvanic skin response is maintained for a particularly long time in respect of that element of the stimulus which is its distinguishing feature. Similarly, during the formation of a conditioned reflex based on the relationship of two light stimuli according to their intensity, the C.G.R. which occurs during the transition from one stimulus to the other is especially persistent. When differentiation depends on the first element of a sequence, this is the element which continues to give rise to reactions for a long period of time. As differentiation becomes established, the C.G.R., becomes weaker again (Trekhova, 1957).

It appears, therefore, that the disinhibition of the orientation reflex and the inhibition of the conditioned adaptation reflexes formed in the course of repetitive light stimulation, all observed as a result of acquisition of signal significance by the stimulus in operation, ensure the selective reactivity of the analyser towards stimuli to which a meaning has been attached.

D. Orientating and Specific Reflexes in the Motor Analyser

When discussing the changes—as a result of reinforcement—in the excitability of the analysers responsible for the perception of signal stimuli, one must consider the effect of the motor reaction itself on analyser excitability. A further problem is the effect of signal stimuli on the activity of the motor analyser.

Proprioceptive stimuli are specific ones for muscular activity. When the weight of a supported load is increased, or when the arm is lifted, there is an increase in the muscle electrical activity. This increased activity is associated with a C.G.R. and generalized α-rhythm depression. The latter can be replaced by a local reaction to proprioceptive stimuli consisting of rolandic rhythm depression. With continued proprioceptive stimulation, both the C.G.R. and the depression disappear, while the muscle electrical impulses proper persist, their features depending on the weight of the load.

Thus, in the same way as other agencies, proprioceptive stimulation gives rise to an orientation reaction, which in this case, appears in the form of a change of muscle tone; this is replaced by the specific adaptation of the musculature in accordance with the load supported. The motor reaction can therefore be said to consist of two elements: the orientation enhancement of excitability of the motor analyser associated with the other elements of the orientation reaction; and the actual reaction proper. What is the effect on the relationship of these two elements when the motor reaction becomes a conditioned response to a signal stimulus?

When the subject is asked to react to a signal by means of a movement, the result is the enhancement of the excitatory states of both, the elements of the orientation reaction and, of the functional system on which the movement is based. At the onset of the process of formation of the conditioned reaction, one can observe the development of muscle tone preparatory to the movement of the hand.

The application of the conditioned signal gives rise to a combination of the orientation reactions. The local reaction in the form of rolandic rhythm depression which precedes the conditioned motor reaction is of special importance.

In this way, a conditioned stimulus gives rise to the orientation reaction which enhances the excitability of the cortical segment of the motor analyser, and prepares the ground for the completion of the special conditioned motor reflex. With stabilization of the reflex, the latent period of the motor reaction, and, the amplitude and duration of the electromyographic activity, also become stabilized. The orientation response to the signal and the proprioceptive effects of the movement itself are extinguished.

Let us consider, as an example, a conditioned motor reflex produced by a light stimulus. The production of the reflex is associated, at its onset, with two orientation reactions, one occurring at the start of stimulation, the other due to the change affecting the muscles concerned. As the conditioned motor reaction becomes established, the two generalized manifestations of the orientation reflex are extinguished. However, as demonstrated by Gastaut *et al.* (1957), the local rolandic rhythm depression persists, indicating the presence of a local conditioned orientation reflex within the motor analyser itself.

During difficult differentiation of light stimuli, the latent period of the motor reaction is markedly increased. The conditioned motor reflex response appears to consist of two phases; the preliminary phase of muscle electrical activity associated with the enhanced orientation reaction and, the phase of execution of the movement, which follows after a short interval. With differentiation established, the orientation reflex is extinguished and the special motor reaction to the conditioned stimulation occurs with a shorter latent period.

The orientation reactions to signal stimuli can be intensified, not only by alteration of the signal stimulus, but also by changing the nature of the re-action required, i.e., a weaker or stronger motor response or, by delaying or arresting it altogether. Any such change gives rise to a C.G.R. and after that, even the application of the usual signal gives rise to a more intense orientation reaction.

Therefore, the motor analyser responsible for the execution of the con-ditioned reaction, and the analyser responsible for the perception of the causative signal stimulus are equally capable of giving rise to the orientation reaction; which furthermore can be enhanced by either, any change affecting the conditioned stimulus or, any alteration of the motor reaction. Conse-quently, it can be stated that the complex of conditioned stimulus and con-ditioned motor response gives rise to a preceding conditioned orientation reflex, in preparation for the action of the motor analyser.

E. **Role of the Orienting Reflex in the Closure and Functioning of the Temporary Connexion**

The association of the orienting with the conditioned reflex raises the problem of the role of the former in the closure of temporary connexions.

This problem has been studied by means of specially designed experiments involving the elaboration of conditioned motor reflexes, with and without preliminary extinction of the orientation reaction to the prospective con-ditioned stimulus.

A marked difference was observed in the rapidity with which the con-nexion was formed in the two cases. In the absence of preliminary extinction of the orientation response to the conditioned signal, the connexion could be produced by 2–3 applications of the verbal reinforcement "Raise your hand". In this case both the conditioned stimulus and the verbal reinforcement gave rise to orienting reactions, as evidenced by the C.G.R.

The process of closure is much slower if the orientation reflex to the future conditioned stimulus has been first extinguished. Closure of the conditioned reflex is then preceded by reappearance of the orientation reaction (Fig. 81). After 10 applications, the sound ceases to produce a C.G.R. or α-rhythm depression, and the orientation reflex can therefore be considered extin-guished (*a, 10*). Verbal reinforcement "Raise your hand", results in the reappearance of the orientation reaction—a C.G.R. and α-block,

R

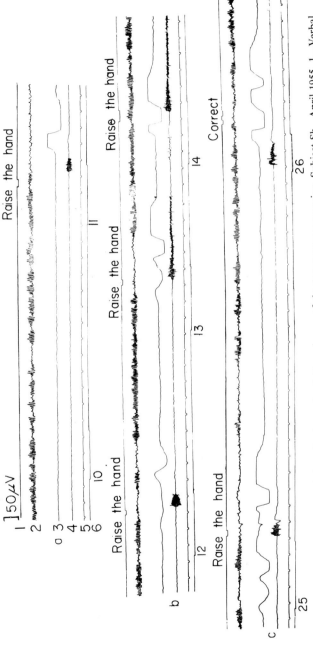

FIG. 81. Reappearance of the orienting reflex before closure of the temporary connexion. Subject Sh., April 1955. 1—Verbal reinforcement. 2—E.E.G. 3—Galvanic skin reaction. 4—E.M.G. 5—Time. 6—Stimulus (sound of 1000 c/s, 70dB).

and in the development of the motor response (*a, 11*). The reinforcement it is true, causes partial disinhibition of the orientation reflex to the future conditioned stimulus, but it becomes particularly intense before the actual closure of the temporal link. The conditioned stimulus initially gives rise to a weak C.G.R. (*b 12*), which with repetition, becomes stronger (*b, 13, 14*). At the same time, the E.M.G. begins to show low amplitude activity. This temporary enhancement does not, however, bring about closure of the connexion. More repetitions are required.

Before the closure is completed the sound begins again to evoke the orientation reflex, with intensification of the C.G.R. and α-rhythm depression (*c, 25*). Any subsequent application of the sound produces an immediate motor response (*c, 26*); concurrently, the α-rhythm depression diminishes.

In this manner the orientation reflex secures a certain level of excitation at the sites of application of the coupled stimuli and thus facilitates the formation of the conditioned connexion.

In a proportion of cases, the preliminary extinction of the orientation reaction to the prospective conditioned stimulus actually prevents the formation of the conditioned motor reflex. As a result of reinforcement, the future conditioned stimulus begins to give rise to a weak orientation reaction, but the increase of reactivity is insufficient and, with repetition, the orientation response becomes extinguished. With continued stimulation, a brisk orientation reaction is only produced by the verbal reinforcing stimulus, and a conditioned reflex is not formed in spite of the great number (more than 60) of coupled stimuli applied (Sokolov and Paramonova, 1956), as shown in Fig. 82.

After many applications of a sound stimulus (1000 c/s 70dB), the orientation reflex becomes extinguished (*20*). Verbal reinforcement is introduced at this stage and gives rise to a motor reaction, associated with a C.G.R. No intensification of the reaction to the signal stimulus can be observed (*22*). With further stimulation by the coupled stimuli one can observe an intensification of the C.G.R. to the sound. This reaction precedes the verbal reinforcement (*30, 31*) but becomes extinguished (*32*). The response to the reinforcing stimulus is consistently maintained but no conditioned reflex is formed even after 65 such sequence stimulations. Another point of interest is the information volunteered by the subject that she was conscious of paying attention to the nature of the verbal reinforcement and not to the sound.

Our findings concerning the difficulties of elaborating conditioned reflexes after the orientation reactions to the prospective conditioned stimuli have become extinguished, are in agreement with the results obtained by Konorsky and Shveikovskaya (1952). These authors have demonstrated that if a non-signal stimulus has already been used as such in relation to a certain reflex,

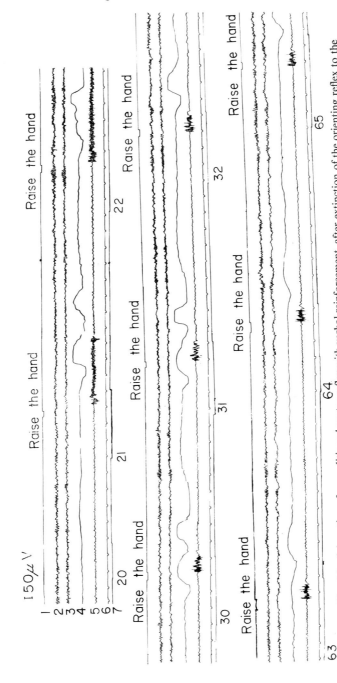

Fig. 82.   No elaboration of a conditioned motor reflex with verbal reinforcement, after extinction of the orienting reflex to the future signal stimulus.   Subject A., May 1955.   From above down: 1—Verbal reinforcement.   2 and 3—E.E.G.   4—Galvanic skin reaction.   5—E.M.G.   6—Time.   7—Stimulus.

the elaboration of a positive reflex to the stimulus is more difficult than if it has been used for the production of some other reflex.

The extent to which the orientation reaction participates in the conditioned reflex reaction was found to be associated with the indication of the link by the secondary signalling system. As demonstrated by Paramonova, the preliminary extinction of the orientation reaction to a signal stimulus results, in a proportion of cases, in the formation of conditioned reflexes associated with conditioned changes in the electrical activity of the muscles. Often, these changes do not reach the consciousness of the subject, and in this case there is no verbal indication of the link between the conditioned stimulus and the response.

The rise of reactivity and sensitivity which can be observed during the period of formation of a conditioned motor reflex is not only a result of the formation of the link, but is itself a necessary condition of the closure of the temporary connexion. The orientation response to the stimulus assists in the formation of the conditioned reflex, and beforehand, one can observe an intensification of the orientation reaction to the future conditioned stimulus.

The reappearance of the orientation reaction to a signal stimulus is an effect of reinforcement which activates the analyser responsible for the perception of the signal. This intensification of the orientation reflex, observed after the application of the reinforcing stimulus, seems to be a result of irradiation of excitation from the cortical representation of the reinforcement to the cortical segment of the analyser in question.

Reinforcement plays a very important part in the development of the orientation reactions to signal stimuli. In man, verbal reinforcement in the form of verbal approval or otherwise, of the response executed, is of particular importance. The effects of identical stimuli undergo considerable changes depending on the character of the verbal reinforcement.

The intensification of the orientation reactions can be observed particularly clearly whenever the conditioned connexion is altered, whether as a result of change of the unconditioned stimulus or of the reinforcement. If a sound, the orientation reflex to which has become extinguished, is replaced by another sound, one of the following two phenomena are observed. Either there is an orientation reaction, but no motor response, or a generalized conditioned reflex to the new stimulus becomes at once established. However, this conditioned motor reaction is not accompanied by the galvanic skin element of the orientation reaction.

Simultaneous records of the motor reaction (pressure on a key)—including exact measurement of its latent period—and of the magnitude of the C.G.R., show that the intensification of the C.G.R. coincident with the change of the conditioned stimulus, is associated with the increase in the latent period of the motor response. In the case of widespread generalization, not accompanied by a C.G.R., the latent period usually remains unaltered in spite of the change of the conditioned stimulus.

The further course of the orientation reflex and the conditioned motor reaction, depends entirely on the nature of the reinforcement given with the new stimulus. If positive reinforcement is forthcoming in the same way as with the stimulus used previously, the orientation reflex (if developed) is rapidly extinguished, the latent period of the motor reaction becomes stable and a generalized conditioned reflex is produced. If, however, the positive reaction to the new stimulus meets with negative reinforcement ("you should not have pressed" or "wrong"), one can observe an intensification of the orientation reaction and a considerable increase in the latent period of the motor reaction. This is due to the fact that the choice of appropriate reaction calls for a finer degree of differentiation than the execution of the generalized conditioned reaction. The differentiation is facilitated by the activation of the orientation reflex and by the development of inhibition within the system of conditioned reflex activity (Fig. 83).

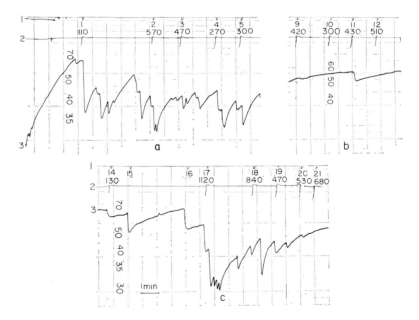

FIG. 83. Changes in the latent period of the motor reaction and in the strength of the orienting reflex on introduction of stimulus differentiation. Subject B., April 1956. 1—Acoustic stimulus. 2—Latent period of motor reaction in sigmas (pressure on a key, whereby the latent period of the motor reaction was measured simultaneously). 3—Galvanic skin reaction. Ordinate: resistance (kilohms).

In Fig. 83*a* may be seen the changes of skin resistance during the course of an experiment. The first application (*1*) of the stimulus gives rise to a motor reaction of long latent period associated with a C.G.R. of high magnitude. With repetition, the latent period and C.G.R. diminish (*4, 5*).

Figure 83*b* shows how, with the motor response established, the reflex is stable and the C.G.R. extinguished (*9*). A change of stimulus (400 c/s) affects neither the motor response nor the C.G.R. (*10*). The second application of the new stimulus, however, gives rise to a C.G.R. (*11*) which is soon extinguished (*12*). When the new stimulus is 200 c/s, its application (*14*) also produces the motor reaction (generalization of the conditioned reflex—Fig. 83*c*). Negative reinforcement ("there is no need to press the key in response to this sound") brings about, in this case, a galvanic skin reaction. Subsequent applications of the 200 (*15*), and 300 c/s (*16*), sounds produce no motor reactions as a result of irradiation of inhibition of the motor reaction. At the same time, however, high amplitude C.G.R.'s can be observed. Similarly, inhibition also follows the application of a positive stimulus of 1000 c/s, and shows as an increase of the latent period of the motor reaction (*17*). This is associated with a particularly intense C.G.R., having characteristic rhythmical fluctuations. With the subsequent applications of the positive stimulus the galvanic skin reactions diminish in strength and become extinguished, and the latent period of the motor reaction diminishes (*18–21*).

Negative reinforcement of positive reactions to a new stimulus, intensifies the orientation response to both old and new agents. The orientation reactions to signal stimuli also undergo intensification at the start of inhibition of a conditioned reflex, i.e., when a positive conditioned reflex receives negative reinforcement. Similarly, an orientation reaction follows alteration of any dynamic stereotype, for the beginning of such alteration is also connected with negative reinforcement of one of the elements of the sequence, hence the intensification of the orientation reaction.

The orientation reflexes, produced by repetitive conditioned stimuli, undergo a number of changes. In the case of coarse differentiation with only one stimulus being reinforced, a positive reflex develops; the orientation reaction —appearing in the form of a galvanic skin response—becomes gradually extinguished, that to the negative stimulus fades first and, finally, that to the positive one as well. However, when differentiation is difficult, the attempts at discrimination between the positive and the negative stimuli manifest themselves in the intensification of the orientation reaction to both, associated with an increase of the latent period of the conditioned motor reactions, and with the development of inaccurate motor responses to some of the stimuli. As differentiation becomes established, the reactions to negative stimuli are the first to diminish and become extinguished.

During difficult differentiation, the afferent generalization of the orientation reflex increases. Consequently, a wider range of stimuli begins to give rise to orientation reactions, although even then, the subject is capable of differentiating very similar stimuli, as indicated by motor reaction. The intensification of generalization during fine differentiation also involves the efferent limb of the orientation reflex. The number of elements of the orientation reaction developing is larger than in the case of coarse differentiation.

What is the explanation of the relationship between the orientation and conditioned motor reaction during signal stimulation? Any alteration of the conditioned stimulus, resulting in intensification of the orientation reflex, acts as if an extraneous stimulus had occurred. The resultant depends on the extent of the difference between the stimulus applied and the conditioned signal. Consequently, a stimulus can present certain features of the signal (depending on its similarity to the signal agent), and of an extraneous stimulus (depending on the differences between it and the signal). Therefore, every novel stimulus acts as an extraneous stimulus, giving rise to the orientation reflex and inhibiting the conditioned reaction, depending on the degree of specialization of the given conditioned link.

The arrest of conditioned reflex activity as a result of a stimulus differing from the signal, appears as complete inhibition of the motor reaction (it generally does not develop at all in the case of a new stimulus), and in a temporary suspension of the motor response to the signal stimulus in use. However, the muscle electrical activity is still seen even though the conditioned reflex motor response to the signal stimulus is absent. Finally, secondary inhibition of the motor reaction is also possible; after a short latent period, there follows a very brief movement associated with a small number of electrical impulses, which becomes rapidly inhibited. In this case, a conditioned motor reaction is inhibited when partly developed—"secondary correction". This rapid inhibition of a conditioned motor reaction during its development is associated with an intensification of the orientation reflex, and the muscle electrical activity observed during secondary correction of movement is accompanied by an increased C.G.R., eye movements and α-rhythm depression (Novikova and Sokolov, 1957).

The effects of the orientation reaction on the conditioned motor reflex are not only of inhibitory nature. Where there is partial inhibition of the conditioned reflex, the orientation reaction can disinhibit the effects of the conditioned stimulus. For instance, where an extraneous stimulus supervenes during differentiation, although there is absence of any obvious movement, electrical activity of the muscles of the hand may be recorded, occurring simultaneously with α-rhythm depression and a C.G.R.—indications of an orientation reaction.

Therefore, simply to say that the orientation reflex is only capable of inhibiting the conditioned motor reaction, would not be true. Its relationship with the motor activity is complex and includes too, the orientation dis-inhibition of the conditioned motor reflex.

The initial phase during differentiation of stimuli is one wherein the orientation reaction appears. The associated rise of excitability spreads widely to the visual, auditory, cutaneous and motor analysers. However, this general rise of excitability inhibits the specific conditioned reaction. When a negative stimulus is given, the result is the inhibition of the conditioned motor reaction associated with irradiation of excitation within the orientation reflex system. The increase in the latent period of the conditioned motor reflex, observed during complicated differentiation, is coincident with an increase in the duration of the orientation reflex. Thus, the latent period in such conditions, includes the duration of the orientation reflex, the latter inhibiting the conditioned motor reflex for this period.

The effect of the orientation reaction on the duration of the latent period can be observed by recording simultaneously, the α-rhythm, C.G.R., and action potentials of the digital flexors. When two auditory stimuli, with tones difficult to differentiate, are applied, the α-rhythm is depressed, the cortical rhythms increase in frequency and the C.G.R. is intensified. These reactions last from the onset of stimulation to the beginning of the motor response. The conditioned motor response itself is considerably inhibited and its latent period is increased. Thus, it can be said that the inhibition of the conditioned motor reflex is associated with the simultaneous excitation of the generalized orientation reaction, which actually inhibits the motor response for a short period of time. The value of this temporary inhibition lies in the fact that it provides a short interval for more exact evaluation of those stimuli which are difficult to differentiate. Once their particular features are recognized the specific motor reaction follows (Sokolov, 1955).

F. Relationship Between Conditioned and Orienting Reflexes

The orientation reflex which reappears during reinforcement, is similar in its properties to that evoked by any non-signal stimulus, and involves both the afferent mechanism and the whole complex of efferent reactions. The reappearance of the orientation response to a signal stimulus is associated with simultaneous increase of sensitivity and reactivity, and is characteristically selective.

The maximum rise of reactivity is observed in the range of stimuli on either side of the signal. The greater the difference between the stimulus used and the signal, the lower the reactivity of the analyser with respect to that particular stimulus. The number of efferent elements also reaches its maximum in response to the signal stimulus. Consolidation of the conditioned reflex is associated with specialization, indicated by the concentration of excitation in the afferent and efferent links of the orientation reflex.

The formation of a conditioned motor reflex is associated with a rise in the level of the tonic orientation reflex—which provides the background for the intensification of the phasic orientation reflexes. The effects of signal stimuli on the body are furthermore increased as a result of the inhibition of the conditioned adaptation reflexes, which usually weaken the action of such stimuli. An indication of the inhibitory role of the adaptation reflexes in modifying the action of stimuli on analysers was shown by the findings of Jouvet and Hernandez-Peon (1957). The work of these authors shows that the amplitude of electrical discharges originating in the cochlear nuclei, which has diminished as a result of repetitive sound stimulation, increases again as soon as the sound is reinforced by an electrical stimulus. Reinforcement thus lifts the blockage of impulses which has been produced by the sound at the first synapse in the auditory path. The increase in the amplitude of the electrical discharges during reinforcement, coincides with the disinhibition of the orientation reflex to the signal stimulus.

The orientation reflex which reappears during reinforcement, serves as an important factor in the formation of the conditioned reflex. Consequently, any sustained inhibition of the orientation reaction interferes with this process. The orientation reaction remains important even after the closure of the conditioned link, and it may reappear at various stages in the differentiation of stimuli.

Intensification of the orientation reaction is closely associated with a temporary inhibition of the conditioned reflex, and shows as an increase in the latent period of the motor reaction. At the same time, however, the orientative rise of cortical excitability has a positive effect, on the excitability of the conditioned reflex arc.

The role of the orientation reflex in the creation of conditioned connexions has been much discussed. Its favourable effect, observed in the course of her experiments by Fursikova (1921), has been clearly demonstrated by Narbutovich and Podkopaev (1936). Guthrie (1930) suggested that the secretory reaction is not a response to the conditioned stimulus but to proprioceptive impulses, arising in association with the motor elements of the orientation reaction. In this view, generalization of the conditioned reflex depends on the occurrence of an orientation reaction in response to the effect of the conditioned stimulus. He proposed a similar explanation for delayed reflexes. According to Pavlov, the participation of such proprioceptive impulses as suggested above, is not a sufficient explanation for the relationship between the period of delay and the moment of application of the unconditioned reinforcement, or for the relationship between the orientation reflex and the phenomenon of generalization. He states, "similar agents produce the conditioned response directly without any trace of an orientation reflex appearing; and when there is an associated orientation reaction the conditioned response is either completely absent or, greatly diminished and increases only *pari passu* with the extinction of the orientation reaction" (Pavlov, 1949, p. 485).

Asratyan (1952; 1955) suggested that the condition reflex is a cortical synthesis of two unconditioned reflexes. One of which—the orientation reaction—is a response to the stimulus during the process of its becoming conditioned, while the other is the specific unconditioned response to the reinforcing stimulus.

Ivanov-Smolenskii criticized this hypothesis, indicating the difficulty of thus explaining those cases where the conditioned reflex becomes stabilized in spite of a marked reduction or even complete absence of the orientation reaction. It is therefore necessary to consider how one may reconcile the inhibition of the orientation reaction, as observed in these conditions, with the consolidation of the conditioned link in which the orientation reaction participates.

It is well known that the interrelationship between the conditioned and orientation reflexes varies at different stages during the process of formation of the conditioned link. This observation was made, for instance, by Myasishchev (1926), who succeeded in demonstrating the inverse relationship between the magnitude of the C.G.R. and the stability of motor reflexes. Further evidence may be seen in the intensification of the C.G.R. during conflict situations requiring a quick change in activity (Merlin, 1953; 1954).

Interesting information concerning the effect of the conditioned reflexes on the course of the orientation reactions has been provided by Tolman. Using the behaviour of the subject investigated as an example, he indicates that routine has an unfavourable influence on investigational activity. On the other hand, in unchanging external conditions, circumstances necessitating various different actions are conducive to the appearance of investigational activity (Tolman, 1955).

Obviously, the question of the constant interplay of the orientation and conditioned reflexes is of immense importance. On the one hand, the conditioned motor reactions affect the orientation reflexes, and on the other, the orientation reactions exert an influence on the course of the conditioned reflex.

In our opinion, the structure of the conditioned reflex arc is not a simple combination of the orientation and specific unconditioned reflexes. Both, the conditioned stimulus, and the response evoked, include specific and orientation elements. During formation of such a reflex arc, distinction must be made between the process of development of the conditioned orientation reaction—which activates both elements of the temporal connexion, and, the specific conditioned reflex—originating from a combination of the specific properties of the conditioned stimulus with the reactions of the motor analyser. As the conditioned reflex becomes automatic, the importance of the orientation reaction diminishes, and the moment of onset of the conditioned stimulus becomes the starting signal for the motor reaction.

If every stimulus is thought of as a combination of specific and non-specific components, with the latter giving rise to the orientation reaction, it is evident that, during the formation of a conditioned reflex, the action of each stimulus accumulates, the specific component being responsible for the conditioned reaction and the non-specific one giving rise to the orientation reflex. As general excitation of the cortex—mediated by the reticular formation as shown in the α-rhythm depression reaction, is one of the elements of the orientation reflex, it becomes clear that the effect of any conditioned stimulus largely depends on the degree of the associated rise in the level of cortical excitation.

The intensification of the orientation reflex during the introduction of differentiation, is explained by the fact that in a proportion of cases, the use of new stimuli not only does not weaken conditioned reflex activity but actually strengthens it. The attempts at differentiation give rise to strong orientation reactions and temporarily inhibit the conditioned reflex. However, at the same time, cortical excitation is enhanced by the orientation reaction which, in certain conditions, thus strengthens conditioned reflex activity.

The effects of monotonous conditioned stimuli, which readily produce a state of cortical inhibition and sleep, can be explained by the weakened cortical activating effect of the orientation reaction.

An important characteristic feature of the orientation reaction to a signal stimulus is its selectivity. Whereas the response is evoked by the stimulus having signal significance, closely related non-signal stimuli are ineffective. This is particularly true in the case of verbal stimuli. The fine discrimination of the properties of stimuli is a function of the cortex. Therefore, the orientation reflex to signal stimuli should be considered as being dependent on the results of preliminary cortical analysis.

It seems that, depending on the results of this cortical analysis, the appropriate information is transmitted to the reticular formation, where the various reactions constituting the orientation reflex originate. Consequently, there occurs a general rise in the reactivity of the body, conducive to perception, and, to the formation of new conditioned reflexes.

PART FOUR

CHAPTER I

Reflex Mechanisms in the Action of Stimuli on Analysers

A COMPLETE picture of how the process of perception is effected, and of the relationship in which reception stands to the mechanisms of conditioned reflex formation, must include the new concept of the actual analyser mechanism which has been produced by modern neurophysiological research (see Brazier, 1955; Gottschick, 1955).

Whereas the classical conception was of the transmission of excitation in analyser systems over paths, each specifically connected with a particular receptor, it is now necessary to envisage at least two paths, a specific and a non-specific, for the conduction of excitation. This may be illustrated by the visual analyser, the specific path of which begins in the photoreceptors of the retina, passes through the retinal system of bipolar and ganglion cells, travels to the lateral geniculate body and thence to the 4th layer of the cortical part of the analyser in the occipital region (Brodmann's area 17). This is the well known specific path for transmission of the specialized visual signals.

This is not, however, the only path for transmission of the excitation produced by light stimulation. The visual path gives off collaterals to the reticular system—that complicated cell structure which begins in the spinal cord and ends in the non-specific nuclei of the thalamus. This system also transmits the excitation to the cortex. But unlike those travelling over the specific path, the impulses reaching the reticular formation via many connecting neurones, do not transmit specialized information connected with the fine discrimination of the properties of the object seen but, terminating in the cortex in non-specific fibre synapses, they regulate the *excitability* of the cortical cells.

Specific paths are thus connected with the transmission of specialized information. Non-specific paths have been shown by Lorente de No (1943, referred to by Fulton, 1951) to reach all layers of the cortex and they transmit toning, activating impulses. The difference between these two systems for the transmission of excitation is revealed by differences in the associated electrical phenomena: the transmission of an impulse in the specific system is characterized by the development of a primary response action potential in the cortex; the transmission of excitation over a non-specific path is characterized by a secondary response and a sustained change in the background rhythmical activity in the cortex, large fast waves replacing the slower rhythm. The change is due to desynchronization—disturbance of the rhythmical discharge of the cortical nerve cells through the influence of the reticular system.

Specific and non-specific paths also differ in respect of the cortical areas in which they produce excitation. The specific response develops at points in the cortex representing the cortical projection of the corresponding points in the receptor surface at the periphery whereas the non-specific effect is generalized over wide areas of cortex. The two systems also differ in the time required for the conduction of excitation. The primary response to light, which is connected with the specific system, reaches a maximum after 67·5 msec. The secondary response, associated with the reticular system, reaches its maximum after 117·5 msec (Monnier, 1956). The change in background rhythmical activity has a latent period of about 300 msec.

The two main parts of the reticular system, the stem part and the thalamic part, are concerned in the transmission of activating influences to cortical neurons, but the effects they produce differ in character. The collaterals from the specific path are given off to these sections of the reticular formation at different levels so that the destruction of one system does not interfere with the action of the other. The brain-stem reticular system influences the entire cortex, producing widespread depression (desynchronization) of slow cortical rhythms. The reticular system of the thalamus has, on the other hand, a more selective action: some parts of it produce local effects on the anterior sensori-motor region and others influence the posterior cortical regions connected with the processing of combined visual and auditory information.

Conditions for the transmission of excitation differ considerably in specific and non-specific paths. In some respects, therefore, it was possible to analyse them independently. In sleep (natural or drug-induced), for instance, conductivity remains high in the specific path and a primary cortical response can be recorded very distinctly. Also, sleep, which involves exclusion of the reticular system, deprives the cortex of the activating influences produced by excitation of the reticular formation. Under these circumstances specific excitation, which is clearly evidenced by the development of a primary cortical response, does not produce any external reaction (in animal experiments). The anaesthetized animal does not react by change in behaviour to the arrival in the cortex of a stimulus specific for a given analyser. In man also, a specific stimulus is not received and fails to evoke change in behaviour when the activating effect of the reticular system is reduced and the cortex inhibited in sleep. It follows, therefore, that, although the specific and non-specific systems of afferentation can in fact be examined independently for purposes of analysis, only joint activity of the two systems can ensure reception of a stimulus and its utilization for the control of behaviour (Adrian, 1954; Hebb, 1955). The analyser concerned with perception thus forms an integral unit only when there is interplay between specific and non-specific excitation systems.

The first principle adding materially to our concepts of the analyser is thus the principle of interaction between specific and non-specific paths for the transmission of excitation.

A second principle—no less important—which extends earlier concepts of the analyser as a strictly afferent system, is that an analyser must be regarded as an afferent–efferent system. The peripheral apparatuses of perception taking part in analyser activity behave as effectors as well as receptors. Applying a term widely used in cybernetics to the analyser, we may say that it operates as a system with *feedback*, the functional state of the receptors being modified by signals from the higher regions (Granit, 1955). These return connexions exist at various levels in the analyser. Fibres turning back from the main path of excitation transmission to nerve cells constitute elementary forms of these feedback connexions (Eccles, 1953).

Return connexions are present in both specific and non-specific systems. Stimulation of the specific nuclei in, for example, the lateral geniculate body or the visual area of the cortex, produces excitation which travels towards the retina (Dodt, 1956). There are feedback connexions between the cortex and the specific system of the thalamus. When the optic nerve is stimulated, recordings from the cortex and the thalamus reveal repeated re-transmission of this impulse ("reverberation effect" of Chang, 1950).

The non-specific (reticular) system, which is connected with the receptor by efferent fibres, also exerts powerful influences on the receptor. The activating influence of the reticular system on the receptor has the effect of lowering its excitation threshold and increasing its lability (Granit, 1955). Equally important are the uninterrupted return connexions between the non-specific reticular system and the cortex. The effects produced through the thalamo-cortical connexions, in the form of continuous cycles of excitation, play an important part in maintenance of the level of excitation at which the dynamic processes for dealing with the specialized information reaching the cortex operate. The proof of the importance of these return connexions between cortex and subcortex in the production of a definite level of excitation is that a cortical segment, deprived of its thalamocortical connexions, loses the power to generate rhythmic waves (Burns, 1951).

The most important conclusion relative to the analyser as an afferent–efferent system is that return connexions, which exist at various levels in the analyser apparatus and provide for autoregulation of the analyser in accordance with the nature of the stimulus acting on it, play a definite part in the activity of the analyser system.

s

It may therefore be suggested that these systems of feedback connexions are important mechanisms for the selective treatment and processing of signals coming from receptor endings affected by external objects.

The direct exchange of afferent signals and efferent "commands", which tune the analyser through the mechanisms of the non-specific and specific systems for the transmission of excitation, is not the only manifestation of the feedback principle. Reflex changes which influence the analyser indirectly, such as changes in the tone of the proprioceptive muscular apparatuses, changes in respiration, vascular changes and so on, are of very great importance.

The reflexes concerned in the control of analyser apparatuses can be divided into two groups, one connected with the specific and the other with the non-specific system for the transmission of excitation. The first group of reflexes is directly connected with the specific system. The feature of these reflexes is that they can only be elicited by stimuli adequate for the particular analyser; they are local in their occurrence and are adjusted to the properties of the agent evoking them. Our experimental work has shown that these reflexes have common properties and constitute the group of adaptational reflexes. An example of the reflexes in this group is the contraction of the pupil on exposure to light, which is effected by the transmission of excitation over the specific path of the visual system.

The other group of reflexes is connected with the conduction of excitation over the non-specific system. The distinct feature of these reflexes is that they are very much generalized and are not adjusted to any definite properties of the agent producing them but, in fact, develop in response to any change in the surroundings. This group includes peripheral vasoconstriction, respiratory arrest, inhibition of general movements, dilatation of the pupil—in short, all the reactions which we regard as individual components of the *orienting reflex* system. The specific and non-specific systems of analyser excitation are thus connected with two groups of reflex controls which have different functional significances and different properties, determined by the properties of the specific and non-specific systems respectively.

The division of the reticular system into a stem part with diffuse action on the cortex and a thalamic part with more localized action is in keeping with our division of orienting reflexes into *generalized* and *local* (Sokolov, 1956). The latter, producing selective adjustment of the analyser, are seen very clearly in acts of voluntary attention in man.

A characteristic feature of reticular system activity is the convergence of impulses originating from a variety of external stimuli, which create a background of definite activity and influence the level of excitation in cortical cells. Orienting reflexes, which sustain the level of excitation in analysers through corresponding somatic and autonomic reflex control mechanisms, should, therefore, be regarded as a special group. These we have described as *tonic* orienting reflexes, as distinct from *phasic* reflexes, connected with the adjusting analyser activity to deal with changing situations (Sokolov, 1955).

It has been shown experimentally that tonic orienting reflexes are reflected in the level of electrical activity in the cortex, which indicates increase of lability and of sensitivity (e.g. in the visual analyser), as well as in the setting of the muscular apparatus of the receptor (e.g. visual fixation).

A third special group is that of the *defensive reflexes*, which have some of the features of adaptation reflexes and are connected with a particular specialized analyser. They are also closely linked with the switching into operation of the non-specific system of excitation and primarily, the diffuse reaction mechanism, including the humoral control of analyser excitability.

Such then is the general concept of the analyser as a system, consisting of specific and non-specific paths for the conduction of excitation and feedback mechanisms concerned in the reflex control of the excitability of different sections of the analyser. Yet, this picture is still only a static expression of the relationships existing between the individual mechanisms and does not reflect the dynamics of the processes in play in analysers during the perception of stimuli and the formulation of behavioural acts.

The processes in operation during analyser activity will vary with the initial relationship existing between the specific and non-specific excitation conducting systems. To simplify matters, we shall begin our analysis with an optimum level of afferentation, creating the conditions required for simultaneous participation of specific and non-specific systems in the analyser excitation.

Let us examine, for example, the effect of a photic stimulus.

The first stimulation produces excitation which is transmitted simultaneously over specific and non-specific paths. As a specific stimulus, the light elicits, apart from local changes in the retina, a reflex process of adaptation to the photic stimulus, one manifestation of which is the contraction of the pupil. As a fresh non-specific stimulus, the light excites the diffuse reticular system which, by its action on the cortex, produces generalized α-rhythm block. Also, by exciting the thalamic reticular system, the light has a particularly powerful effect on the level of excitation in the cortical part of the visual analyser. This effect of the light coincides with increased lability of the cortex and of the peripheral part of the analyser, the result being that the information arriving over the specific system of excitation is adequately processed and perception of the given stimulus is ensured.

The stimulation reaching the reticular system involves the vascular centres which also play their part in increasing the general reactivity of the nervous system through circulatory redistribution to increase cerebral blood supply.

In addition to this general reaction, the effect of which coincides with the direct activation of the cortex by the reticular system, there is general involvement of other analysers in the reaction. A new stimulus produces a galvanic skin reaction, apparently connected with increase of cutaneous sensitivity; there is general arrest of movement and turning of the head and eyes for fixation of the object; the activation of proprioceptors is indicated by increase of muscle tone and there is respiratory arrest connected with activation of the olfactory analyser; that the taste analyser is activated is indicated by the orientational secretion of saliva.

The relationships between these reactions change even in the course of the continued action of the same light stimulus. First of all, the non-specific reticular system responsible for the generalized orienting reaction goes out of action. This is due primarily to adaptation at the periphery (contraction of the pupil, reduction of the concentration of visual purple) which reduces the physical strength of the stimulus acting on the retina. In addition, however, it must be assumed that there is blocking of the impulses travelling over the collaterals to the reticular system. This, however, affects mainly the stem part of the system producing generalized α-rhythm block; the thalamic system connected with the local orienting reflex goes out of action more slowly.

Our experimental investigations have shown that a light stimulus, when its action was prolonged, still continued to reduce α-rhythm to small amplitude in the visual region even after vascular, galvanic skin and respiratory reactions had disappeared and the tracings had resumed their normal form, which meant that the local system of activation connected with the cortical division of the visual analyser was still active.

When the phasic reactions leading to activation of all analysers had disappeared the continuously acting light still maintained a higher level of afferentation in the visual analyser through the non-specific system of the thalamus, toning it and increasing the excitability of the visual system.

Exclusion of the light and change to darkness also produced immediate α-rhythm block together with all the other components of the orienting reflex through the diffuse reticular system. As the state of darkness continued, the effect of the diffuse reticular system disappeared and α-rhythm became larger than originally by virtue of the fact that in the dark the locally acting activating system receives fewer afferent impulses than in the light, and inhibition develops in the cortex. Only after some time in the dark did the amplitude of the α-rhythm decline somewhat as a result of peripheral adaptation, (dilatation of the pupils and restoration of the visual purple) increasing the physical effect on the eye of feeble light stimuli and also as a result of impulses coming from the retina even in the dark, all of which indicates increased afferentation of the thalamic reticular system leading to a higher level of excitation in the occipital region.

Light and darkness thus have complex effects on the visual analyser, these effects being determined by the interrelationships between the specific analyser system and its adaptational reactions, and by the activities of the various parts of the non-specific reticular system which influence the level of excitation in the analyser.

That light has a dual action on the visual analyser—reducing its sensitivity by virtue of adaptation reactions and, at the same time, increasing the excitability of the nerve elements in the analyser—is proved by these experiments on change in the sensitivity of the visual analyser produced by exposure to light. It was shown that the eye was sensitized both by weak liminal stimuli and also by supraliminal photic stimulation after the adaptational reduction of sensitivity produced by the latter had disappeared (Sokolov *et al.*, 1955). This sensitization is connected with activation of the non-specific system, the excitation of which, revealed by reactions of α-rhythm depression, coincided with the effect of increased sensitivity.

The proof that the excitability of the visual analyser is increased by reticular system activity is the linking of increased photic sensitivity in the visual analyser during the action of sound with reactions of α-rhythm depression. Sound, which produces α-rhythm depression in the occipital region through non-specific reticular system activity, also produces some increase of visual analyser sensitivity. Extinction of the reaction of α-rhythm depression is associated with loss of this sensitizing effect (Sokolov, 1955; Steklova, 1957).

That light increases the excitability of the visual analyser is indicated by results we obtained with rhythmic photic stimulation. Rate assimilation by the cortex—an indication of the functional state of the cortical neurons—was better in the light and poorer in darkness. The importance of the non-specific system in the adjustment of the analyser produced by light, is proved by experiment in which acoustic stimuli produced orienting reflexes, which included activation of the reticular system, and thereby increased lability so that the optimum rate of photic driving was observed (Sokolov, 1957; Danilova, 1957).

The effect of a stimulus thus consists of specific excitation together with the associated adaptational changes, and a non-specific activating effect which tones the cortex and constitutes an important element in the creation of optimum conditions for perception.

Not only do sense organs provide information about surrounding objects but they also maintain a certain level of activity in the organism. Experiments carried out in Pavlov's laboratory (Pavlov, 1949) in which simultaneous destruction of all the main exteroceptors resulted in reduced cortical excitability and the development of inhibitory processes, are of particular interest in this connexion. Electrophysiological investigations on the effect of deafferentation have shown that destruction of the reticular system and complete deafferentation ("encéphale isolé" preparation) yielded identical results, with development of slow waves, typical of the inhibitory state (Roger *et al.*, 1956).

This interplay of specific and non-specific systems of excitation in analysers and their material influence on the process of stimulus perception was also clearly evident in experiments with vascular reflexes, in which the relationships between non-specific reactions (components of the orienting reflex) and specific (adaptational) reflexes, directly connected with the quality and strength of the acting stimulus, could be distinguished and examined (Vinogradova and Sokolov, 1957; Sokolov, 1955).

Prolonged photic stimulation cannot, however, reveal the true complexity of the dynamics of stimulus perception. It is much more important to study the features of perception in relation to a stimulus which is administered repeatedly.

The first effect of repetition of a stimulus is attenuation of the non-specific response which we regard as the orienting reflex and which consists of quite a number of components. As application of the stimulus is continued, changes occur in the relative degrees of participation of the stem and thalamic reticular systems. First to disappear are the diffuse reactions connected with the brain-stem reticular system. The evidence of this is the disappearance of the diffuse α-rhythm depression and extinction of vascular, respiratory motor and other components of the orienting reflex. The local influences of the thalamic reticular system remain in evidence. This replacement of the generalized by a local orienting reaction is seen very clearly in experiments extending the work of Gastaut (1952) on rolandic rhythm (Roger *et al.*, 1958). Comparison of the effects of repeated light stimulation and passive movement showed that the diffuse reactions of α-rhythm block and many other components of the orient-ing reflex which developed in relation to the first applications of the stimuli, were replaced by localized reactions in the corresponding cortical projection areas. Complete extinction of these local reactions of activation was extremely difficult. At most, there was considerable attenuation of these reactions at the moment when the photic or proprioceptive stimulus was withdrawn.

What is the mechanism for the extinction of non-specific reactions? Experi-mental work in Pavlov's laboratories (Pavlov, 1947) has shown that the cortical segments of analysers play a very important part in extinction of the orienting reflex. When the cortex was removed, orienting reactions were extinguished with difficulty or remained practically unextinguished. It can not, however, be said that inhibition of orienting reactions is directly determined by the development of inhibition in the cortex. On the contrary, the process of orienting reaction inhibition is connected with active cortical influences on subcortical systems and requires a definite level of cortical excitation. The development of an inhibitory state in the cortex, which frequently ends in sleep, is itself the result of extinction. This is confirmed by our experiments with repeated stimulation, which we termed "over-extinction" of the orienting reflex to indicate continued application of the stimulus even after the reaction to it had been extinguished. The presentation Experiments in which the vascular component of orienting reflexes to sounds were recorded (Vinogradova and Sokolov, 1955) and others, in which galvanic skin reactions and reactions of α-rhythm block to proprioceptive stimuli were recorded (Roger *et al.*, 1958), have yielded similar results.

Various components of an orienting reflex were seen to be extinguished with repetition of a non-signal (indifferent) stimulus. More particularly, the reactions to sound in the form of vasoconstriction ceased to develop. A proprioceptive stimulus first ceased to evoke generalized block, although it continued to produce cutaneogalvanic reflexes and local block of rolandic rhythm. Continued application of the stimuli led to disappearance of the galvanic skin reaction also. Finally, complete or almost complete extinction of the reaction of local rolandic rhythm block could be observed.

Continuation of the extinction after the orienting reactions had been extinguished and had disappeared produced paradoxical results. The presentation of acoustic stimuli when the subject was lapsing into a somnolent drowsy state again began to elicit the vascular reactions which had earlier been extinguished. Despite the continued application of stimuli and the deepening of the inhibitory state of the cortex, as clearly evidenced by the posture and gestures of the subject, the vascular reactions were not extinguished and might even be intensified.

The behaviour of the galvanic skin reaction and the electrical reaction of the cortex to proprioceptive stimulation were of even greater interest. Continued repetition of non-signal passive raising of the arm, even after the orienting reactions to this stimulus had been extinguished, led to development of cortical inhibition as revealed by change in its background electrical activity. θ- and δ-waves replaced the α-waves which had previously predominated in the background. The subject was somnolent. On this background there was paradoxical restoration of the galvanic skin reactions which had previously been extinguished. The restoration of these reactions coincided with the development during proprioceptive stimulation of an "arousal" reaction with bursts of α- and β-activity in the occipital as well as the motor region. These experiments show that inhibition of an orienting reflex is associated with an active state of the cortex and, conversely, cortical inhibition attenuates the effect of orienting reflex extinction. The impulses produced by stimulus action are apparently blocked in the reticular system by the active intervention of the cortex.

Extinction of an orienting reflex thus leads to the development of general cortical inhibition, and the development of cortical inhibition weakens the elaborated conditioned reflex inhibition of the orienting reflex.

The importance of impulse blocking in the mechanism of orienting reflex extinction has been demonstrated in the experiments of Jouvet and Hernandez-Peon (1957) in which action potentials were reduced by repeated acoustic stimulation, even at the first relay in the auditory path.

The extinction of orienting reflexes on repeated application of the stimulus can thus be explained by the blocking of impulses in the non-specific path. The first to be blocked are the impulses going to the stem part of the reticular system. Our experimental work has shown that this block requires a certain definite level of cortical activity. The development of cortical inhibition enfeebles the blocking mechanism.

The importance of the cortex in the intensification and attenuation of orienting reflexes has been proved by many experiments with electrical stimulation of the cortex: at any point in the cortex the first stimulations elicited complex orienting reflexes. As the number of stimulations increased, the generalized orienting reaction disappeared and only the local reactions connected with the particular analyser, for example the erecting of the ears on stimulation of the auditory region, persisted (Lagutina, 1955). The effects of adequate receptor stimulation and non-specific electrical stimulation of the cortex in respect of the orienting reflex and the changes produced therein were very similar.

The part played by the cortex in excitation or inhibition of orienting reflexes can be explained by the numerous corticoreticular connexions. The importance of the cortex in excitation of the reticular system has been confirmed by Bremer (1954), who observed that the "arousal" effect of acoustic stimulation was attenuated after removal of the auditory cortex.

Apparently, therefore, excitation of an orienting reflex can be produced both via collaterals from the specific path concerned (this is indicated by the excitation of the reticular formation produced by afferent stimulation after decortication) and by cortical impulses produced as a result of the transmission of excitation over the specific system, the proof of which is that an orienting reflex can be reproduced by direct electrical stimulation of the cortex.

The inhibition of an orienting reflex, which is connected with blocking of the impulses entering the reticular formation, is the result of the active influence of the cortex on the subcortex. As more and more impulses reaching the reticular system are blocked, the activating influence of the reticular formation on the cortex is correspondingly reduced. There is production of functional deafferentation similar to that observed on destruction of the reticular formation (Bremer, 1954). The general level of cortical excitation then declines, its active intervention in control by the blocking of impulses is reduced and, travelling over the non-specific path, the stimulation again begins to elicit orienting reactions in the form of arousal effects on a general background of reduced activity, associated with the initial phase in the development of sleep inhibition.

Proof that the cortex is concerned in inhibition of orienting reactions is also afforded by the delicate selective extinction of the orienting reflex to one particular stimulus. In experiments with point cutaneous stimuli we found that even a slight change in the position of the point stimulated, again produced a reaction (Sokolov, 1956). It is difficult to explain such a high degree of reaction selectivity by reference to the reticular system alone, the structure of which is diffuse. It must, therefore, be recognized that the evolution of an orienting reaction is dependent on cortical feedback to the reticular system which, in turn, influences the level of cortical excitation. The activating influence of the reticular system on the state of cortical neurons is thus itself dependent on the state of the cortex.

That inhibition of an orienting reflex is dependent on a certain level of excitation in the cortex is indicated by the following observation. When we apply the same stimulus (e.g. light) we observe that the various components of the orienting reflex to that particular stimulus are extinguished. The excitation limited to the visual region, evoked by the light through the local thalamic system, is that which persists longest. The apparent contradiction—the light produces inhibition (extinction of the diffuse orienting reflex) and also excitation (local α-rhythm block in the occipital region) disappears when it is considered that inhibition of the various components of the orienting reflex requires active cortical excitation. A distinction should, therefore, be made between inhibition as a state of the cortical neurons (cortical tone) and inhibition as a reflex form of negative control.

What then is the mechanism responsible for the blocking of impulses on repeated application of a stimulus?

The first point to be noted is that the phenomena observed during the elaboration of inhibitory conditioned reflexes are very similar to those associated with extinction of orienting reflexes. The basis of this similarity is that, in extinguishing an orienting reaction, we are essentially dealing with the elaboration of a conditioned cortical reflex which will have an inhibitory effect on the development and fate of excitation in the non-specific system connected with the orienting reflex. Extending this view, we may say that the extinction of an orienting reflex at cortical level consists of the elaboration of conditioned inhibition of the unconditioned orienting reaction. Conditioned orienting reflexes are of particular interest in this connexion. Our investigations (Sokolov, 1956) on the elaboration of orienting reflexes showed that two forms of conditioned orienting reflexes could be produced by combinations of indifferent non-signal stimuli, namely conditioned excitation and conditioned inhibition of the orienting reflex.

In the former case the previously inactive stimulus itself became the exciter of an orienting reflex. In the latter, the conditioned stimulus weakened the orienting reflex to the new stimulus following it, and which alone produced a powerful orienting reaction. The extinction of an orienting reflex by repeated application of the same stimulus, may be regarded as the result of linkage of certain cortical areas with the complex of adaptational mechanisms, reducing the effect of the stimulus. In other words, conditioned inhibition of an orienting reflex may be regarded as the premature introduction of mechanisms which usually come into operation when the particular stimulus has acted for a considerable period of time and the orienting reaction to the stimulus has disappeared. It has already been indicated that an orienting reaction only develops in the early period of stimulus action. A conditioned reflex accelerates this process by intervening beforehand to limit development of the orienting reflex.

Adaptation merits attention in the analysis of these attenuating mechanisms. Our experimental work revealed a connexion between adaptation phenomena and inhibition of the orienting reaction. This connexion becomes evident in the mechanism of conditioned adaptation reflexes. An example of such a reflex is the constriction of the pupil in response to a conditioned acoustic stimulus, or the reduction of light sensitivity in response to a conditioned acoustic stimulus previously combined with light. Conditioned adaptation reflexes can be formed within the limits of the same analyser. Thus, combination of a weak and a stronger light may intensify the effect of the former.

Conditioned adaptation reflexes to time are of great importance. In these reflexes the moment of the start of the stimulus is the signal for its termination and conditions the animal for transition to the new level of intensity. Conditioned adaptational reflexes are presumably one of the mechanisms responsible for reduction of the stimulus effect in the peripheral parts of the analyser, with consequent modification of the course of the orienting reflexes. If this be so, one would expect to find connexions between the elaboration of conditioned adaptational reflexes and extinction of the orienting reflex, and conversely, between inhibition of conditioned adaptational and disinhibition of orienting reflexes.

There is experimental confirmation of this general relationship. Elaboration of the conditioned adaptational reflex proceeded as the applications of the stimulus increased and the orienting reflex was extinguished. Sudden replacement of the stimulus rendered the elaborated conditioned adaptational reflex inadequate to the changed conditions, the effect of stimulus action increased and an orienting reflex developed. Disinhibition of orienting reflexes following the action of a powerful stimulus can, to some extent, be explained by the fact that the extra-stimulus inhibited the adaptational conditioned reflexes and thus intensified the effects of the succeeding stimuli. By disturbing the stereotype of the conditioned adaptational reflex, the extra-stimulus intensified the impulses exciting the orienting reflex.

Evidence that, in extinguishing the orienting reflex, we are actually elaborating a system of connexions limiting the effect of the stimulus, was provided by our eyelid reflex inhibition experiments. When specific instructions to refrain from blinking were given, the combination of a sound with a puff of air directed on to the eye led to complete inhibition of the eyelid reflex to the unconditioned stimulus. Through conditioned adaptational changes in the ocular muscles, the sound helped to inhibit eyelid movement. When the air-puff was delivered alone, there was no conditioned reflex preparation in the absence of the acoustic stimulus, and eyelid and orienting reflexes were observed to develop simultaneously.

The same effects were observed with a combination of weak and strong sounds. After the galvanic skin reactions to the components had been extinguished (which meant that adaptational changes limiting the effect of the stimulus had been elaborated), application of the louder sound alone without the preceding weaker sound elicited a powerful orienting reaction. The absence of the "warning" materially altered the effect of the stimulus on the analyser and led to the development of an orienting reflex (Sokolov, 1956).

Our experiments did not deal with the question of whether all the mechanisms concerned with extinction of the orienting reflex could be explained by the elaboration of cortical conditioned connexions. Inhibition of the orienting reflex can probably also develop at lower levels, as has been demonstrated experimentally on decerebrate rabbits (Kvasov, 1955). It is also probable that there are other blocking mechanisms as well as conditioned adaptation reflexes.

The similarity of the generalization phenomena occurring during the elaboration of conditioned reflexes and during extinction of the orienting reflex merit attention in relation to the question of the connexion between extinction of the orienting reflex and the elaboration of adaptation conditioned reflexes. We know that when a reflex is elaborated with a combination of one stimulus and reinforcement, the conditioned reflex will also develop in response to stimuli close to the signal stimulus. And the closer spatially the points in the cortex representing these stimuli are to one another, the more is this so. When the orienting reflex to one such group of stimuli is extinguished, the inhibition spreads to the neighbouring parts and its strength is directly proportional to the proximity of the particular stimulus to that used during extinction. Extinction of orienting reactions from the skin on the palm also leads to their disappearance in the case of stimulation administered on the fingers. At more remote points on the skin the reaction increases in magnitude the further the point of application of the stimulus is from that used during extinction. This irradiation of the extinction of orienting reflexes is presumably connected with irradiation during elaboration of the conditioned adaptation reflexes.

When a stimulus is applied many times, its effect is modified as a result of the elaboration of conditioned inhibition of the orienting reflexes and the formation of conditioned adaptation reflexes. These changes in the analyser can be expressed numerically in terms of changes in sensitivity, reactivity and lability.

It follows, therefore, that the action of a stimulus on the analyser is a reflex process responsible for the ultimate perception of the stimulus.

What happens when the action of a non-signal stimulus is given reinforcement in the form of a verbal order belonging to another agent, producing a powerful orienting reaction, or painful reinforcement associated with the development of a defensive reflex? In other words, what is the nature of the processes which characterize the readjustment of stimulus perception during the elaboration of a conditioned reflex to that stimulus? As we see it, the elaboration of a new motor reflex does not differ in principle from the elaboration of the conditioned orienting and conditioned adaptational reflexes which develop when any non-signal stimulus is applied repeatedly. The only difference lies in the analysers participating, and in the adaptational significance of the different conditioned connexions.

The elaboration of conditioned reflexes—conditioned adaptation reflexes, reflexes to time and conditioned inhibition or excitation of orienting reflexes— begins in the course of the application of a non-signal stimulus. The actual effect of repeated non-signal stimuli is mediated by a system of conditioned reflex connexions which regulate the magnitude of the effect of the stimulus on the organism. Reinforcement following a stimulus which has become indifferent merely complicates and varies the system of connexions already created. But the features described by us in our analysis of the action of non-signal stimuli are essentially the same as those seen during the elaboration of motor reflexes.

The effectiveness of reinforcement depends on the systems of connexions formed during its application (that is on how frequently and in what combinations the reinforcement is applied). Experiments in which we applied powerful electrodermal stimuli which, as the application continued, produced increasingly powerful defensive reactions without trace of the orienting reflex which developed when these stimuli were first applied, showed that the effect of the stimulus when it became reinforcement was very different from its effect when presented as an unconditioned stimulus (Vinogradova and Sokolov, 1957). The general principles discussed earlier in relation to the reflex adjustment of the effects of stimuli resulting from repetition are thus equally applicable whether the stimuli be reinforcing or conditioned.

The combination of a conditioned stimulus with reinforcement leads to complicated interaction between the combined elements, with disturbance of previously established connexions and the establishment of new ones.

Let us examine, by reference to plethysmographic findings, the combination of an acoustic stimulus with electrodermal reinforcement after the sound has become an indifferent stimulus and the current has begun to elicit a frank defensive reaction without trace of any orienting reflex. The mere fact of combining the sound and the electrodermal stimulation altered the effect of the reinforcement, which became weaker as a defensive stimulus and assumed the properties of an exciter of the orienting reflex. But the reinforcement also altered the effect of the signal preceding it. The first effect of the application of reinforcement was intensification of the orienting reflex to the stimulus which had already acquired signal significance. Influenced by the reinforcement with current, the sound first began to evoke progressively stronger orienting reactions. A noteworthy feature here was the change in sensitivity: the conditioned stimulus thresholds fell sharply as a result of its reinforcement with current, so that very weak sounds produced definite orienting reactions (Sokolov, 1956).

Some special experiments on the visual analyser of man showed that speech reinforcement also increased sensitivity (Sokolov *et al.*, 1955). The specific effect of a light stimulus, which has acquired signal significance, in producing a greater reduction of photic sensitivity was intensified (Golubeva, 1955).

Reinforcement of a stimulus or the conferring of signal significance on it by preliminary instructions increased the lability of cortical neurons, as evidenced by the ability of the occipital region to readjust its rhythms to a higher frequency of light flicker (Sokolov, 1955, 1957; Danilova, 1957).

Intensification of orienting reflexes to the conditioned signal and reinforcement in the early stages of the elaboration of the connexion is a universal phenomenon, evident both in different elements of the orienting reaction and with different reinforcements. Speech reinforcement, for example, delivered after a light which, by virtue of many repetitions, had almost ceased to cause a reaction of α-rhythm depression, sharply intensified the depression effect to the photic stimulus, and restored the galvanic skin reflex to light.

The phenomenon is similar to one we have described in which one acoustic stimulus, which had ceased to produce an orienting reflex, was combined with another, louder, sound which produced a distinct orienting reaction. Galvanic skin reflex recordings showed that there was elaboration of a conditioned galvanic skin reflex, indicative of intensification of the orienting reflex to the conditioned stimulus. This intensification of the orienting reflex did not suggest simple disinhibition of the particular reflex as a result of the altered conditions of stimulus application, but exhibited features indicative of the elaboration of a conditioned orienting reflex.

The increase of sensitivity and reactivity of the analyser perceiving a conditioned stimulus, observed to result from the reinforcement of this stimulus, is connected with inhibition of the conditioned adaptation reflexes which were elaborated by repeated applications of the stimulus and which restricted its effect to the analyser. It should again be emphasized here that the adaptational effect of light on the eye increases when this light becomes the conditioned signal for a motor reaction (Sokolov, 1955). That this is in harmony with the intensification of the effect of sound on subcortical and cortical divisions of the auditory analyser resulting from its reinforcement by an electrodermal stimulus, has been convincingly demonstrated by the electrophysiological animal experiments of Jouvet and Hernandez-Peon (1957).

The mechanisms attenuating the orienting and special effects of the stimulus, which have been elaborated in the course of many repetitions, are abolished by reinforcement. The result is that the stimulus enters the paths of non-specific excitation and again becomes the exciter of an orienting reaction. This effect of the conditioned stimulus is intensified as a result of the elaboration by the reinforcement of a conditioned orienting reflex.

Confirmation that the signal stimulus begins to have a more powerful excitant effect on the reticular formation is afforded by restoration, or intensification, of the reaction of α-rhythm depression to the signal stimulus (Voronin and Sokolov, 1955).

The general features of the electrical reactions in the cortex in response to the action of signal stimuli (α-rhythm block when α-rhythm is prominent and intensification of α- and β-waves when θ- and δ-waves predominate in the background) are completely similar to those seen in the orienting reflex. The effect of the reinforcement is to increase the involvement of the reticular formation in the reaction and to lead to the formation of conditioned reflex activation of the reticular system in addition to the special conditioned, for example motor, reflex.

The accentuation of the orienting reflex to the signal stimulus and the formation of a conditioned orienting reflex constitute only the first stage in the formation of the conditioned reflex.

Examination of the vascular conditioned reflex to the defensive reinforcement reveals that a special conditioned defensive reflex is elaborated by the repeated combinations of conditioned stimulus and reinforcement. A sound, which at first had a more intense orienting effect when reinforced by current, itself began to elicit a defensive reaction. The orienting reflexes to the conditioned stimulus and to the reinforcement disappeared. Similar features are seen in the elaboration of a conditioned motor reflex with speech reinforcement. As the conditioned motor reflex becomes more firmly established, the α-rhythm depression produced by the stimulus diminishes, the cutaneogalvanic reflex disappears and the motor reaction is fully developed with a short, stable latent period (Voronin and Sokolov, 1955). The orienting reflex which develops in the early stage of the elaboration of the conditioned reflex is thus extinguished as the special conditioned reaction becomes firmly established and stabilized. The special conditioned reaction, on the other hand, becomes more firmly established and stronger with increase in the number of combinations of conditioned stimulus and reinforcement.

The influence of the reinforcement on the reticular formation diminishes as the number of combinations increases. Consequently, the electrical reaction in the cortex disappears when the special conditioned reaction is firmly established. It follows, therefore, that the electrical reactions seen in the cortex during the formation of a conditioned reflex are merely an expression of the participation of orienting reactions in the occurrence of the special conditioned reaction.

The different forms of electrical reactions in the cortex reflect different forms of the orienting reflex—generalized or local. The continued presence of the more resistant α-rhythm depression in response to a signal light indicates that the local orienting reaction in the visual analyser is much more resistant than the generalized reaction produced in the visual analyser by an acoustic stimulus. But even this local reaction has properties of an orienting reaction, as it disappears or is very much attenuated when the conditioned reflex is firmly established.

This extinction of the orienting reflex to a signal stimulus, which is produced by weakening of the effects on the reticular formation, only occurs when the conditioned connexion is sufficiently stable and the demands for discrimination of signal stimuli are very small. It is essentially subject to the same laws of extinction as orienting reactions to non-signal stimuli. With the signal stimulus, however, the rate of extinction is much slower. The orienting reflex is then maintained by the reinforcement following the conditioned stimulus, and by return afferentation from the response reaction which its reinforcement produces.

The orienting reflex is, however, restored as soon as we alter the structure of the conditioned connexion by substituting reinforcement for one of the conditioned stimuli, by changing the conditioned stimulus or, finally, by altering the conditions in which the response reaction occurs. There is particular intensification of the orienting reflex when one stimulus is reinforced positively and another closely similar to it is reinforced negatively. This applies to all forms of reinforcement and includes the elaboration of a conditioned motor reflex with speech reinforcement. When two stimuli have to be differentiated, the orienting reflex and the special conditioned reflex exhibit divergent features. The latent periods for the motor reaction in the conditioned reflex are increased quite considerably, the indications being that inhibition is developing in this system.

The inhibition of the special conditioned reflex is associated with inhibition of the conditioned adaptational reflexes which are elaborated in the course of the applications of any stimulus to an analyser and which include its effect on the non-specific system. Concurrently with the inhibition of the special conditioned reflex and the inhibition of the conditioned adaptational reflexes there is intensification of the orienting reaction. Consequently, the process of inhibition which is so clearly evident in the conditioned reflex arc cannot be detected in the general level of cortical excitation, which is greatly increased and is characterized by greater background depression and more powerful orienting reactions on application of stimuli. All this is indicative of the increased level of cortical excitation produced through activation of the reticular system.

In this way we arrive at the important conclusion that processes of excitation and inhibition in the system of the orienting reflex may stand in reciprocal relationships to processes of excitation and inhibition in the conditioned reflex arc. This conclusion is supported by experiments of many kinds. Thus, stabilization of the conditioned reflex is associated with extinction or attenuation of the electrical reactions in the cortex. The more closely the conditioned stimuli which have to be differentiated stand to one another, the more powerful is the excitation of the orienting reflex and the stronger the inhibition processes in the system of the conditioned motor reflex, the signs of which are lengthening of the latent period and loss of a number of reactions in response to positive stimuli. That the α-rhythm depression actually reflects the increased level of excitation observed when closely similar stimuli have to be differentiated is proved by the increase of lability in the systems of cortical neurons as revealed by intensified driven rhythm reactions in response to light flicker of higher frequency (Danilova, 1957).

The explanation for the persistence of the orienting reflex when the differentiation of conditioned stimuli is difficult is that the stabilization of connexions which normally restrict stimulus action when non-signal stimuli are used or when a conditioned reflex not requiring fine discrimination of stimuli is being elaborated, is rendered difficult by the replacement of stimuli.

Cortical mechanisms which can activate the reticular system and thereby create conditions for the maintenance of a high level of excitation are an important factor in the intensification of the orienting reactions in difficult stimulus differentiation.

The difference between orienting reactions to positive and orienting reactions to negative stimuli, when differentiation has been firmly established, constitutes important proof of the participation of the cortex. Our experimental work has shown that, as the differentiation of conditioned motor reactions proceeds and reactions develop only in response to the positive signals, orienting reactions, including α-rhythm block, develop only in response to the positive stimulus. It is difficult to assume that fine differentiation of signals can be effected in the reticular system itself, as would appear to follow from the scheme of the conditioned reflex suggested by Gastaut *et al.* (1957). The more likely view is that the signal reaching the cortex from the positive stimulus, itself influences the reticular system and thus intensifies the orienting reflex. This is shown by experiments in which verbal stimuli were purposely used as positive and negative stimuli, as their discrimination requires the participation of complex cortical mechanisms. The positive verbal stimuli likewise elicited more powerful reactions of depression than the negative stimuli (Marushevskii, 1957). Selective excitability of the reticular system, the activity of which is evidenced more particularly by α-rhythm block, was thus produced in the course of the elaboration of a conditioned reflex which required the participation of cortical mechanisms.

Selectivity of the orienting reaction is connected with the selective character of the conditioned reflex. This is typified by the experiments described earlier in which weak threshold signal stimuli produced powerful vascular components in the orienting reflex whereas louder sounds did not elicit any appreciable reactions (Vinogradova and Sokolov, 1955). This was also observed when light sensitivity was measured: weak light stimuli close to threshold produced more persistent reactions of α-rhythm depression than other more clearly perceived photic stimuli (Mikhalevskaya, 1957).

A conditioned stimulus thus produces reactions, first as the unconditioned exciter of an orienting reaction and, secondly, as its conditioned exciter. The former effect may be explained by movement of excitation over collaterals to the reticular system and the latter by cortical connexions which intensify or attenuate the unconditioned effect of the stimulus. The functioning of the conditioned reflex involves continuous interaction between specific and non-specific paths for the transmission of excitation, which is reflected in the dynamics of the orienting and specific reflexes.

Not only does the conditioned stimulus evoke a more powerful orienting reaction by increasing the excitation of the cortical point connected with perception of the conditioned stimulus, but it also sets the level of excitability required for effectuation and control of the response reaction through the mechanism of the conditioned orienting reflex. This is seen very clearly in recordings of rolandic rhythm, which is depressed during action of the conditioned stimulus serving as the signal for movement. The depression is seen even when only one movement is elicited (Gastaut, 1952; Gastaut *et al.*, 1957). Our experiments in which light was combined with passive movement of an arm showed that, after a number of combinations, the light acquired the properties of an exciter of local depression of the rolandic rhythm. This effect disappeared, however, when the combinations were continued, but was restored by the action of an extra-stimulus in the manner of an orienting reflex.

That the specific conditioned reflex and the electrographic expression of the conditioned orienting reflex were unconnected was revealed by dissociation of the peripheral muscular conditioned reflex and conditioned depression of the rolandic rhythm. Conditioned block of rolandic rhythm occurred even in the absence of conditioned muscular reactions (Roger *et al.*, 1958).

When a conditioned reflex is firmly established, the conditioned stimulus
T

may elicit a conditioned reaction with minimum cortical analysis of the stimulus, a position which corresponds to the stage of extinction of the orienting component. Cortical control, however, remains. Of interest in this connexion are certain cases of erroneous movements, developing when the conditioned stimulus is suddenly changed after the subject has been given only the positive stimulus repeatedly. Under these conditions the conditioned stimulus produced a short burst of muscle potentials of large amplitude in the electromyogram, with a minimum latent period. There was, however, secondary correction of this reaction while the reflex was still in the course of developing. The muscle potentials were inhibited and there was simultaneous development of an orienting reaction (Novikova and Sokolov, 1957).

What does this experiment indicate? It would appear that the excitation from the conditioned stimulus, firmly established by reason of its constant application, was transferred to effector paths without adequate analysis, and perception of the signal as differing from the model was somewhat delayed because of the extinction of the orienting reflex. The lack of correspondence detected in the course of further action of the stimulus was the stimulus for the orienting reflex and for the reticular system. There was simultaneous development of inhibition in the paths of the conditioned reflex, just in time to arrest the commencing reaction. It follows, therefore, that cortical control of a conditioned reflex is effected through excitation of the orienting system.

Although reciprocal relationships between the level of excitation of the orienting reflex and the excitation in the conditioned reflex system were observed in a number of cases, it must be emphasized that a certain level of excitation of the orienting reflex is essential for the formulation and functioning of the conditioned reflex. By increasing cortical excitability at the receiving point for the conditioned signal and at the points for control of the response reaction and the effect of reinforcement, the orienting reflex provides the necessary conditions for the fine perception of the conditioned stimulus and the feedback impulses from the motor system.

Preliminary extinction of the orienting reaction makes it difficult to elaborate a conditioned reflex to the stimulus for which the orienting reflex has been extinguished. Conversely, there is successful closure of the conditioned reflex if the orienting reflex is adequately pronounced. When a connexion is closed, even after preliminary extinction of the orienting reflex to the conditioned stimulus, restoration of the orienting reflex can be observed before development of the conditioned connexion (Sokolov and Paramonova, 1956).

In many cases, the elaboration of a conditioned reflex can be observed even when the orienting reflex has been extinguished and there is a general inhibitory drowsy state. Experiments by Vinogradova and Paramonova have shown that the conditioned stimulus is not distinctly perceived by the subject and that the conditioned connexion is not reflected in the subject's verbal system. A similar phenomenon was observed by us in the case of preliminary extinction of the orienting reflexes both to the conditioned stimulus, a light, and to the reinforcement, passive raising of the arm, when this produced the development of an inhibitory state, as evidenced by slow waves in the subject's electroencephalogram. In a number of cases we were able to observe a reflex movement of the arm which the subject assessed as an involuntary twitch, or of which he was completely unaware (Roger *et al.*, 1958). The orienting reflex mechanism, which is essential for perception of the conditioned stimulus and control of the response reaction, has thus an important influence on the quality of the conditioned connexion formed.

Our analysis shows that the process of perception, considered as one of reception in the widest sense, cannot be reduced to elementary concepts of the centripetal conduction of afferent impulses. The effect of the stimulus on the analyser is a complicated reflex process involving a large number of reflex adaptations in complex interaction.

An important place in the process of perception is occupied by conditioned orienting and conditioned adaptational reflexes, closure of which may be effected within the limits of the same analyser and thus render it capable of detailed and adequate representation of the effects of external agents. The general principles of conditioned reflex activity can, therefore, be used for the analysis of some mechanisms of perception. And the discovery of the complex structure of mechanisms for stimulus perception will enable us to achieve a more profound understanding of the structure of the conditioned reflex arc in man.

A Neuronal Model of the Stimulus and the Orienting Reflex

1. Questions in the Objective Study of Sensory Integration

An important problem in central nervous system research is that of "sensory integration" (Adrian, 1947)—the synthesis of elementary stimuli into a system which, when integrated, determines the reaction of the organism.

"Gestalt" psychologists have demonstrated the importance of the relationships between the various elements in perception (Koffka, 1935). As, however, they limited their research to the description of subjective phenomena, it was impossible for them to discover the intrinsic mechanisms in this phenomenon.

Pavlov's doctrine on conditioned reflexes made it possible to develop objective methods of examination for the processes of sensory analysis and synthesis, based on the elaboration of differentiated conditioned reflexes to simple and compound stimuli. Thus, Ivanov-Smolenskii (1927) has shown that a system of elementary stimuli constitutes a specific stimulus to which, as a single whole, a conditioned reflex can be elaborated. The conditioned reflex method opened up a wide field for the objective study of analyser activity in a variety of animal species (Voronin, 1953, 1957). It should be noted that the investigation of sensory integration by means of conditioned reflexes was based on preliminary, often prolonged, elaboration of differentiated reactions with the result that the true limits of afferent analysis and synthesis were often masked.

The ability of the organism to differentiate external stimuli can, however, manifest itself by the development of an orienting reaction on change of stimulus even before the elaboration of differentiation, as well as in the form of differential conditioned reactions. Pavlov wrote: ". . . there is an essential difference between the recognition by the nervous system of a difference between external agents generally and the differentiation of these agents by means of conditioned reflexes. The former is revealed by the stimulatory process in the form of an orienting reaction, an investigatory reflex, which only secondarily has an inhibiting or disinhibiting effect on conditioned reflexes. The latter is expressed by the development of an inhibitory process

282

which is the result, so to speak, of a struggle between stimulation and inhibition" (Pavlov, 1947, p. 116).

Use of the orienting reaction, without requiring the elaboration of differentiated conditioned reflexes, makes it possible to exclude complicating factors and more directly to study the ability of the nervous system to synthesize and analyse stimuli acting on it.

2. The Orienting Reflex and its Components

The concept of the orienting (investigatory) reflex was introduced by Pavlov in 1910. Its feature is that, developing on any change of stimulus, it takes exactly the same form irrespective of whether the stimulus used is stronger, weaker or of different quality.

The development of an orienting reaction is a sign that the nervous system has detected a change in the stimulus, that it has differentiated one stimulus from another. Also, the moment at which the orienting reaction develops indicates the time at which this differentiation was first effected.

An orienting reflex consists of somatic (movements of the body, head, eyes, ears etc.), autonomic (cardiovascular and respiratory changes, cutaneogalvanic reaction), electroencephalographic (depression or exaltation of α-rhythm, changes in cortical reactivity) and also, sensory components in the form of enhanced analyser sensitivity and lability. In addition, an orienting reflex may also manifest itself indirectly by the inhibition or disinhibition of conditioned reflexes.

The isolation of the orienting reflex as an independent functional system (Anokhin, 1949, 1959), distinct from adaptational and defensive reflexes, is based on two of its properties, namely its identical nature for any change of stimulus and, its ability to undergo extinction. This distinction can be demonstrated most effectively by combined recording of vascular reactions in hand and head (Vinogradova and Sokolov, 1957).

The first applications of a variety of stimuli (heat, cold, pain, sound) produce orienting reactions in the form of vasoconstriction in the hand and vasodilatation in the head. The specific features of the different reflexes emerge with repetition of the stimuli, when the orienting reflex is extinguished. Sound, which previously produced only an orienting reaction, ceases entirely to produce vascular changes; heat produces vasodilatation and cold, vasoconstriction (adaptational thermoregulating reflex). Pain produces vasoconstriction in both the hand and head as a component of a defensive reaction. The application of an extra-stimulus, which disinhibits the orienting reflex, restores the original orienting types of reaction (vasoconstriction in the hand and vasodilatation in the head) in response to all stimuli. A cutaneogalvanic reaction (method of Tarkhanov or Féré), eye movements, respiratory change and α-rhythm depression in the occipital and motor regions are observed at the same time as the vascular changes. Occasionally, there is also an increase of muscle tone. All these reactions, as components of the orienting reflex, are regularly extinguished by repetition of the stimulus and are restored when it is changed.

A study of the rate of extinction and the localization of the various components of the orienting reflex have revealed two types of reflex, namely generalized and local. The former comprises the activation of several analysers whereas in the latter there is activation of systems only in the analyser directly concerned. The first application of a tactile stimulus (contact stimulator), for example, produces generalized α-rhythm depression, eye movement, arrest of respiration and a cutaneogalvanic reaction. After 15–30 applications all that remains is the local effect in the EEG of the sensorimotor region. Later, this reaction is also extinguished and is only restored when there is change of stimulus or change in the experimental setting.

The functional significance of all these components of the complicated orienting reaction lies in increase of the discriminatory powers of the analysers and the provision of optimum conditions for perception of stimuli. This takes the form of increased reactivity, sensitivity and lability in both central and peripheral parts of the analysers.

Comparative study of the background EEG spectrum in the occipital region and the reactive changes produced by light flicker by means of Walter's harmonic analyser, shows that the first application of light flicker on an EEG background of excitation characterized by α-rhythm of low amplitude, leads to still greater α-rhythm depression and the development of a rhythmic response at a frequency of 18 c/s. The light effect diminishes with repeated application. This is associated with change in the background rhythmic activity to α-rhythm of large amplitude. Under these conditions the light does not elicit a response with a rate of 18 c/s, the α-rhythm frequency being only slightly increased. After the administration of a sound stimulus which produces an orienting reaction, there is again background predominance of low-amplitude α-rhythm of greater frequency, and light flicker produes marked photic driving to a rate of 18 c/s. The reactivity of the cortical divisions of the visual analyser were thus increased by an orienting reaction (Sokolov, 1958).

The activation of analyser systems by an orienting reaction extends also to their peripheral segments. Experiments on rabbits, using contact lenses acting as lid retractors and electrode carriers, established that the lability of the retina was increased by an orienting reaction. The evidence of this was that light flicker of relatively high frequency (20–40 c/s) began to produce more powerful reactions after the delivery of a sound stimulus. Examination of the reaction by harmonic analysis of the rabbit electroretinogram (ERG), by means of a modified Walter analyser capable of analysing oscillations of from 1·5 to 480 c/s, revealed that this intensification of the retinal responses can only be observed during a certain limited period following the sound stimulation. This intensification effect was not discernible if the acoustic stimulus had previously been applied repeatedly and the orienting reaction extinguished.

The detailed analysis of the ERG for a frequency of 5 c/s was of exceptional interest. With this low frequency flicker, the sound usually failed to change, or might even reduce the ERG amplitude slightly. Analysis of the form of the ERG by the superimposition of 50 segments taken during 10-sec periods of light flicker, revealed peculiar pointing of the "B" wave resulting from more rapid return of the tracing to the baseline, an effect which we also observed when the light intensity was increased. The ERG cycle was thus shortened for low frequencies by an orienting reaction, and the retina could respond to a higher flash frequency.

The activation of the central and peripheral parts of the analyser by an orienting reflex is reflected in a general increase of sensitivity with lowering of absolute thresholds. As this increased sensitivity is of limited duration and disappears with extinction of the orienting reflex, a "test stimulus method" was used for its examination (Sokolov, 1958). A light stimulus, the strength of which was 0·8 threshold, was delivered before and after the sound producing the orienting reaction. The subject was instructed to clench his hand as soon as he saw the light. The experiment was carried out after complete dark adaptation. If, by virtue of preliminary application, the sound did not elicit an orienting reaction as evidenced by α-rhythm depression in the occipital region, the test stimulus remained subliminal. If, however, the sound stimulus was altered (e.g. intensified) and began to produce α-rhythm depression in the occipital region, the sensitivity of the visual analyser was increased, on this background of depression, and the test stimulus was detected by the subject: it increased the depression still further and produced a conditioned motor reaction recorded in the form of muscular contraction. As the orienting reaction to the new sound was in turn extinguished and the depression diminished, sensitivity was also reduced: the latent period for the motor reaction to the test stimulus increased and later a conditioned reaction failed completely to develop. The test stimulus remained subthreshold. Thus, the effect of increased sensitivity disappeared with extinction of the orienting reflex. The orienting reflex is thus a system of reactions promoting directly, (cortical rhythm, ERG) or indirectly, (cerebral blood supply) the most favourable conditions for stimulus reception.

3. Selective Extinction of the Orienting Reflex

The above analysis shows that the extinction of the orienting reaction is of selective character. This means that the reaction can still be elicited by other stimuli which had not previously been used after its extinction to one stimulus. Repeated applications of an acoustic stimulus of fixed frequency and loudness led to disappearance of all components of the orienting reaction and a state of apparent non-reactivity. A sound of the same intensity but different pitch then produced a distinct orienting reaction which, within certain limits, increased in intensity the greater the difference between the new sound and that used in the experiment (Sokolov and Paramonova, 1959).

A similar process but of slower development (in that the main criterion used was the local orienting reflex in the form of α-rhythm depression) could be observed in response to point stimulation of the retina effected by means of a projection perimeter. In the third experiment the first application of the light at 40° from the central fixation point produced a generalized reaction with respiratory change, eye movement, a cutaneogalvanic reaction and α-rhythm depression. There was no reaction to the 9th application. It did not develop when the point of stimulation was transferred to 35°. Stimulation of a point at 50°, however, produced a reaction and more powerful responses developed from stimulation of points at 60° and 70°.

This selective extinction cannot be explained by local reduction of excitability at certain points in the analyser. Evidence against this view is afforded by an experiment in which the absolute threshold was measured after selective extinction of the orienting reaction to one particularly, quite considerable intensity. For instance, after 21 applications a sound of 70 dB and 100 c/s ceased to produce changes in the EEG, cutaneogalvanic reaction and other components of the orienting reflex. However, at that moment a sound of threshold intensity (O dB) and the same frequency as before produced the entire group of reactions. The same result was obtained with photic stimuli close to the absolute threshold (1–70 thresholds). After extinction of the reaction to a light of 160 units (about 30 times threshold) in the 5th experiment, a weaker stimulus of 120 units (about 5 times threshold) produced a reaction in the form of α blocking and the development of a cutaneogalvanic reaction. It can be concluded, therefore, that selective extinction of the orienting reflex is not merely a result of simple local changes in analyser excitability.

4. A Neuronal Model of the Stimulus

We have introduced the concept of the "neuronal model of the stimulus" to explain the phenomenon of selective extinction (Voronin and Sokolov, 1958). By neuronal model is meant a certain cell system whereby the information is stored concerning the properties of a stimulus which has been applied many times. The term suggests that the nervous system produces an exact model of the properties of external objects acting on the sense organs. Let us examine some of the properties of such a neuronal model. If the same stimulus, e.g. stimulation of a certain point in the retina with a stimulus of definite intensity, is always used for experimental extinction of the orienting reaction, the duration of the stimulus and the intervals between individual stimuli will be recorded at the time in the neuronal model. Whatever parameter of the stimulus we change, an orienting reaction develops at the moment when the stimulus administered ceases to coincide with the "neuronal model" built up in former applications. The neuronal model is, therefore, a polyvalent model of the stimulus in which all or a considerable group of its properties are represented.

Analysis of the effect which sudden shortening or lengthening of the duration of stimulus action has on the development of the orienting reaction is of the greatest interest from the "neuronal model" standpoint. When the duration of stimulus action was reduced, a reaction developed at the moment when the action of the stimulus had previously been stopped. When the duration of stimulus action was suddenly prolonged, a reaction developed at the moment when the stimulus began to exceed the duration in the model built up previously. The general rule could, therefore, be formulated that an orienting reflex developed when a stimulus delivered at a given moment failed to coincide with the previously created "neuronal model of the stimulus". The "neuronal model" concept is closely connected with a phenomenon which can be described as the extrapolating properties of the nervous system (Krushinskii, 1959). Instances in which the same stimulus was repeated at strictly constant intervals of time are of interest in this connexion. After the orienting reaction to the stimulus had been extinguished, the omission of one stimulus from its usual place led to the development of an orienting reaction, which showed that the model was tuned to the complex sequence of future events. A system reflecting the most probable sequence of future actions is presumably built up in the nervous system in the course of repeated applications. At any moment this system is compared with the stimulus actually in operation. When there is lack of coincidence, an orienting reaction develops in order to facilitate reception of the elements responsible for this disturbance.

The nervous system thus elaborates a forecast of future stimuli as a result of repeated stimulation and compares these forecasts with the stimuli actually in operation.

The concept of a neuronal model of the stimulus also enables us to explain the features seen in the development of an orienting reaction when a compound stimulus is used. When combinations of a weak and a loud sound are used, the orienting reactions to both components are gradually extinguished. If now the weak stimulus is applied alone, a reaction develops at the point where the loud stimulus is lacking. If the strong stimulus is delivered without being preceded by the weak stimulus, a reaction develops despite the fact that the same strong component did not produce a reaction when it followed the weaker component.

Another example of the formation of a neuronal model for the action of compound stimuli is afforded by the extinction of reactions to words. When the orienting reactions to various words differing in sound but similar in meaning were extinguished, the use of a word with a different meaning produces a reaction. The orienting reaction in this case is elicited by the lack of coincidence between the already created neuronal model fixing a group of words with common meaning and the newly applied word from a different group.

It is appropriate, in a discussion of the neuronal model of the stimulus, to consider the concept of the dynamic stereotype introduced by Pavlov, which is based on analysis of reflex activity in relation to repetitive stimulation, delivered regularly under exactly the same conditions (Pavlov, 1949).

The dynamic stereotype concept is essentially based on evidence concerning the stereotyped reproduction of reactions, but the term "neuronal model of the stimulus", is concerned with the persistent retention of traces of external stimulation—in so far as it explains the development of non-stereotype orienting reactions, and is a further development of Anokhin's concepts of the "acceptor of action" (Anokhin, 1959). That both phenomena are, however, based on common mechanisms is clearly revealed by analysis of the interrelationship between conditioned and orienting reactions.

5. The Filtering Properties of the Neuronal Model

The fact that the orienting reaction only disappears for the stimulus which had previously been used in the experiment, suggests the selective blocking of impulses from the afferent system to effector mechanisms for the orienting reaction. The neuronal model would, therefore, function as a selective filter. The characteristics of the filter can be defined by changing one parameter of the stimulus used for extinction and recording the magnitude of the reaction which develops. When the test stimulus differed only slightly from the model, the reaction was very slight. The greater the difference between the model and the stimulus delivered, the larger the reaction. Similar characteristics can be obtained for each of the properties of the stimulus (duration, strength, etc.) and the neuronal model, therefore, acts as a compound filter, arresting or blocking the reaction to the definite combination of properties which is characteristic of the given stimulus. This filtration applies not only to the simple properties, but to combinations of these properties, as has been noted in connexion with the action of compound stimuli.

It must be emphasized that the orienting reaction may also fail to reflect the finest differentiations of which the afferent system is capable. The fact is that, when a stimulus is used repeatedly, there may be general reduction of excitability in the centres for the orienting reflex in addition to the formation of the neuronal mode—the basis for possible future elaboration by the nervous system of the impulses signifying discrepancy which are responsible for the orienting reaction. Consequently, the weak impulses produced by slight discrepancies may prove non-effective by virtue of the reduction in the general excitability of the orienting reaction. The neuronal model, which can be created for intermittent stimuli as well as for a constant stimulus, also takes account of the number of times stimuli of different kinds are used in an experiment. When the experimental stimulus was kept strictly constant, a just detectable change might, under favourable circumstances, produce an orienting reaction. When various stimuli were used, the orienting reaction to the property which was varied in the experiment was extinguished collectively. Comparison of stimuli used a different number of times in an experiment showed that the stimulus of which there were fewer applications acted more effectively.

6. The Scheme of the Orienting Reflex

The ability of the nervous system to "model" compound stimuli, in the course of the extinction of the orienting reaction, compels us to recognize that the cortex is the most important element in these processes. Extinction of the orienting reaction is impossible in decorticate dogs (Pavlov, 1949). The efferent mechanisms of the orienting reflex are situated in the nuclei of the brain-stem reticular formation. Excitation of these nuclei may be produced through collaterals from the specific paths. This, however, is not the only path. It must be remembered that these nuclei can also be stimulated through descending corticoreticular fibres, excited by the suggested "impulses of discrepancy" arising from failure of the stimulus to coincide with the neuronal model in the cortex. With the formation of a new model corresponding to the actual stimulus administered, the impulses of discrepancy disappear.

The impulses travelling over collaterals from specific paths are, as a result of repetition of the stimulus, apparently blocked by a conditioned inhibitory reflex mechanism. The active role of the cortex in the inhibition of the orienting reaction is confirmed by experiments in which cortical control was temporarily abolished by sleep inhibition, as well as in experiments on decorticate animals.

When the orienting reaction is extinguished, all the reactions disappear gradually but the EEG background is still active. If, however, the extinction process is continued further, the EEG background tends to be changed by the development of slow waves, indicative of the development of an inhibitory state in the cortex. With the development of this inhibitory background there is paradoxical restoration and intensification of orienting reactions as revealed by exaltation of α-rhythm, a cutaneogalvanic reaction, respiratory changes and vascular reactions, all of which are stably maintained in this transitional state between waking and sleep. If a powerful stimulus is made to act at this stage, an active EEG is restored and the unextinguished reactions disappear.

It may be asked to what extent does the development of slow waves actually point to the development of an inhibitory process? Evidence on this point is afforded by cortical reactions to light flicker at various stages of sleep inhibition. It has been shown experimentally that the development of slow waves is connected with reduction of cortical reactivity and lability.

The influence of the cortex in selectively blocking impulses is apparently directed primarily to control of the passage of excitation over collaterals to the reticular system. This is proved by the fact that extinction of the orienting reflex by direct electrical stimulation of the reticular system is not observed in intact animals.

Let us examine the effect of a photic stimulus in relation to our suggested schema, which is based on findings by Polyakov and Shkol'nik-Yarros (1959). The elements of the schema are: (a) conduction over specific paths of the information used for modelling and (b) comparison of the incoming specific excitation with the neuronal model.

Depending on the results of the comparison, there may be:

(a) the development of signals of discrepancy when the stimulus fails to coincide with the model and activation of the reticular system through corticoreticular connexions. Cessation of the collateral block as a result of disturbance of the conditioned inhibitory connexion. Enhancement of the discriminatory power of the analysers through the system of feed-back connexions.

(b) absence of signals of discrepancy when the stimulus coincides with the model. Collateral block by an inhibitory conditioned reflex mechanism.

Among the various effects connected with the reticular system special mention must be made of its feed-back influence on the receptor, involving both specific paths and the sympathetic nervous system, to which Orbeli (1949) has drawn particular attention in his theory of the adaptation-trophic function of the autonomic nervous system.

Discussion of the conditioned reflex mechanism for extinction of the orienting reaction must include mention of the numerous investigations by Pavlov and his school (Rozental', 1932; Chechulin, 1923; Popov, 1921) demonstrating the connexion between extinction of the orienting reflex and internal inhibition.

The stimulus used for extinction is at once a conditioned stimulus and an unconditioned agent, leading to development of unconditioned inhibition of the orienting reaction, which disappears when the action of the stimulus is prolonged. This inhibition may possibly be connected with the development of hyperpolarization of the synaptic endings of collaterals entering the reticular system. The unconditioned inhibition which develops may be intensified in accordance with signals from the cortex which depend on the specific information reaching it at the onset of stimulation. The fact that, as the number of applications of the stimulus increases, its extinction always takes the form of gradual shortening of the reaction—although the initial moment is the most difficult to inhibit, constitutes indirect evidence in favour of the view expressed.

In this inhibitory conditioned connection, the onset of stimulation, which previously had repeatedly produced a process of unconditioned inhibition of the orienting reaction, became a signal "switching on" the mechanism of this inhibition in anticipation of its need. The duration of this same stimulation, which previously evoked a process of unconditioned inhibition, was equivalent to the reinforcement in ordinary conditioned reflexes. When the stimulus was changed, this inhibitory connection, which usually blocked the reticular system in good time, failed to operate, and the stimuli began to elicit orienting reactions, the effect being, therefore, one of disinhibition of these reactions.

7. The Neuronal Model of the Stimulus and the Conditioned Reflex

The process of conditioned reflex elaboration is one of complex interaction between the orienting and specific unconditioned reflexes elicited by the action of both the prospective conditioned stimulus and the prospective unconditioned stimulus which later becomes the reinforcement. This process can be observed most clearly in man when the vascular reactions in the hand and head are recorded simultaneously in the course of the elaboration of a conditioned defensive reflex to electrodermal stimulation. In order that the entire process may be observed in a pure form, the orienting reactions to both the future conditioned stimulus, a sound, and the future unconditioned stimulus, the current, are extinguished, so that the sound generally ceases to produce a reaction and the current begins to elicit regular vascular defensive reactions instead of orienting reactions. When the sound and current are first combined, the orienting reactions to both sound and current are intensified. The specific conditioned defensive reaction is only elaborated after many combinations, the proof of its formation being the development of vasoconstrictor reactions in the head and hand in response to the sound alone. If a new distinct stimulus is introduced at this stage, there is again initial activation of the orienting reflex to both the new and the previously used positive stimulus, and a large number of applications are required before the stage is reached when the positive stimulus produces a conditioned defensive reflex, and the new stimulus is completely inactive. This relationship between conditioned and orienting reflexes proves that the orienting reflex is an intrinsic part of a conditioned reflex as well as being an independent reflex (Voronin and Sokolov, 1955).

The relationship between orienting and conditioned reflexes may be stated in the following way. Until a conditioned reflex is firmly established, consolidated and automatized, it is accompanied by the development of orienting reactions to both conditioned and unconditioned stimulus. Stabilization of the conditioned connexion coincides with disappearance of the orienting reaction. All changes in the conditioned reflex system are accompanied by development or intensification of the orienting reflex, and the time the latter persists is proportional to the difficulty of the system of reflexes to be elaborated.

This evidence suggests that the repeated application of the conditioned stimulus leads to the formation of a neuronal model of the stimulus. A conditioned reaction only develops when the stimulus applied coincides with the model. If the stimulus and model are not identical, impulses signifying discrepancy develop and an orienting reaction occurs. The conditioned reaction is arrested at the same time. If the new stimulus is reinforced in the same way as the old, there is rapid formation of a single common model, which may also incorporate the rate of application of stimuli, a fact noted when non-signal sounds differing in frequency were used alternately. If, however, the new stimulus is given negative reinforcement, a more complicated situation develops: two independent models are formed, one corresponding to the positive sitmulus and the other to the negative. When both models have been formed, both positive and negative conditioned reactions proceed without any trace of an orienting reflex as there are no impulses of discrepancy. If a further stimulus is introduced, it produces a reaction only if it does not coincide with either model. The nature of its conditioned reaction is determined by the model with which it coincides.

Certain special experiments yielded confirmatory evidence of the correctness of this scheme. When one point on the retina was chosen as the origin of a positive stimulus and others adjacent to it were made negative ones, it was found that, as the reflex became consolidated, the most powerful orienting reactions developed in response to stimuli situated between the positive and negative stimuli, or in other words, to stimuli which did not correspond to the model of either the positive or negative stimulus. There was also a secondary zone of powerful orienting reactions produced by stimulation of the outermost points in the field of vision, seldom used in the experiment. The orienting reactions in the former zone developed by virtue of non-coincidence with either positive or negative stimulus, the latter group as a result of divergence from the more general model of the negative stimuli.

Conditioned motor reflexes with the shortest latent period and greatest intensity developed in response to stimuli close to the model of the positive stimulus. The motor reactions which developed where the orienting reactions were powerful were sluggish, slight and abortive, and had long latent periods.

Beyond, there was a zone in which both conditioned and orienting reactions were absent. And finally, there was no development of conditional reactions in the outermost zone of powerful orienting reactions.

Similar relationships were created when we made one stimulus negative and the others positive (inhibitory standard method: Paramonova, 1959). The inhibitory standard to which the gradually formed neuronal model corresponded was a sound of 100 c/s. At first only sounds differing greatly from the inhibitory standard elicited conditioned motor reactions. All the related stimuli, including the inhibitory standard itself, produced orienting reactions. Then orienting reactions gradually ceased to occur with the inhibitory standard. Sounds near to the standard began to elicit orienting reactions unaccompanied by conditioned reactions, and slightly more remote stimuli produced conditioned motor and orienting reactions simultaneously.

These relationships were extremely prominent during the elaboration of conditioned vascular defensive reflexes with electrodermal reinforcement. When the stimulus coincided with the model of the positive, current-reinforced acoustic stimulus, a special form of conditioned reaction developed, in which there was complete absence of the cutaneogalvanic reaction, the direct sign of the orienting reflex. Stimuli between the positive and inhibitory standards produced powerful vascular reactions of orienting type and cutaneogalvanic reactions. Stimuli coinciding with the inhibitory model elicited neither vascular nor cutaneogalvanic reactions. Stimuli of extreme peripheral frequencies produced reactions of orienting type and cutaneogalvanic reactions. The concept of two models, inhibitory and positive, affords a satisfactory explanation for the structure of the reaction zones observed.

Analysis of conditioned motor reflexes to photic stimuli, close to the absolute threshold from the standpoint of the neuronal model theory, is of particular interest. When the threshold is being determined, the subject reacts by movement to all stimuli, including the very weakest. Supraliminal stimuli are readily associated with the model and two or three repetitions of such a stimulus are sufficient to produce a motor reaction without trace of orienting reaction. When stimuli close to threshold are used, the formation of a model is more difficult and even a thousand stimuli in a series of successive experiments may fail to extinguish the orienting reaction.

The part played by the neuronal model of the stimulus in conditioned and orienting reactions may be represented schematically in the following way.

There is formation of a model of the conditioned stimulus during the establishment of a conditioned reflex. Direct stimulation of the reticular formation is at the same time blocked. Impulses of discrepancy do not arise. Coincidence of a stimulus with the established model leads to development of a conditioned reaction without inclusion of the activating system. When the stimulus is changed, an orienting reaction develops because of lack of coincidence between the stimulus and the model, or because of the difficulty of forming a new model. The blocking effect of the cortex on the reticular formation is reduced and the conditioned reaction is arrested. The reticular system produces a reaction of activation which spreads through the cortex and brings into operation its finer discriminatory power.

REFERENCES

ADRIAN, E. D., *The physical background of perception.* Oxford (1947).

ADRIAN, E. D., *Brain mechanisms and consciousness.* pp. 237–243. Oxford (1954).

ALEKSEYEV, M. A., *J. Higher Nervous Activity (Zh. vyssh. nervn. deyat.)* **3**: 6 (1953).

ALEKSEYEV, M. A., *J. Higher Nervous Activity (Zh. vyssh. nervn. deyat.)* **5**: 4 (1955).

ALEKSEYEV, M. A. and ARAPOVA, A. A., Scientific papers of the Pavlov physiological laboratories (*Tr. fiziol. labor. im. I. P. Pavlova*) Vol. 4 (1949).

ALLPORT, F. H., *Theories of perception and the concept of structure: a review and critical analysis with an introduction to a dynamic-structural theory of behavior.* p. 709. New York and London (1955).

ANDREYEV, L. A., Proceedings of 15th International Physiological Congress (*XV Mezhdunarodnyi fiziol. kongress. Tezisy soobshchenii*). Moscow (1935).

ANOKHIN, P. K., Scientific papers of the Pavlov physiological laboratories (*Tr. fiziol. labor. im. I. P. Pavlova*). Vol. 10. (1941).

ANOKHIN, P. K., Problems of higher nervous activity (*Problemy vysshei nervnoi deyatel'nosti*). Moscow (1949).

ANOKHIN, P. K., Scientific papers of the Pavlov physiological laboratories (*Tr. fiziol. labor. im. I. P. Pavlova*), Vol. 2, 1 and 2. Moscow (1952).

ANOKHIN, P. K., Problems of Psychology (*Voprosy psikhologii*) **6** (1955).

ANOKHIN, P. K., *J. Higher Nervous Activity (Zh. vyssh. nervn. deyat.)* **6**: 1 (1956).

ANOKHIN, P. K., *Physiol. J. U.S.S.R. (Fiziol. zh. SSSR)* **42**: 1 (1956).

ANOKHIN, P. K., *J. Higher Nervous Activity (Zh. vyssh. nervn. deyat.)* **7**: 1 (1957).

ANOKHIN, P. K., *Internal inhibition as a physiological problem* (Vnutrenneye tormozheniye kak problema fiziologii). Medgiz, Moscow (1959).

ANREP, G. V., *Russian Physiological Journal (Russk. fiziol. zh.)* **1**: 1–2 (1917).

ARKHANGEL'SKII, V. N., GOL'TS, YE. T., and RAYEVA, N. V., Problems in sense organ physiology and pathology (*Problemy fiziologii i patologii organov chuvstv*). Moscow (1936).

ASAFOV, A. M., ZIMKINA, A. M. and STEPANOV, A. I., *Physiol. J. U.S.S.R. (Fiziol. zh. SSSR)* **41**: 3 (1955).

ASRATYAN, E. A., Archives of Biological Sciences (*Arkh. biol. nauk*) **30** (1939).

ASRATYAN, E. A., Proceedings of 15th Congress on Problems of Higher Nervous Activity (*Trud. 15-go soveshch. po problemam vyssh. nervn. deyat.*). Moscow and Leningrad (1952).

ASRATYAN, E. A., *J. Higher Nervous Activity (Zh. vyssh. nervn. deyat.)* **5**: 4 (1955).

ATAYEV, M. M., *J. Higher Nervous Activity (Zh. vyssh. nervn. deyat.)* **5**: 1 (1955).

BABSKII, YE. A., *Physiol. J. U.S.S.R. (Fiziol. zh. SSSR)* **40**: 3 (1954).

BAKER, L. M. and TAYLOR, W. M., *J. Esp. Psychol.* **48**: 361–366 (1954).

BEKESY, G. A., *Acta Otolaryng.* **35**: 411–422 (1947).

BEKHTEREV, V. M., *Objective psychology* (Ob"yektivnaya psikhologiya). Moscow (1928).

BELYAVSKII, YE. A. and KHBILIVITSKII, T. YA., *Problems in the study and development of personality* (Voprosy izucheniya i vospitaniya lichnosti). Vol. 1–2 (1930).

BENTELEV, A. M. *Physiological Journal of U.S.S.R. (Fiziol. zh. SSSR)* **42**: 5 (1956).

BERGER, G., *Recent advances in biology* (Uspekhi sovremennoi biologii) **2**, 3 (1933).

BERITOV, I. S., *General physiology of the muscular and nervous systems* (Obshchaya fiziologiya myshechnoi i nervnoi sistem). Moscow and Leningrad (1948).

BERITOV, I. and VOROB'YEV, O., *Scientific papers of the Beritashvili Institute of Physiology* (Trudy In-ta fiziologii im. Beritashvili). Vol. 5. Tbilisi (1943).

BERLYNE, D. E., *J. Comp. Physiol. Psychol.* **48**: 238–246 (1955).

BERLYNE, D. E., *Brit. J. Psychol.* **45**: 256–265 (1954).

BERNSHTEIN, N. A., *The Structure of movements* (O postroyenii dvizhenii). Medgiz (1947).

BIRYUKOV, D. A., J. *Higher Nervous Activity* (*Zh. vyssh. nervn. deyat.*) **2**: 4 (1952).

BOGOSLOVSKII, A. I., *Physiol. J. U.S.S.R.* (*Fiziol. zh. SSSR*) **20**: 6 (1936).

BOIKO, YE. I., Bulletin of the Academy of Paedagogic Sciences of R.S.F.S.R. (*Izv. APN RSFSR*) **53**. Moscow (1954).

BONVALLET, M., DELL, P. and HIEBEL, G., *E.E.G. Clin. Neurophysiol.* **6**: 119–144 (1954).

BRAILOVSKII, YA. Z. and LEVINA, R. I., Bulletin of Otorhino-laryngology (*Vestn. oto-rino-laringol.*) **5**, 7 (1953).

BRAZIER, M. A. B., *Electrical activity of the nervous system.* Pitman London (1951).

BREMER, F., *Brain mechanisms and consciousness.* Oxford (1954).

BRONSHTEIN, A. I., *The sensitization of sensory organs* (Sensibilizatsiya organov chuvstv). Leningrad (1946).

BURNS, B. D., J. *Physiol.* **112**: 156–175 (1951).

BUTLER, R. A. and HARLOW, H. F., J. *Comp. Physiol. Psychol.* **47**: 258–263 (1954).

BYKOV, K. M., *Cortex and viscera* (Kora golovnogo mozga i vnutrennyye organy). Medgiz (1947).

CHANG, H. T., J. *Neurophysiol.* **15**: 5–26 (1952).

CHANG, H. T., J. *Neurophysiol.* **13**: 235–257 (1950).

CHECHULIN, S. I., Archives of Biological Sciences (*Arkhiv biol. nauk*) **23**: 1–3 (1923).

CHISTOVICH, L. A., *Physiol. J. U.S.S.R.* (*Fiziol. zh. SSSR*) **41**: 4 (1955).

CHISTOVICH, L. A., *Physiol. J. U.S.S.R.* (*Fiziol. zh. SSSR*) **42**: 8 (1956).

CHUGONOV, S. A., *Clinical electroencephalography* (Klinicheskaya elektroentsefalografiya). Medgiz (1950).

CLARK, W., *Infra-red photography: its principles and applications.* New York and London (1946).

DANILOVA, N. N., Conference on the electrophysiology of the central nervous system (Konf. po voprosam elektrofiziologii tsentral'noi nervnoi sistemy. Tez. dokl.). Leningrad (1957).

DAVIS, H., TASAKI, I. and GOLDSTEIN, R., Cold Spring Harbor Symposia on quantitative biology **17**: 143–154. New York (1952).

DEDOBRISHVILI, Ts., 14th Conference on higher nervous activity (14-e soveshchaniye po probl. vyssh. nervn. deyat. Tez. i referaty dokladov) (1953).

DELAFRESNAYE, J. F. (Editor). *Brain mechanisms and consciousness.* Blackwell Scientific Publ., Oxford (1954).

DOBRYAKOVA, O. A., Bulletin of the Academy of Paedagogic Sciences of R.S.F.S.R. (*Izv. APN RSFSR*) (1947).

DOBRYAKOVA, O. A., Problems of physiological optics (*Problemy fiziol. optiki*) **6** (1948).

DODT, E., J. *Neurophysiol.* **19**: 301–307 (1956).

DOLIN, A. O., Archives of Biological Sciences (*Arkhiv biol. nauk*) **42**: 1–2 (1936).

DOLIN, A. O., Papers delivered at a conference on psychology (Tezisy dokladov na soveshchanii po psikhologii). Moscow (1955).

DURUP, G. and FESSARD, A., *C. r. Soc. Biol.* **122**: 756–758 (1936).

ECCLES, J. C., *The neurophysiological basis of mind. The principles of neurophysiology.* p. 314. Oxford (1953).

FADDEYEVA, A. A., Problems of physiological optics (*Probl. fiziol. optiki*) **11** (1955).

FARBER, D. A., *Physiol. J. U.S.S.R.* (*Fiziol. zh. SSSR*) **38**: 3 (1952).

FECHNER, G. T., *Die elemente der psychophysik.* Leipzig (1889).

FEOKTISTOVA, YE., *Advances in reflexology and nervous system physiology* (Novoye v refleksologii i fiziologii nervnoi sistemy). 3rd Collection (1929).

FÉRÉ, C., *C. r. Soc. Biol.* **40**: 217–219 (1888).

FIGURIN, N. L. and DENISOVA, M. P., *Stages in the development of behaviour in infants up to one year* (Etapy razvitiya povedeniya detei v vozraste ot rozhdeniya do odnogo goda). Medgiz (1949).

FLECK, S., J. *Gen. Physiol.* **48**: 163–168 (1953).

FULTON, J. F., *Physiology of the nervous system.* New York (1951).
FURSIKOV, D. S., *Russian Physiol. J.* (*Russk. fiziol. zh.*) **4**: 1–6 (1921).
GADZHIYEV, I. M., *Features of photochemical conditioned reflexes in man* (Osobennosti fotokhimicheskikh uslovnykh refleksov u cheloveka). Moscow (1955).
GALAMBOS, R., *J. Neurophysiol.* **19**: 424–437 (1956).
GAMBURG, A. A., *Autonomic conditioned reflexes in oligophrenics* (Proba izucheniye vegetativnykh uslovnykh refleksov u oligofrenov). Satarov (1953).
GANTT, W. H., *Experimental basis for neurotic behavior. Origin and development of artificially produced disturbances of behavior in dogs.* p. 211. New York and London (1944).
GASTAUT, H., *Rev. Neurol.* **87**: 176–187 (1952).
GASTAUT, H. and BERT, J., *E.E.G. Clin. Neurophysiol.* **6**: 433–444 (1954).
GASTAUT, A., NAQUET, R., ROGER, A., DONGIER, C., REGIS, A., MORRELL, F., JUS, A. and JUS, C., *J. Higher Nervous Activity* (*Zh. vyssh. nervn. deyat.*) **7**: 2 (1957).
GASTAUT, A., ROGER, A., DONGIER, C. and REGIS, A., *J. Higher Nervous Activity* (*Zh. vyssh. nervn. deyat.*) **7**: 2 (1957).
GERSHUNI, G. V., *Physiol. J. U.S.S.R.* (*Fiziol. zh. SSSR*) **35**: 5 (1949).
GERSHUNI, G. V., *Problems of physiological acoustics* (*Probl. fiziol. akustiki*) **2**: (1950).
GERSHUNI, G. V., *J. Higher Nervous Activity* (*Zh. vyssh. nervn. deyat.*) **5**: (1955).
GERSHUNI, G. V., *Problems of physiological acoustics* (*Probl. fiziol. akustiki*) **3**: (1955).
GERSHUNI, G. V., *J. Higher Nervous Activity* (*Zh. vyssh. nervn. deyat.*) **7**: 1 (1957).
GLEZER, V. D., *Physiol. J. U.S.S.R.* (*Fiziol. zh. SSSR*) **38**: 5 (1952).
GLEZER, V. D., *Physiol. J. U.S.S.R.* (*Fiziol. zh. SSSR*) **39**: 5 (1953).
GOLIKOV, N. V., *Physiological basis of electroencephalographic theory. Problems in the theory and practice of electroencephalography* (Fiziologicheskiye osnovy teorii elektroentsefalografii. Voprosy teorii i praktiki elektroentsefalografii). University Press, Leningrad (1956).
GOLUBEVA, E. A., *Study of reflex mechanisms in the action of light on the visual system in man* (Issledovaniye reflektornykh mekhanizmov deistviya sveta na zritel'nyi analizator cheloveka). Moscow (1955).
GOLUBEVA, E. A., Reflex mechanisms in the functioning of the visual system. Proceedings of Conference on Psychology (O reflektornykh mekhanizmokh raboty zritel'nogo analizatora. Materialy soveshchaniya po psikhologii). Academy of Paedagogic Sciences Press, R.S.F.S.R. (1957).
GOREV, V. P., Bulletin of Experimental Biology and Medicine (*Byull. eksp. biol. i med.*) **7**: 6 (1939).
GOTTSCHICK, J., *Die leistungen des nervensystems.* Jena (1955).
GRANIT, R., *Acta Psychol.* **2**: 1, 117–118 (1955).
GRANIT, R. and HEHATSCH, H. D., *J. Neurophysiol.* **19**: 356–366 (1956).
GRANIT, R., *Sensory mechanisms of the retina. With an appendix on electroretinography.* Oxford Univ. Press, London and Toronto (1947).
GRANIT, R., *Receptors and sensory perception.* Yale Univ. Press, New Haven (1955).
GRINSHTEIN, A. M., *Paths and centres of the nervous system* (Puti i tsentry nervnoi sistemy). Moscow (1947).
GRINSHTEIN, A. M., *J. Neuropathol. Psychiat.* (*Zh. neiropatol. i psikhiat.*) **56**: 12 (1956).
GULYAYEV, P. I., *Physiol. J. U.S.S.R.* (*Fiziol. zh. SSSR*) **42**: 3 (1956).
GURTOVOI, G. K. and KRAVKOV, S. V., *Problems of physiological optics* (*Probl. fiziol. optiki*) **9**: (1950).
GUTHRIE, E. R., *Psychol. Rev.* **37**: 412–428 (1930).
GYURYADZHAN, A. A., Proceedings of Conference on Problems of Higher Nervous Activity (Soveshchaniye po problemam vyssh. nervn. deyat. Tez. dokl.). Moscow and Leningrad (1953).
HARDY, W. G. and BORDLEY, J. E., *Acta Otolaryng.* **40**: 346–360 (1951–1952).
HARLOW, H. F., Proceedings of 14th International Congress on Psychology. pp. 152–153 (1955).
HARTRIDGE, H., *Recent advances in the physiology of vision.* Churchill, London (1950).

HEAD, H., *Studies in neurology*. London (1920).

HEBB, D. L., *Psychol. Rev.* **62**: 243–254 (1955).

HUIZING, H. C., *Acta Otolaryng.* **40**: 297–306 (1951–1952).

HULL, C. L., *A behavior system. An introduction to behavior theory concerning the individual organism*. Yale Univ. Press, New Haven (1952).

HULL, C. L., *Principles of behavior. An introduction to behavior theory*. New York and London (1943).

HUNT, C. C., Cold Harbour Spring Symposia on Quantitative Biology **17**: 113–123 (1952).

IL'YANOK, V. A., *Interaction between cortical analyser centres* (Vzaimodeistviye korkobykh tsentrov analizatorov) (1953).

ISTOMANOV, S. N., *The effect of sensory nerve stimulation on the vascular system in man* (O vliyanii razdrazhenii chuvstvuyushchikh nervov na sosudistuyu sistemu cheloveka). St. Petersburg (1885).

IVANOV-SMOLENSKII, A. G., *Russian Physiol. J.* (*Russk. fiziol. zh.*) **10**: 3–4 (1927).

IVANOV-SMOLENSKII, A. G., *Proceedings of the Pavlov physiological laboratories* (Trudy fiziologicheskikh laboratorii im. I. P. Pavlova). **2**, 2. (1927).

JASPER, H., *E.E.G. Clin. Neurophysiol.* **1**: 405–420 (1949).

JASPER, H., *Epilepsy and Brain Localization*. Chap. 14. Churchill, London (1949).

JASPER, H., NAQUET, F. and KING, E. E., *E.E.G. Clin. Neurophysiol.* **7**: 99–114 (1955).

JASPER, H. and SHAGASS, C., *J. Esp. Psychol.* **28**: 373–388 (1941).

JOUVET, A. and HERNANDEZ-PEON, R., *Mecanismes neurophysiologiques concernant l'attention, l'habituation et le conditionnement*. Marseille (1955, 1957).

KASATKIN, N. I., MIRZOYANTS, N. S. and KHOKHITVA, A. P., *J. Higher Nervous Activity* (*Zh. vyssh. nervn. deyat.*) **3**: 2 (1953).

KAZ'MIN, G. I. and FEDOROV, V. K., 14th Conference on Problems of Higher Nervous Activity (14-e soveshchaniye po problemam vysshei nervnoi deyatel'nosti). Moscow and Leningrad (1951).

KEDROV, A. A. and NAUMENKO, A. I., *Problems in the physiology of the intracranial circulation and their clinical interpretation* (Voprosy fiziologii vnutricherepnogo krovoobrashcheniya s klinicheskim ikh osveshcheniyem). Moscow (1954).

KEKCHEYEV, K. Kh., *Bulletin of the R.S.F.S.R. Academy of Paedagogic Sciences* (*Izv. APN RSFSR*) **8** (1947).

KLOSSOVSKII, B. N., *The cerebral circulation* (Tsirkulyatsiya korvi v mozgu). Moscow (1951).

KOFFKA, *Principles of Gestalt psychology*. Kegan Paul, Trench, Trübner and Co. New York (1935).

KOGAN, B. A., *The irradiation and concentration of extinctive inhibition* (Ob irradiyatsii i kontsentratsii ugasatel'nogo tormozheniya). St. Petersburg (1914).

KONORSKI, J. and SZWEJKOWSKA, G., *Acta Biol. Exp.* **16**: 95–113 (1952).

KOTLYAREVSKII, L. I., *Archives of Biological Sciences* (*Arkhiv biol. nauk.*) **39**: 2 (1935).

KOZHEVNIKOV, V. A., *Electrophysiological study of the formation of temporary connexions to acoustic stimuli in man* (Elektrofiziologicheskoe izucheniye obrazovaniya vremennykh svyazei na zvukovyye razdrazhiteli u cheloveka). Leningrad (1951).

KOZHEVNIKOV, V. A., *Physiol. J. U.S.S.R.* (*Fiziol. zh. SSSR*) **41**: 2 (1955).

KOZHEVNIKOV, V. A., *Problems of physiological acoustics* (*Probl. fiziol. akustiki*) **3**: (1955).

KRAVKOV, S. V., *Principles of general sense organ psychophysiology* (Ocherk obshchei psikhofiziologii organov chuvstv). U.S.S.R. Academy of Sciences Press, Moscow and Leningrad (1946).

KRAVKOV, S. V., *Interaction between sense organs* (Vzaimodeistviye organov chuvstv). U.S.S.R. Academy of Sciences Press, Moscow and Leningrad (1948).

KRAVKOV, S. V., *The eye and its function* (Glaz i yego rabota). U.S.S.R. Academy of Sciences Press, Moscow and Leningrad (1950).

KRASNOGORSKII, N. I., *The process of delay and the localization of the cutaneous and motor analysers in the cortex of the dog* (O protesesse zaderzhivaniya i o lokalizatsii kozhnogo i dvigatel'nogo analizatora v kore bol'shikh polusharii u sobaki). St. Petersburg (1911).

KRATIN, YU. G., *Physiol. J. U.S.S.R. (Fiziol. zh. SSSR)* **41**: 5 (1956).
KRUSHINSKII, L. V., *Recent Advances in Biology (Uspekhi sovr. biol.)* **26**: 2 (5) (1948).
KRUSHINSKII, L. V., *Problems of cybernetics* (Problemy kibernetiki). Vol. 2. Moscow (1959).
KUPALOV, P. S., *J. Higher Nervous Activity (Zh. vyssh. nervn. deyat.)* **1**: 6 (1951).
KUPALOV, P. S. and GANTT, W. H., *Brain* **50**: 44–52 (1927).
KVASOV, D. G., *Physiol. J. U.S.S.R. (Fiziol. zh. SSSR)* **38**: 4 (1952).
KVASOV, D. G., *Proceedings of All-Union Congress of Physiologists, Biochemists and Pharmacologists* (Vses. s"ezd fiziol., biokhim. i farmakol., Tez. dokl.) (1955).
KVASOV, D. G., *Physiol. J. U.S.S.R. (Fiziol. zh. SSSR)* **42**: 8 (1956).
LAGUTINA, N. I., *Proceedings of All-Union Congress of Physiologists, Biochemists and Pharmacologists* (Vses. s"ezd fiziol., biokhim. i farmakol. Tez. dokl.) (1955).
LAPTEV, I. I., *Problems of higher nervous activity* (Problemy vysshei nervnoi deyatel'nosti). Moscow (1949).
LAPTEV, I. I., *Problems of higher nervous activity* (Problemy vysshei nervnoi deyatel'nosti) (1949).
LAZAREV, P. P., *Investigations on adaptation* (Issledovaniya po adaptatsii). U.S.S.R. Academy of Sciences Press (1947).
LEBEDINSKII, A. V., *Archives of Biological Sciences (Arkhiv biol. nauk)* **49**: 1 (1938).
LIBERMAN, A. YE. and STREL'TSOVA, N. I., *J. Higher Nervous Activity (Zh. vyssh. nervn. deyat.)* **2**: 6 (1952).
LICHKO, A. YE., *Scientific papers of the Pavlov Institute of Physiology* (Trud. In-ta fiziol. im I. P. Pavlova) **1**: (1952).
LINSLEY, D. B., *Ann. Rev. Physiol.* **17**: 311–338 (1955).
LIVANOV, M. N., *Bulletin of the U.S.S.R. Academy of Sciences* (Izv. Akad. Nauk. SSSR) **6** (1944).
LIVANOV, M. N., *Scientific papers of the 15th Conference on higher nervous activity* (Trud. 15-go soveshchaniya po problemam vyssh. nervn. deyat.) Moscow and Leningrad (1952).
MAIOROV, F. P., *Scientific papers of the Pavlov physiological laboratories* (Trud. fiziol. labor. im. I. P. Pavlova) **9**: (1940).
MAIOROV, F. P., *History of the conditioned reflex doctrine* (Istoriya ucheniya ob uslovnykh refleksakh). Academy of Medical Sciences Press, Moscow (1954).
MAIORCHIK, V. YE. and SPIRIN, B. G. *Problems of Neurosurgery (Vopr. neirokhirurg.)* **3** (1951).
MAIZEL', N. I., *Typological features of higher nervous activity in man* (Tipologicheskiye osobennosti vysshei nervnoi deyatel'nosti u cheloveka). R.S.F.S.R. Academy of Paedagogic Sciences Press (1956).
MAKAROV, P. O., *Neurodynamics of the visual system in man* (Neirodinamika zritel'noi sistemy cheloveka). Leningrad (1952).
MAKAROV, P. O., *Proceedings of 4th Conference on physiological optics* (Chetvertoye soveshchaniye po fiziologicheskoi optike). Leningrad (1955).
MARUSEVA, A. M., *Problems of physiological acoustics (Probl. fiziol. akustiki)* **3** (1955).
MARUSEVA, A. M. and CHISTOVICH, L. A., *Proceedings of the 14th Conference on Pavlov doctrine* (Tez. 14-go soveshchaniya po problemam ucheniya I. P. Pavlova). Leningrad (1951).
MARUSEVA, A. M. and CHISTOVICH, L. A., *J. Higher Nervous Activity (Zh. vyssh. nervn. deyat.)* **4**: 4 (1954).
MARUSHEVSKII, M. O., *Problems of psychology (Vopr. psikhologii)* **1** (1957).
MERLIN, V. S., *Physiol. J. U.S.S.R. (Fiziol. zh. SSSR)* **40**: 2 (1954).
MERLIN, V. S., *UCH. ZAP.* Kaz. Gos. Univ. **113**, 3 (1953).
MIHAMA, H. and KOTAKE, Y., *Kwansei Gakuin Univ. Ann. Stud.* **2**: 1–20 (1954).
MIKHALEVSKAYA, M. B., *Proceedings of a Conference on the orienting reflex* (Tez. dokl. na konf. po probl. oriyentirovochnogo refleksa). Moscow (1957).
MILYAVSKAYA, V. O., *Problems in the study and development of personality* (Voprosy izucheniya i vospitaniya lichnosti). Leningrad (1930).
MIRZOYANTS, N. S., *J. Higher Nervous Activity (Zh. vyssh. nervn. deyat.)* **4**: 5 (1954).
MKRTYCHEVA, L. I., *Proceedings of 4th Conference on physiological optics* (Chetvertoye soveshch. po fiziol. optiki). Leningrad (1955).
MOKHOVA, G. M., *J. Higher Nervous Activity (Zh. vyssh. nervn. deyat.)* **6**: 2 (1956).

MONTGOMERY, K. C., *J. Comp. Physiol. Psychol.* **48**: 254–260 (1955).
MONTGOMERY, K. C., *J. Comp. Physiol. Psychol.* **47**: 60–64 (1954).
MONNIER, M., *Problems in modern physiology of the nervous and muscular systems* (Problemy sovremennoi fiziologii myshechnoi i nervnoi sistem). Tbilisi (1956).
MORRELL, F. and JASPER, H. H., *E.E.G. Clin. Neurophysiol.* **8**: 201–215 (1956).
MORUZZI, G. and MAGOUN, H. W., *E.E.G. Clin. Neurophysiol.* **1**: 455–473 (1949).
MOTOKAWA, K. and HUZIMORI, B., *Tohoku J. Exp. Med.* **50**: 215–223 (1949).
MUNDY-CASTLE, A. C. and McKIEVER, B. Z., *J. Exp. Psychol.* **46**: 15–24 (1953).
MUSHKINA, N. A., *J. Higher Nervous Activity* (*Zh. vyssh. nervn. deyat.*) **6**: 1 (1956).
MUSHKINA, N. A., *J. Higher Nervous Activity* (*Zh. vyssh. nervn. deyat.*) **6**: 1 (1956).
MUSYASHCHIKOVA, S. S., *Problems of interoception physiology* (Voprosy fiziologii interotseptsii). Moscow and Leningrad (1952).
MYASISHCHEV, V. N., *Advances in reflexology and nervous system physiology* (Novoye v refleksologii i fiziologii nervnoi sistemy). Leningrad (1926).
MYASISHCHEV, V. N., *Advances in reflexology and nervous system physiology* (Novoye v refleksologii i fiziologii nervnoi sistemy). 3rd Collection. Leningrad (1929).
MYASISHCHEV, V. N., *Electrodermal indices of the mental state in man* (Elektrodermal'nyye pokazateli nervno-psikhicheskogo sostoyaniya u cheloveka). Moscow (1945).
NARBUTOVICH, I. O., *Scientific papers of the Pavlov physiological laboratories* (Trud. fiziol. labor. im I. P. Pavlova) Vol. 8 (1938).
NARBUTOVICH, I. O. and PODKOPAYEV, N. A., *Scientific papers of the Pavlov physiological laboratories* (Trud. fiziol. labor. im. I. P. Pavlova) **4**: 2 (1936).
NIKOLAYEVA, N. I., *Physiol. J. U.S.S.R.* (*Fiziol. zh. SSSR*) **41**: 1 (1955).
NOVIKOVA, L. A. and SOKOLOV, YE. N., *J. Higher Nervous Activity* (*Zh. vyssh. nervn. deyat.*) **7**: 3 (1957).
NOVIKOVA, L. A. and FARBER, D. A., *Physiol. J. U.S.S.R.* (*Fiziol. zh. SSSR*) **42**: 5 (1956).
ORBELI, L. A., *Problems of higher nervous activity* (Voprosy vysshei nervnoi deyatel'nosti). Moscow (1949).
PARAMONOVA, N. P., *The elaboration of fine differentiations without special reinforcement* (O vyrabotke tonkikh differentsirovok bez spetsial'nogo podkrepleniya) (1959).
PAVLOV, I. P., *Complete works* (Poln. sobr. trud.) U.S.S.R. Acad. Sci. Press, Moscow and Leningrad (1947–1949).
"PAVLOV WEDNESDAYS" (Pavlovskiye sredy). Vol. 3. U.S.S.R. Acad. Sci. Press, Moscow and Leningrad (1949).
PEIMER, I. I. and FADDEYEVA, A. A., *Physiol. J. U.S.S.R.* (*Fiziol. zh. SSSR*) **42**: 3 (1956).
PENFIELD, W. and RASMUSSEN, T. *The cerebral cortex of man. A clinical study of localization of function.* New York (1950).
PENFIELD, W., *Brain* **77**: 1–17, (1954).
PERL, E. R., GALAMBOS, R. and GLORIG, A., *E.E.G. Clin. Neurophysiol.* **5**: 501–512 (1953).
PIERON, H., *The sensations: their functions, processes and mechanisms.* Frederick Muller Ltd. London (1952).
POLYAKOV, G. I., *Recent advances in biology* (Uspekhi sovremennoi biologii). Vol. 42 (1959).
POPOV, N. A., *Bulletin of Bakinsk University* (Izv. Bakinsk. gos. univ.) **1** (1921).
POPOV, N. A., *Russ. Physiol. J.* (Russk. fiziol. zh.) **2**: 1–2 (1921).
POPOV, N. F., *Investigations on the physiology of the cerebral cortex in animals* (Issledovaniya po fiziologii kory golovnogo mozga zhivotnykh). Moscow (1953).
PRESSMAN, YA. M., *Proceedings of 4th Conference on physiological optics* (Chetvertoye soveshch. po fiziol. optike). Leningrad (1955).
PSHONIK, A. T., *The cerebral cortex and receptor function* (Kora golovnogo mozga i retseptornaya funktsiya organizma). Moscow (1952).
RAMON Y CAHAL, S., *Histologie du systemenerveux de l'homme et des vertébrés.* Paris (1909).
RAPPOPORT, YE. YA. and ROBINSON, N. A., *Bulletin of the Institute of Experimental Medicine* (*Byull. VIEM*) 11–12 (1935).
RAVICH-SHERBO, I. V., *Typological features of higher nervous activity in man* (Tipologicheskiye osobennosti vysshei nervnoi deyatel'nosti cheloveka). R.S.F.S.R. Acad. Paed. Sci. Press, Moscow (1956).

REGELSBERGER, H., Der bedingte Reflex und die vegetative Rhythmik des Menschen dargestellt am Electrodermatogramm. Wien, pp. 1725 (1952).

REMY, M., *Mschr. Psychiat. Neurol.*, **129**, pp. 207–215 (1955).

ROBINSON, J. and GANTT, W. H., *Bull. Johns Hopkins Hosp.*, **80**, pp. 231–253, (1947).

ROGGER, A., ROSSI, G. F. and ZIRONDOLI, A., *Electroenceph. clin. neurophysiol.* **8**: pp. 1–13 (1956).

ROGOV, A. A., *Vascular conditioned and unconditioned reflexes in man* (O sosudistykh uslovnykh i bezuslovnykh refleksakh cheloveka). U.S.S.R. Acad. Sci. Press, Moscow and Leningrad, (1951).

ROITBAK, A. I., *Electrical phenomena in cerebral cortex* (Bioelektricheskiye yavleniya v kore bol'shikh polusharii). Tbilisi (1955).

ROKOTOVA, N. A., *J. Higher Nervous Activity* (*Zh. vyssh. nervn. deyat.*) **2**: 5 (1952).

ROKOTOVA, N. A., *Physiol. J. U.S.S.R.* (*Fiziol. zh. SSSR*) **40**: 6 (1954).

ROZENTAL', I. S., *Archives of Biological Sciences* (*Arkhiv biol. nauk*) **29**: 3 (1929).

ROZENTAL', I. S., *Archives of Biological Sciences* (*Arkhiv biol. nauk*) **30**: 1 (1930).

ROZENTAL', I. S., *Archives of Biological Sciences* (*Arkhiv biol. nauk*) **32**: 2 (1932).

ROZHDESTVENSKAYA, V. I., *Physiological mechanisms in conditioned reflex change in the sensitivity of peripheral vision* (K voprosu o fiziologicheskihk mekhanizmakh uslov-noreflektornogo izmeneniya chuvstvitel'nosti perifericheskogo zreniya). R.S.F.S.R. Acad. Paed. Sci. Press: **53** (1954).

ROGER, A., SOKOLOV, YE. N. and VORONIN, L. G., *J. Higher Nervous Activity* (*Zh. vyssh. nervn. deyat.*) **8**: 1 (1958).

RUSINOV, V. S., *Proceedings of Conference on the electrophysiology of the central nervous system* (Konf. po voprosam elektrofiziologii tsentral'noi nervnoi sistemy. Tez. dokl.) Leningrad (1957).

SAKHIULINA, G. A., *Bull. Exp. Biol. Med.* (*Byull. eksp. biol. i med.*) **17**: 6 (1944).

SAMSONOVA, V. G., *J. Higher Nervous Activity* (*Zh. vyssh. nervn. deyat.*) **3**: 5 (1953).

SAMSONOVA, V. G., *J. Higher Nervous Activity* (*Zh. vyssh. nervn. deyat.*) **6**: 2 (1956).

SEMENOVSKAYA, YE. N., *Problems of physiological optics* (*Probl. fiziol. optiki*) **3**: (1946).

SEMENOVSKAYA, YE. N., *The importance of attention in changes in sense organ sensitivity* (Rol' vnimaniya v izmenenii chuvstvitel'nosti organov chuvstv). R.S.F.S.R. Acad. Paed. Sci. Press: **8** (1947).

SEMENOVSKAYA, YE. N. and STRUCHKOV, M. I., *Problems of physiological optics* (*Probl. fiziol. optiki*) **8** (1953).

SEREBRENNIKOV, S. S., *Scientific papers of the Pavlov physiological laboratories* (Trud. fiziol. labor. im. I. P. Pavlova) **19**: (1940).

SECHENOV, I. M., *Selected works* (Izbr. proizv.). Vol. 1. U.S.S.R. Acad. Sci. Press (1952).

SHAKHNOVICH, A. R., *Physiol. J. U.S.S.R.* (*Fiziol. zh. SSSR*) **42**: 8 (1956).

SHERRINGTON, C. S., *The integrative action of the nervous system.* Cambridge Univ. Press, England (1948).

SHIROKOV, A. A., *J. Psychoneurol.* (*Zh. psikhonevrol.*) **13**: 4 (1937).

SHKOL'NIK-YARROS, YE. G., *Proceedings of 4th Conference on physiological optics* (Chet-vertoye soveshch. po fiziol. optike) Leningrad (1955).

SHPIL'BERG, P. I., *Physiol. J. U.S.S.R.* (*Fiziol. zh. SSSR*) **28**: 2–3 (1940).

SHPIL'BERG, P. I., *Physiol. J. U.S.S.R.* (*Fiziol. zh. SSSR*) **28**: 2–3 (1940).

SKIPIN, G. V., *Scientific papers of the Pavlov physiological laboratories* (Trud. fiziol. labor. im. I. P. Pavlova) **3**: 1 (1928).

SKIPIN, G. V., *Scientific papers of the Pavlov physiological laboratories* (Trud. fiziol. labor. im. I. P. Pavlova) **10**; (1941).

SKIPIN, G. V., *J. Higher Nervous Activity* (*Zh. vyssh. nervn. deyat.*) **6**: 1 (1956).

SMIRNOV, K. S., *Some features in the formation of pupillary conditioned reflexes in man* (O nekotorykh osobennostyakh obrazovaniya zrachovykh uslovnykh reaktsii u cheloveka). Moscow (1952).

SMIRNOV, V. A., *The pupils: normal and pathological* (Zrachki v norme i patologii). Medgiz (1955).

SMIRNOV, G. D., *Recent advances in biology* (*Uspekhi sovrem. biol.*) **42**: 3 (6) (1956).

SNYAKIN, P. G., *Functional mobility in the retina* (Funktsional'naya mobil'nost' setchatki). Medgiz. (1948).

SOKOLOV, E. N., *Acta Psychol.* **11**: 1 (1955).

SOKOLOV, YE. N., *Proceedings of Conference on psychology* (Doklady na soveshch. po psikhologii). Moscow (1954).

SOKOLOV, YE. N., *Problems of psychology* (*Vopr. psikhologii*) **1** (1955).

SOKOLOV, YE. N., *J. Higher Nervous Activity* (*Zh. vyssh. nervn. deyat.*) **6**: 4 (1956).

SOKOLOV, YE. N., *Proceedings of Conference on the orienting reflex* (Tez. dokl. na konf. po probl. oriyentirovochnogo refleksa). Moscow (1957).

SOKOLOV, YE. N., *Papers of a Conference on psychology* (Materialy soveshch. po psikhologii). R.S.F.S.R. Acad. Paed. Sci. Press, Moscow (1957).

SOKOLOV, YE. N., *Orienting reflex and problems of higher nervous activity* (Oriyentirovochnyi refleks i voprosy vyssh. nervn. deyat.) (1958).

SOKOLOV, Ye. N. and PARAMONOVA, N. P., *The neuronal model of the stimulus* (Nervnaya model' stimula). (1959).

SOKOLOV, YE. N. and VINOGRADOVA, O. S., *Residual hearing in deaf and dumb children* (Ostatochnyi slukh u tugoukhikh i glukhonemykh detei). R.S.F.S.R. Acad. Paed. Sci. Press (1957).

SOKOLOV, E. N., DANILOVA, N. N. and MIKHALEVSKAYA, M. B., Electrographic study of light sensitivity (Issledovanie svetovoi chuvstvitel'nosti metodom elektrografii). Paper read at the Conference of Physiological Optics. L. (1955).

SOKOLOV, YE. N., DANILOVA, N. N. and MIKHALEVSKAYA, M. B., *Problems of psychology* (*Vopr. psikhol.*) **2** (1957).

SOKOLOV, YE. N. and PARAMONOVA, N. P., *J. Higher Nervous Activity* (*Zh. vyssh. nervn. deyat.*) **6**: 5 (1956).

SOLOVEICHIK, D. I., *Scientific papers of the Pavlov physiological laboratories* (Trud. fiziol. labor. im. I. P. Pavlova) **2**: 2 (1928).

SPASSKAYA, N. D., *The galvanic skin reflex in schizophrenics* (Kozhno-gal'vanicheskii refleks u bol'nykh shizofreniei). Moscow (1955).

STEKLOVA, R. P., *Proceedings of Conference on the orienting reflex* (Tez. dokl. na konf. po probl. oriyentirovochnogo refleksa). Moscow (1957).

STEVENS, S. S., (1951) *Handbook of Experimental Psychology*. John Wiley & Sons. New York & London

STRAUMIT, A. YA., *Proceedings of 16th Conference on higher nervous activity* (16-e soveshchaniye po problemam vysshei nervnoi deyatel'nosti. Tez. dokl.) (1953).

TARKHANOV, I. R., *Bull. Clin. Foren. Psychiat. Neuropathol.* (*Vestn. klin. i sudebn. psikhiatr.* chaniye po problemam vysshei nervnoi deyatel'nosti. Tez. dokl.) (1953). *i nevropatol.*) **7**: (1889).

TATO, J. M., *Arch. Ohr-, Ns.- u. Kehlheilk.* **164**: 477–486 (1954).

TEPLOV, B. M. and BORISOVA, M. N., *Problems of psychology* (*Vopr. psikhol.*) **1** (1957).

TEREKHOVA, O. P., *Problems of psychology* (*Vopr. psikhol.*) **1** (1958).

TOLMAN, E. C., *Acta Psychol.* **2**: 1, 31–40 (1955).

TSIRESHKIN, B. D., *Bull. Otorhinolaryngology* (Vestn. oto-rino-laringologii) **4** (1953).

UKHTOMSKII, A. A., *Collected works* (Sobr. soch). Vol. 2. Univ. Press, Leningrad. (1951).

UR'YEVA, F. M., *Physiol. J. U.S.S.R.* (*Fiziol. zh. SSSR*) **20**; 5 (1936).

VAVILOV, S. I., *Microstructure of light* (Mikrostruktura sveta). Moscow (1950).

VINOGRADOV, N. V., *Scientific papers of Pavlov physiological laboratories* (Trud. fiziol. labor. im. I. P. Pavlova) **5**: (1933).

VINOGRADOVA, O. S., *Proceedings of Conference on the orienting reflex* (Tez. dokl. konf. po problemam oriyentirovochnogo refleksa). Moscow (1957).

VINOGRADOVA, O. S., *The orienting reflex and problems of higher nervous activity* (Oriyentirovochnyi refleks i voprosy vyssh. nervn. deyat.) (1958).

VINOGRADOVA, O. S. and SOKOLOV, YE. N., *Problems of psychology* (*Vopr. psikhol.*) **2** (1955).

VINOGRADOVA, O. S. and SOKOLOV, YE. N., *Problems of physiological acoustics* (*Probl. fiziol. akustiki*) **3** (1955).

VINOGRADOVA, O. S. and SOKOLOV, YE. N., *J. Higher Nervous Activity* (*Zh. vyssh. nervn. deyat.*) **5**: 3 (1955).

VINOGRADOVA, O. S. and SOKOLOV, YE. N., *Physiol. J. U.S.S.R.* (*Fiziol. zh. SSSR*) **43**: 1 (1957).

VLASOVA, M. M., *Bull. R.S.F.S.R. Acad. Paed. Sci.* (*Izv. APN R SFSR*) **53**. Moscow (1954).

VOITONIS, L. G., *Prehistory of intellect* (Predystoriya intellekta). U.S.S.R. Acad. Sci. Press, Moscow and Leningrad (1949).

VORONIN, L. G., *Analysis and synthesis of compound stimuli in the normal and damaged cerebrum of the dog.* (Analiz i sintez slozhnykh razdrazhitelei normal'nymi i povrezhdennymi polushariyami mozga sobaki). Moscow (1948).

VORONIN, L. G., *Analysis and synthesis of compound stimuli in higher animals* (Analiz i sintez slozhnykh razdrazhitelei u vysshikh zhivotnykh). Medgiz, Moscow (1953).

VORONIN, L. G., *Lectures on the comparative physiology of higher nervous activity* (Lektsii po sravnitel'noi fiziologii vysshei nervnoi deyatel'nosti). Moscow State University Press, Moscow (1957).

VORONIN, L. G. and SOKOLOV, YE. N., *Bull. Moscow University* (*Vestn. Mosk. un-ta*) **9** (1955).

VORONIN, L. G. and SOKOLOV, YE. N., *International symposium on electroencephalography* (Mezhdunarodnyi simpozium po elektroentsefalografii). Moscow (1958).

VORONIN, L. G. and SOKOLOV, YE. N., *Moscow University Bulletin* (Vestn. MGU) **9** (1955).

WALTER, W. G., *The living brain.* Duckworth, London, (1953).

WALTER, W. G., *Brain mechanisms and consciousness*, p. 345–369. Oxford (1954).

WANG, G., STEIN, P. and BROWN, V., *J. Neurophysiol.* **19**: 340–349 (1956).

WEVER, E. J. and LAWRENCE, M., *Physiological acoustics.* Princeton (1954).

WIENER, N., *Cybernetics or control and communication in the animal and the machine.* New York and Paris (1948).

WOODWORTH, R. S., *Experimental psychology.* Methuen, London (1939).

YAKOVLEV, P. A., *Bull. Ophthalmology* (*Vestn. optalmol.*) **17**: 4 (1940).

YOUNG, F. A. and BIERSDORF, W. R., *J. Comp. Physiol. Psychol.* **47**: 264–268 (1954).

ZAGORUL'KO, L. T., *Physiol. J. U.S.S.R.* (*Fiziol. zh. SSSR*) **23**: 6 (1937).

ZAGORUL'KO, L. T., LEBEDINSKII, A. V. and TURPAYEV, YA. P., *Physiol. J. U.S.S.R.* (*Fiziol. zh. SSSR*) **16**: 6 (1933).

ZELENYI, S. P., *Proceedings of 3rd All-Union Congress of Physiologists* (Trud. III Vses. s"ezda fiziologov) (1928).

ZIMKIN, N. V., *Physiol. J. U.S.S.R.* (*Fiziol. zh. SSSR*) **17**: 5 (1934).

ZIMKINA, A. M., *Papers of a Conference on psychology* (Materialy sovershch. po psikhologii). R.S.F.S.R. Acad. Paed. Sci. Press, Moscow (1957).

ZISLINA, N. N., *J. Higher Nervous Activity* (*Zh. vyssh. nervn. deyat.*) **5**: 5 (1955).

ZISLINA, N. N., *Problems of higher nervous activity in normal and abnormal children* (Problemy vyssh. nervn. deyat. normal'nogo i anomal'nogo rebenka) R.S.F.S.R. Acad. Paed. Sci. Press, Moscow (1956).

Index

(*Abbreviations:* a.—adaptation; c.—conditioned; d.—defence; o.—orientation; r.—reflex.)

Adaptation reflexes 14, 15, 36, 109
  compared with o. and d.r. 14, 15
  depression of pupillary components 102
  retinal 109
  specialized 94
    in measurement of sensitivity 23
Adrenaline in cortical activation 9
α-Rhythm
  blockage in o.r. 109
  as component of o.r. 86
  and continuing illumination 94
  depression 78, 79
    in response to flicker 89
    irradiation 130
    in occipital area 71
    as o. reaction 72
    spontaneous 99
    with weak stimuli 227
  enhancement in o.r. 79
  in phasic o.r. 118
  re-emergence and a. processes 98
  and retinal adaptation 100
Analyser
  activation of cortical end of 80
  as afferent–efferent system 263
  as combination of afferent systems 19
  selective sensitization of 241
  as self-regulating system 8
  systems, activation of 284
  threshold, estimation of 25
  tuning reflexes 14
Antidromic wave 200
"Arousal"
  effect 270
  reaction 269
Audiogram 185, 198
Auditory
  analyser function investigated 185–86
  stimulation 76

Blink reflex 73, 76, 110
  conditioned 147, 149
  properties 71
  and puff of air 78

Central reaction 111
Cephalic–hand vasoconstriction of d.r. 46
C.G.R. *see* Galvanic skin reflex
"Concentration reaction" 11
Conditioned adaptation reflex 18, 147, 216
  intra-analyser 20
  pattern 141
  in sensory a. process 141
  to time 272
Conditioned defence reflex, formation 173
Conditioned defensive reactions 19
Conditioned motor reflex
  latent period 238
  response 246–47
Conditioned orientation reflex 151, 200, 238
  in man 17
Conditioned reflex
  elaboration of 274, 291
  formation 276
    stages 199–200
  functioning of 279
  in measurement of sensitivity 24
  relation with o.r. 292
  in single analyser system 20
  stabilization of 238
"Conditioned reinforcement" 189
Cortex
  activity's effect on o.r. 16
  control of functional state of retina 7
  electrical responses to light and darkness 110
  excitability and darkness 92
  excitation level and inhibition of o.r. 271
  in intensification and attenuation of o.r 270
  tuning to flicker frequencies 91

Defence dominant focus 52
Defence reaction
  cephalic–hand vasoconstriction in 46
  combined with o.r. 46
  in measurement of sensitivity 24
Defence reflex 46, 64
  and o. and a.r. compared 14–15

interaction with o. and thermoregulation 65
Defensive reflexes 265
Discrimination
  of c. stimuli 167
  of painful stimuli 169
Dominance factor 53
Dominant
  defence focus 53
  focus 52
    development of 184
Dynamic stereotype 288

E.E.G. and o.r. 79, 84
Electromyographic tracings 73
Extinguishing inhibitor 127
Eye movements 73

Féré's phenomenon 53

Galvanic skin reaction 53, 54
  automatic registration of 54
  component of o.r., reactivity of 195
  connexion with brain areas 69
  and d.r. 59
  different from cephalic vasomotor response 62
  extinction of 56, 60
    to signal stimulus 195
  features 54–55
  intensification 62
    with painful stimuli 193
  main laws of 56
  and o.r. 61
  reciprocal relation with c. motor r. 194
  and sensitization of skin analyser 56
  similarity to vascular component of o.r. 55
  threshold 61

Hypothalamic reactions 69

Illumination on dark-adapted eye 132–133
Indifferent stimulus 35
"Inextinguishable" reactions 120
  inhibition of 121
Inhibition
  conditioned 153
  of efferent elements 128
  of o.r., lowers sensitivity 131
    and reticular formation 130
  widespread 120

Inhibitory process
  afferent and efferent limbs of o.r. compared 129
  and extinction of o.r. 124
Inter-analyser connexion 21
Irradiation
  of general o.r. 88
  of excitation 127

Kravkov's adaptometer 73

Lability 28
  measurement of 28
  of an analyser 28
  of reflex arc 28
Light
  and darkness, effects 110
    as complex stimuli 112
  effects on o.r. 106
  intermittent stimulation effects 113
  repeated, on dark-adapted eye 132–33
Light—strong light, bioelectrical manifestations 144
Limiting method 31
Loudness recruitment 182

Motor conditioned reflex, formation 185

Neuro-humoral control system 10
Neuronal model 287
  as multi-dimensional filter 289
Neurosis 122
Non-signal stimulus reinforcement 150
Non-specific
  excitation 69
  nerve fibres 69, 128
  o.r. 69
  paths 261
    interaction with specific paths 263
  reactions 68
    extinction of 268
  system, rr. connected with 264
"Novelty" significance of 132

Orientation reaction
  and cortical lability 91
  development to signal stimulus 251
  and differences between reactivity and sensitivity 28
  effect on latent period 255
  enhancement by liminal stimuli 227
  generalized and local, summation of 84

local 82
 and generalized differences in E.E.G. 84
 not reflected in E.E.G. 79
 to proprioceptive stimulation 246
 relation with c. motor r. during signal stimulation 254
Orientation reflex
 and a. to repetitive illumination 135
 arc 123
 and bio-electrical cerebral reaction 78
 compared with a. and d.r. 14–15
 components of 12–13
 complex of 118
  components of 109
 conception of 282
 c. intensification of 153
 and control of sensitivity 116
 development factor 132
  in response to changing stimulus 147
 differentiation from specific r. 88
 effect of cortical activity on 16
 efferent limb, concentrated excitation in 241
 excitation processes of 158
 extinction 12, 118, 123, 269, 286
  after painful stimulus 182
  associated with c.a.r. formation 159
  and c.a.r. 158
  and fall of sensitivity 123
  and irradiation of inhibition 125–26
  process of 120
  and sensitivity of analyser 23, 119
  and tonic and phasic balance 119
   interaction 119
 "extinguishing stimuli" of 127
 generalized 108
  conditioned 155
  as cortical depression 80
  irradiation of 88
 generalized and local 79, 284
  and α-rhythm 86
  division into 264
  effects of light stimulation on 106, 108
 as independent functional system 283
 inhibition connected with a. phenomena 272
  and driving effect 89
 intensification of 16
 and c.r. inhibition 256
 interaction with a.r. 110, 132
  a.r. and d.r. 71
  thermoregulation and d.r. 65
 interrelation with c.r. 257
  specific and d.r. 66

local 108
 conditioned 155
 as rolandic rhythm depression 80
 similar to specific reactions 82
 not reflected in E.E.G. 79
 over-extinction 120
  stability of 121
 paradoxical reappearance 121
 persistence in specific analyser 80
 phasic 116
  and α-rhythm 118
  exemplified by C.G.R. component 116
  and tonic 265
  related to tonic 117
 photic driving 92, 93
 produced by application or omission of reinforcement 149
  repetitive c. stimuli 253
 reciprocity with c. reflex 278
 relation to specific a.r. in visual analyser 208
  c.r. 154
 role in creating c. connexions 256
 tonic 117, 243
  and formation of c. motor r. 256
  and phasic 265
  and slower rhythms 118
 ultimate aim of 13
 vascular component of 39
"Orientation sensitivity" 178, 197
 inversely related to "d. sensitivity" 182
 relation with "painful" sensitivity 183
Orienting investigatory reflex 11
 conception of 283

Pain threshold 182
Pattern of reflexes 171
Perception as system of reflex acts 5
Perielectronic activity in higher centres control of receptors 7
Peripheral
 adaptation 110, 112
  mechanisms 96
 reactions in sensitivity measurement 23
Photic driving
 effect 108
 nature of 88
 and o.r. 92
 positive effect of light on 93
Photic stimulation
 driving effect during 218
 effect of 265
 rhythmic, effects of 89
Poly-effector recording 30

Positive induction 126
Primary cortical response 23
Propriomuscular control of the eye 8
Pupillary reactions
  and a. processes 98
  cinematographic investigations 96
  during light stimulation 99
  to light–darkness sequence 137
  as specialized reactions 99

Reactivity
  absolute sensitivity as index of 27
  changes in 27
  of d. and o.r. 50
  differing from sensitivity 28
  increased by o.r. 102
  measurement of 26
  of the r. arc 27
Reflex control
  within the analysers 10
  of receptors 6
Reflex ring 8
Reflex tuning of sensitivity of analysers 17
Reinforcement
  conditioned 189
  effectiveness of 274
  influence on reticular formation 277
Reinforcing stimuli classified 171
Respiratory reaction
  correlation with E.E.G. 73
  to normal stimulation 72
  recorded 73
Reticular formation 9, 88, 109, 258, 261
  and afferent inhibition 126
  of brain stem 262
  and cortical excitability 237
  and inhibition of o.r. 130
  of thalamus 262
  and non-specific excitation 69
Reticular system 289
Rolandic fissure rhythm depression 80

Secondary signalling system 251
Sensitivity
  absolute threshold 182
  changes due to o. and a. 102
    studied experimentally 50
    and vascular indications 49
  defined 22
  differing from reactivity 28
  differences between specific, o. and d.
    types 201
  estimation of 24

to light measured during a. 100
  and interaction of o. and specialized
    rr. 105
methods of measuring 22–26, 31
pattern of change in, and c.r. 178
and reactivity increase to c. stimulus 275
to repeated stimulation, measured 50
variations and painful stimuli 186–87
Sensory conditioned reflex 18
"Sensory integration" 282
Signal stimulus 163
  and o.r. 164
    extinction 164
Signalling in afferent system(s) 20
Special conditioned reflex, inhibition 277
Specific
  adaptation reflex 64
  path for specialized visual signals 261
    interaction with non-specific 263
    reactions 69, 113
      latent period of 69
      similar to o.r. 82
  reflexes, weakening of 137
  sensitivity, reduction of 123
  system, rr. connected with 264
Sound, repetitive stimulation 109
Stimulus
  complex nature 68
  as a complex 113
Subsensory reactions 178, 181
  types of 228

Tarkhanov's galvanic skin reaction 53, 72,
  76
Temporary connexions, closure 247
Thalamic reticular formation 109
Thalamo-cortical
  connexions 263
  projective apparatus 9
Thermal stimulus, single long-acting 64
Thermoregulatory reflex
  interaction with o.r. 45, 65
  as specific a.r. 64
Threshold
  defined 22
  determined by minimal changes 31
  estimation of 25
  of excitability 25
  of reaction 25
  true analyser, estimation of 25
Test stimulus technique 105, 234
Time, c.a.r. to 274

Unitary reaction 19

Vascular
  changes in hand and head, simultaneous recording 37
  component of o.r. 39
    extinction 39, 40
  reaction, classification of reinforcing stimuli 171
    thermoregulatory 43
Vasomotor
  components relationship between o., a. and d.rr. 163
  reactions 186

  reciprocal 39
    connexion with o.r. of opposite side 41
Visual analyser
  "autosensitization" of 226
  light-stimulation effects on sensitivity of 223
  orientation changes in 202
  peripheral a. 96
  reactivity of 221

Walter analyser 74